What people said about
The National Food Strategy
(the Dimbleby Report)

'The Dimbleby report is a wake-up call to this country and government to do something about our food system and the epidemic of obesity and ill health destroying our country. We eat more ultra-processed unhealthy food than any other European country and it is getting relatively cheaper and more deadly each year.'

Tim Spector, Professor of Genetic Epidemiology at King's College London and author of *Spoon Fed*

'From field to fork, extraordinary work is being done to try and build a better food system for everyone, be it Jamie Oliver promoting education and a balanced diet, Henry Dimbleby's ambitions for safe, healthy and affordable food, or Marcus Rashford whose mission off the football field is to tackle child hunger.'

HM King Charles III

'Analytically tight, empirically thorough, the Dimbleby Report is not only a masterly study of the UK's food problem, but constructs a framework wide enough to be deployed for studying the food problems societies face everywhere. The report's recommendations are detailed, convincing, and would be entirely implementable if we cared about ourselves and the world around us.'

Sir Partha Dasgupta, Frank Ramsey Professor Emeritus of Economics, University of Cambridge, and author of *The Economics of Biodiversity*

'What is it going to take for these children to be prioritised? Instead of removing support through social security, we should be focusing efforts on developing a sustainable long-term road map out of this child hunger pandemic. I am, today, pledging my support for three recommendations from the National Food Strategy.'

Marcus Rashford, Manchester United and England

'This is no time for half-hearted measures. If both government and businesses are willing to take bold action and prioritise the public's health, then we have an incredible opportunity to create a much fairer and more sustainable food system for all families.'

Jamie Oliver, Chef

'This report is visionary and courageous and also much needed. It provides hope at a time when Covid 19 has exposed our vulnerability as a nation, which is in part the result of our poor diet. It is also deeply practical, offering solutions that can reverse a broken system and vested interests that currently result in healthy food being least available to those who most need it.'

Dr Michael Dixon, Chair of the College of Medicine

'Dimbleby offers a nuanced and imaginative way forward, one which harnesses the capacity of farmers and land managers to be a major part of the solution in tackling these challenges, while being fairly rewarded for their hard work and ingenuity. Many farmers are up for the challenge, but will need these recommendations to be implemented to make this possible.'

Helen Browning, CEO Soil Association

'Good food isn't just about deliciousness. It's also about health – our own health, and the health of the environment. This fascinating report elevates food to where it belongs – at the forefront of public debate.'

Yotam Ottolenghi, Chef

'The best government document that's ever come out.'

Prue Leith, Chef, writer, presenter

RAVENOUS

First published in Great Britain in 2023 by

Profile Books
29 Cloth Fair, London EC1A 7JQ

www.profilebooks.com

3 5 7 9 10 8 6 4 2

Typeset in Sabon Roman and Fira Sans
to a design by Henry Iles.

A CIP catalogue record for this book is available from the
British Library.

ISBN 978-1800816510
eIBSN 978-1800816534

Printed and bound in Great Britain by Clays Ltd, Elcograf S.p.A.

FSC
www.fsc.org
MIX
Paper from
responsible sources
FSC® C018072

RAVENOUS

How to get ourselves and our planet into shape

Henry Dimbleby

with Jemima Lewis

P

PROFILE BOOKS

TO JOHNNY, DORY
AND GEORGE

Contents

Introduction 9
Trapped in the system: *A brief explainer*. 19

PART ONE: OUR BODIES

1. A miracle and a disaster 31
How solving the last crisis in the food system
caused the current one

2. Boiling the frog 40
How did we get so fat?

3. You can't outrun a bad diet 51
Exercise will make you healthier, but it won't cure obesity

4. Appetite 63
Our ancient biology can't cope with the modern
environment

5. Anatomy of an egg sandwich 73
Ultra-processed food and the gut microbiome

6. Inequality 85
Eating well is much harder if you are poor

7. Should Nanny tell us what to eat? 96
The argument for state intervention

8. Hacking the system 105
How to legislate to break the Junk Food Cycle

9. Hacking the body 114
If politicians don't act, drug companies will

PART TWO: OUR LAND

10. How humanity ate the world 123
The food system is the greatest cause of
environmental destruction

11. The invisibility of nature 132
What does our food really cost?

12. Warming meals 144
The many ways in which food production
contributes to climate change

13. Peak meat? 151
Why we need less livestock farming

14. Sentient food 163
The miseries of intensive farming

15. Making the most of our land 178
For our own self-interest we need to make
space for nature

16. You can't eat butterflies 191
Protecting nature doesn't have to compromise food security

17. Can we have it all? 203
Only if we stop being so wasteful

PART THREE: OUR FUTURE

18. Goujons of hope 213
Can alternative proteins save us?

19. Stewards of the land 227
The government must ask more of farmers,
but protect them better

20. The power of love 241
Good food cultures don't just happen:
they are made by us

21. Utopia or dystopia? 253
Our future is coming for us. We must get
ready to meet it

Appendix 271
How to change the food system: actions for government

Acknowledgements 283

Sources and endnotes 287

Index 311

Introduction

When you lift a forkful of food to your mouth, what are you actually doing? Feeding yourself, of course. Perhaps chewing unconsciously as you scroll on your phone; or perhaps sitting down for a proper meal with family; or perhaps not using a fork at all, but munching a packaged snack while on the move.

Whichever it is, you probably think it's your decision. This is even – no, especially – true if you are eating something you know is not good for you. The guilt is experienced privately, inside your head. It may be part of an internal conversation you have been having for years, berating yourself for poor decisions and failures of willpower. And even though this reproachful voice makes you miserable, you believe it. You have free will, after all. So why do you keep making the wrong choices?

Here's why. You are not alone. You are certainly not free. You are part of a system so vast, so complex, so powerful and so intimately woven into everyday life that you hardly even know it's there. Every choice you make, everything you buy and eat, is informed by the tweaking and nudging of this giant machine, in which each of us is an unwitting cog.

You may not want to hear this. The idea of free will is precious to us, no matter how elusive it proves. No one wants to feel like a victim of unseen forces. But you are, and so am I. All living creatures on this planet, from the plankton in the oceans to the rulers of nations, are prisoners of the food system. And not just because we must eat to live.

The food system is no longer simply a means of sustenance. It is one of the most successful, most innovative and most destructive industries on Earth. To understand its scale, just look at the graphics on the page opposite.

The top one shows the estimated combined weight of humans and wild animals (defined here as land-dwelling vertebrates and birds) on the planet in 10,000 BCE. This was the start of the Holocene era, when global temperatures entered an unprecedented era of stability; the moment in history where the seasons became milder and more predictable, and agriculture therefore became possible. At this point, there were 2.5 million humans on Earth – a population dwarfed by the multitude of wild animals.

The lower graphic shows the situation today – to the same scale. The population of humans has swollen to 8 billion. The food system created by *Homo sapiens* has enabled us to become Earth's dominant species.

We learned to cook plants and animals, which made it much easier for us to digest nutrients, which in turn enabled us to shrink our guts and grow bigger brains instead. We used these brains to teach ourselves how to farm the food we needed. Liberated from the relentless work of hunter-gathering, we began to trade surplus food for other goods and services, and develop more complex social networks. Civilisation, as we came to call it, was born.

But as humans have thrived, almost all other forms of wildlife have declined. You can see on this chart that the biomass of wild animals has withered by 85 percent,

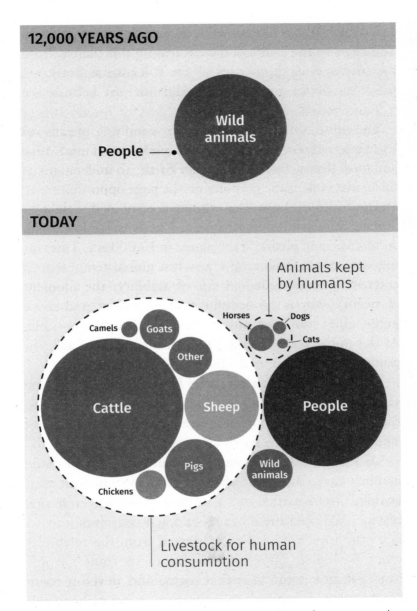

12,000 years ago the total weight of humans was tiny compared to the weight of wild animals (top). Today, the combined weight of land animals bred for food dwarfs that of wild animals and birds. ('Others' includes turkeys, ducks, geese, buffalo, etc. Ocean life and invertebrates are not included.)

thanks initially to our enthusiastic hunting of megafauna,* and then to the damage our increasingly rapacious food system has done to the natural world. These days our pets weigh almost as much as all the wild animals on the planet.

Land that used to sustain multitudes of species is now cultivated only for humans. Most animal life, too, serves the same purpose. The combined weight of animals bred for food is now twice the weight of all of the humans at any given time, and more than twenty times the combined weight of all wild vertebrates and birds.

The success of the food system goes hand in hand with its destructive power. The bigger it gets, the greater the environmental impact. It's not just biodiversity that is collapsing under the weight of our eating habits. Globally, the food system is the second-biggest emitter of greenhouse gases (after the fuel industry), and the primary cause of deforestation, drought, freshwater pollution and the depletion of aquatic wildlife.

All this, in turn, threatens our food security. The Covid pandemic, followed by the Russian invasion of Ukraine, were sharp reminders that a plentiful food supply is not something we can take for granted. Climate change is predicted to deliver even bigger shocks to the global food system, in the form of extreme weather events and catastrophic harvest failures. And then there's the toll that cheap, highly processed food is taking on our bodies.

The cheapest, most abundant ingredients in the modern food system are sugars, refined carbohydrates such as flour,

---

* Between 50,000 and 8000 BCE, our ancient ancestors are thought to have hunted more than 178 of the world's largest mammals to extinction – including mammoths, mastodon and the giant ruffed lemur. This is known as the 'Quaternary Megafauna Extinction'.

and fats. These are ingredients that humans are biologically programmed to crave. Our species evolved in a world where calories were hard to come by, and we are predisposed to pounce on anything high in fat and sugar.

Over 80 percent of processed food sold in the UK is unhealthy.* This is not because food manufacturers are evil: it is a simple matter of supply and demand. Unhealthy food is easier to sell. Companies therefore invest more into developing and marketing it. This in turn expands the market further still. The bigger the market, the greater the economies of scale. Highly processed foods – high in salt, refined carbohydrates, sugar and fats, and low in fibre – are on average three times cheaper per calorie than healthier foods. This is one reason why bad diet is a particularly acute problem among the poorest.

Diet-related disease is now the biggest cause of avoidable illness and death in the developed world. By 2035, the UK's National Health Service is projected to spend more on treating type 2 diabetes, just one condition caused by bad diet, than it does on all cancers today.

There are those who insist this is an issue of personal responsibility. That the answer is to 'educate the masses' in how to eat well, and leave the rest to individual willpower. But this fails to acknowledge, let alone explain, the sheer scale of the problem. In 1950, less than 1 percent of the UK population was clinically obese. Today, that figure stands at 28 percent. Are we to believe that, in the intervening years, the British public has suffered a massive collapse of willpower? Of course not. People haven't changed; the food system has.

---

* This figure is based on analysis of the nutrient profiles of products sold by 18 large food companies, representing half the processed food products sold in Britain. 'Unhealthy' products are defined as those that the World Health Organization deems unsuitable to market to children.

This is not to say we are powerless in the jaws of the machine. On the contrary: to a large extent we *are* the machine. Our appetites and behaviours are crucial to how the food system arranges itself. If we adjust them, we can adjust the system. But to do that we need to understand how the system actually works.

In 2019, the UK government asked me to write a comprehensive food strategy for the nation. I was already well acquainted with some parts of the immense apparatus through which, in the modern world, food is produced and consumed. As the co-founder and former CEO of Leon restaurants, and as the lead non-executive director at Defra (the Department for Environment, Food and Rural Affairs), I had seen from both a commercial and a political perspective how the millions of cogs in the food system meet and turn.*

Still, the scale of my task was daunting: to analyse the system from top to bottom, field to fork, and find solutions for an increasingly urgent problem: *How can we feed ourselves affordably, without destroying both our own health and the health of our planet?*

Assisted by a team of brilliant civil servants, and an advisory panel of scientists, farmers, academics, business

---

* Prior to this review, I had, with John Vincent, conducted another review for government in 2013 – *The School Food Plan*. This led, among other things, to the introduction of free school meals for all children up to Year 2, and cooking lessons being made a right for all children up to the age of 14. In 2018, I co-founded the charity Chefs in Schools with Nicole Pisani (former head chef at Yotam Ottolenghi's restaurant, Nopi) and Louise Nicholls, the headteacher of a federation of primary schools in east London. Chefs in School recruits professional restaurant chefs to work in schools and train existing staff in school kitchens, with the aim of improving both school lunches and food education. As a result of all this, I have spent a lot of time over the years in school kitchens.

leaders and charity and public sector workers, I set about my investigations. It felt a bit like that scene in *Modern Times*, where Charlie Chaplin falls into the factory machinery and has to pass all the way through before he can come out the other side. Together with my colleagues, I travelled the country visiting farms, food banks, high-rise greenhouses and alternative protein laboratories. We held focus groups all over the country, read academic papers from around the world, analysed data, ran mathematical models, questioned received wisdoms and inspected policy ideas, looking for hidden bear traps.

Then, in the early spring of 2020, when I was halfway through this research, an unforeseen complication arose: the first wave of Covid crashed onto our shores, bringing panic in its wake. Within weeks, supermarket shelves were being stripped bare, supply lines faltering under the strain. Over an eight-day period of hectic policymaking, the government first asked people to avoid going to pubs and restaurants, then shut these venues by law, and finally exhorted the nation to 'stay at home' entirely.

This meant the whole structure of the UK food system was abruptly bent out of shape. The 'out of home' food sector (restaurants, cafes, takeaways and pubs), which had previously supplied 20–25 percent of the UK's food, was closed overnight. School kitchens, which provide up to 50 percent of children's food during term time, were closed too. Wholesale ingredients for hospitality businesses – milk for coffees, flour for bakeries, prime cuts of beef – were suddenly stuck in warehouses, factories and farms, in danger of spoiling. Meanwhile, consumers, obliged to have all their meals at home, struggled to find basic ingredients such as mince or tinned tomatoes.

I helped Defra set up a group called the Food Resilience Industry Forum, whose job was to ensure that the nation got fed. The government suspended competition laws to allow the different players within the food sector to share information and find solutions. Every morning I sat in on the 8.15am conference call between civil servants and leaders in the food system: logistics companies, supermarket chains, farmers and food producers. You could almost hear the gears crunching as the machinery of production and distribution was forced into a new mode of operation.

In the event, the food system adapted to the pressures of lockdown with extraordinary agility. From the outside, it looked like something that happened naturally. Supply lines started running smoothly again, shelves filled up, the crisis passed. But watching from behind the scenes was first alarming, then awe-inspiring. Logistics companies offered to help wholesalers, who had been selling to restaurants, divert their goods into new markets; supermarkets helped move stock into local corner shops; hospitality businesses – even as they stared into the financial abyss – teamed up with civil servants and local councils to get hot meals to the neediest. The scale and beauty of the food system was laid out before me in those meetings, and I marvelled at it. I saw how delicately interlinked its various parts are, but also how adaptable it is. The food system can change, at speed – but only under intense pressure, and with sufficient collective will.

What the world needs now is a much more fundamental adaptation. We need once again to muster our ingenuity, to reshape the way we produce, sell and consume food, so that it stops making us and our world sick.

The scale of this challenge can hardly be overstated. There are so many different issues to tackle, and often the solutions appear to be at odds with each other. We must solve the health crisis created by our modern Western diet; end the environmental damage caused by intensive agriculture; ensure that good food is affordable for everyone; repair the damage we have already done to the land; restore biodiversity; and use our land to help fight climate change. We need to improve our food security, proofing ourselves against events affecting global supply chains. But we also need to repurpose some of our least productive farmland to provide habitats for our ailing wildlife, and to help mop up carbon emissions from those industries (such as air travel and heavy industry) that will depend on fossil fuels for the foreseeable future.

To most people – including most politicians – this looks like an impossible to-do list. The sheer complexity of it is paralysing. Fear of unintentionally creating new problems, pressure from the food industry, public scepticism and a truculent media ready to punish any whiff of nanny-statism, have combined to stymie successive governments. Even as the country grows fatter and sicker, and the costs to the NHS become increasingly unmanageable, politicians are afraid to act.

The so-called 'Government Food Strategy' that was unveiled in June 2022, in response to my review, is not a strategy at all. It is merely a handful of disparate policy ideas, many of them chosen because they are unlikely to raise much of a media storm. That doesn't mean those ideas are worthless. Some are more interesting and important than might appear at first sight. The government accepted my recommendation to create a Land Use Framework, for example, which is critical to balancing the multiple demands on our land. If they do it right, it will be ground-breaking. But it won't be enough on its own. The government's 'strategy' is far too scant, fragmented and cautious to meet the scale of the problem.

And yet, the system is fixable. In fact, change is inevitable. Sooner or later the cost to the nation of our current eating habits, measured both fiscally and in ruined lives, will become politically unsustainable. The only question is how much harm we are prepared to inflict on ourselves before we muster the courage to intervene. Do we really want to wait until a crisis turns into a catastrophe? The faster we move to tackle both obesity and environmental damage at their source, the faster we can begin to repair that damage.

The ideas and solutions I propose in this book are based on evidence collected from around the world. They have been subjected to minute examination and merciless number crunching. The cultural reflexes and untested assumptions that shape so many of our feelings about food have been deliberately set aside, in order to understand what really works – and what doesn't.

One of the reasons change is so hard is that our instinctive beliefs about what is healthy or sustainable are often wrong. 'Low fat' is seldom healthier than full fat, for example; and 'local' food can have a bigger carbon footprint than the imported stuff.

I want to clear away the myths and misconceptions that obscure our understanding of the food system. I will take you behind the scenes and show you the mechanisms that act together, accidentally or otherwise, to make us eat what we eat. I will explain why our modern diet has created a global crisis of diet-related disease and environmental destruction. But I will also demonstrate that these outcomes are not inevitable. We do not have to remain trapped in this food system. I will show you how we can escape.

Trapped in the system: *a brief explainer*

'A bad system', said the American statistician W.E. Deming, 'will beat a good person every time.' One reason for this is that good people often don't realise they are in a system. We experience our lives as a somewhat haphazard series of interactions with people, places, events and circumstances. It seldom feels mechanical or preordained, the way one imagines a system would. What actually is a 'system', come to that, apart from a faceless, intangible entity that can be blamed for all the ills of the world?

The simplest definition of a system is any set of things working together as a larger whole, towards some purpose or end. It might be man-made: the railway system, for example, is made up of tracks, trains, stations, train drivers and so on, all combining to get us about. Or a system can occur naturally – like photosynthesis in plants.

The food system is the sum of all of the elements that combine to produce, process, market and sell the food we eat. It contains many smaller systems within the system, and can be said to include everything from the bacteria in the soil to the layout of a supermarket aisle. The sheer scale and ubiquity of the food system gives it a kind of invisibility: we live deep inside it, and it is hard to get enough distance to see it as a whole.

When I started working on the National Food Strategy, I was urged by many experts to take a 'systemic approach'. But when I asked what that approach would look like I got lots of different answers. Some pointed to the (now famous in the field) Foresight Obesity System Map, which was produced in work commissioned by government in 2007 to tackle obesity. This intricate spider's web of a chart (see below) does a great job of illustrating the

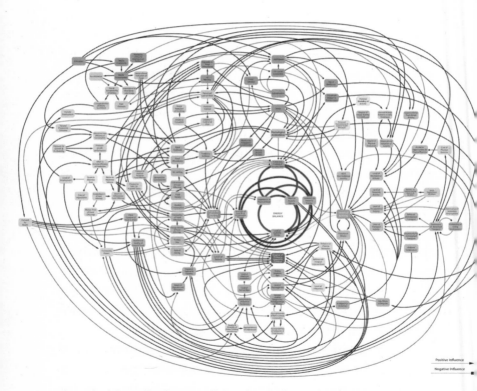

The mind-bogglingly complicated Foresight Obesity System Map, drawn up for a 2007 government report on obesity. It contains 108 variables connected by approximately 300 causal links.

multifactorial nature of obesity – just glancing at it makes the pulse race and the eyeballs swivel – but it is of limited help in devising policy. In fact, the 'it's complicated' approach to changing systems can be so demoralising that it actually stops us making progress. If change is this hard, is it even worth trying?

Another chart that was often pressed on me shows how responsibility for decision-making on food policy is spread, like a thin layer of jam on toast, across government (see overleaf). There is no single department with responsibility for food, goes the argument. Instead, every department gets a shout, and so chaos ensues. I do think there is much to learn from this excellent chart. It would undoubtedly be easier to make good decisions about food policy if the chain of command wasn't such a mess. But the food system is not unique in being regulated by multiple arms of government. An understanding of these relationships is important in policymaking, but not fundamental to understanding the system itself.

What I *have* found helpful to that end is a basic understanding of 'system dynamics'. This is a branch of science developed in the early 1950s at the Massachusetts Institute of Technology (MIT), which uses mathematical models to understand complex system behaviour. It breaks all systems down into four component parts, each of which may be repeated many times: a 'stock' (which is a quantity of something); a 'flow' (the movement of that something from one place to another); 'feedback loops' (which control the flow); and the 'purpose' or 'output' of the system.

Stocks within a system don't need to be homogeneous, or even material. It is possible to model what happens in a system when the 'stock' of trust in a regulator declines, for example, or when the stock of skill in a workforce increases. Feedback loops also come in many forms, including laws,

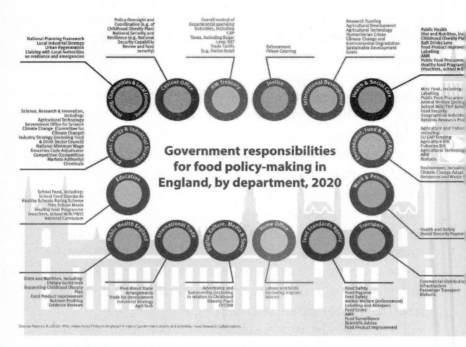

Government responsibilities for food policy-making in England, by department, 2020

National Planning Framework
Local Industrial Strategy
Urban Regeneration
Liaising with Local Authorities
on resilience and emergencies

Policy Oversight and
Coordination (e.g. of
Childhood Obesity Plan)
National Security and
Resilience (e.g. National
Security Capability
Review and food
security)

Overall control of
departmental spending
Subsidies, including
CAP
Taxes, including Sugar
Levy; VAT
Trade Tariffs
(e.g. Excise Duty)

Enforcement
Prison Catering

Research Funding
Agricultural Development
Agricultural Technology
Humanitarian Crises
Climate Change and
Environmental Degradation
Sustainable Development
Goals

Public Health
Diet and Nutrition, inc
Childhood Obesity Pla
Soft Drinks Levy
Food Product Improve
Labelling
AMR
Public Food Procurem
Healthy food Program
(Vouchers, school mil

Science, Research & Innovation,
including:
Agricultural Technology
Government Office for Science
Climate Change (Committee for
Climate Change)
Industry Strategy (including Food
& Drink Sector Council)
National Minimum Wage
Groceries Code Adjudication
Competition (Competition
Markets Authority)
Chemicals

Misc Food, including:
Labelling
Public Food Procurem
Animal Welfare (policy
School Milk/F&V Sche
Food Security
Geographical Indicatio
Systems Research Pro

Agriculture and Fisher
including:
EU CAP Funding
Agriculture Bill
Fisheries Bill
Agricultural Technolog
AMR
Biofuels

Environment, including
Climate Change Adapt
Resources and Waste S

School Food, including:
School Food Standards
Healthy Schools Rating Scheme
Free School Meals
Healthy food Programme
(vouchers, school milk/F&V)
National Curriculum

Health and Safety
Social Security Paymen

Diets and Nutrition, including:
Dietary Guidelines
Supporting Childhood Obesity
Plan
Food Product Improvement
Nutrient Profiling
Evidence Reviews

Post-Brexit Trade
Arrangements
Trade for Development
Industrial Strategy
Agri-Tech

Advertising and
Sponsorship (including
in relation to Childhood
Obesity Plan)
OFCOM

Labour and Skills
(including migrant
labour)

Food Safety
Food Hygiene
Feed Safety
Animal Welfare (enforcement)
Labelling and Allergens
Food Crime
AMR
Food Surveillance
Scientific Advice
Food Product Improvement

Commercial distributio
Infrastructure
Passenger Transport
Biofuels

Departments shown: Housing, Communities & Local Government; Cabinet Office; HM Treasury; Justice; International Development; Health & Social Care; Business, Energy & Industrial Strategy; Environment, Food & Rural Affairs; Education; Work & Pensions; Public Health England; International Trade; Digital, Culture, Media & Sport; Home Office; Food Standards Agency; Transport

Source: Parsons, K. (2020). Who Makes Food Policy in England? A map of government actors and activities. Food Research Collaboration.

This chart, produced by Kelly Parsons from City University, London, illustrates the difficulty of making coherent food policy when responsibility is distributed between so many different departments. The Treasury, for example, decides on taxes (such as the sugary drinks levy); the Department for Digital, Culture, Media and Sport decides whether the advertising of junk food to children should be restricted; the Department for Education decides who is eligible for free school meals and is responsible for ensuring their quality; and the Department of Health and Social Care clears up the mess.

social customs, information (a speedometer prompting a driver to slow down) and biological signals (the hormone prolactin telling a mother's body to produce more milk).

There are two kinds of feedback loop: 'balancing' and 'reinforcing'. *Balancing feedback loops* (also known as *negative feedback loops*, although their effects can be positive) serve to maintain stocks at certain levels. They limit, or reverse, the direction of travel. Our appetite, for example, responds to certain chemicals in our blood and gut which regulate how much we eat. If we eat too much, we feel full, and that stops us eating more. If we eat too little, we get hungry and go in search of more food. (Clearly, this feedback mechanism doesn't always work as well as it should, as we will see in *Chapter Four*.)

Reinforcing feedback loops amplify the direction of travel (they are also known as positive feedback loops, although they can have negative effects). They create both vicious circles (I eat more → I get fatter → that makes me sad → I eat more → I get fatter) and virtuous circles (more people buy free range eggs → investment increases in free range egg production → the cost of free range eggs comes down → more people buy free range eggs). These reinforcing feedback loops can create runaway systems that are very hard to stop, such as nuclear fission or melting polar ice caps.

Minuscule changes in starting conditions can, over time, lead to big differences in outcomes. Systems can appear stable, and then collapse without warning. Attempting to control them (even loosely) is extremely difficult, and many well-intentioned endeavours fail.

But that doesn't mean we shouldn't try. Systems science also shows us that different systems from very different fields tend to exhibit similar and predictable behaviours. There is a common set of identifiable patterns in which systems fail, for example. And, depending on the structure of the system, some interventions are more likely than others to lead to positive change.

In her book *Thinking in Systems*, Donella Meadows (part of the original MIT team) drew on thousands of studies to identify archetypal ways in which systems can malfunction. She called these *System Traps*. They can cause incredible damage, but because they are buried in a system we take for granted, we often fail to identify them as the culprit. When things go wrong, we instinctively want to blame people or events, rather than looking for a flaw in the system.

This is one reason why political (and public) responses to structural problems are so often ineffective. 'Blaming, disciplining, firing, twisting policy levers harder, hoping for a more favourable sequence of events, tinkering at the margins – these standard responses will not fix structural problems,' wrote Meadows. 'But system traps can be escaped – by recognizing them in advance and not getting caught in them, or by altering the structure – by reformulating goals, by weakening, strengthening, or altering feedback loops, [or] by adding new feedback loops.'

Our current food system is riddled with system traps, as we shall see in the coming chapters. These are some of the worst offenders:

Policy Resistance This trap occurs when balancing feed-back loops keep bringing the system back to the same spot, no matter how hard you try to shift it. Take tradition-al drug prevention policies. No matter how many wars on drugs are fought, drug dealing remains a problem. This is because, if enforcement is successful, it reduces the stock (drugs) within the system, which increases its value and incentivises drug smugglers to circumvent the system. Together, these countermoves produce a standoff, and the stock remains unchanged. Everyone makes a huge effort to achieve their own objectives, but the system is unmoved.

The Tragedy of the Commons This phrase was coined by the American ecologist Garrett Hardin in a 1968 article of the same name, although the problem was first identified by the nineteenth-century English economist William Forster Lloyd. It occurs when a finite resource is accessible to everyone. Rather than preserve the resource, each actor in the system is incentivised to take as much of it for themselves as they can before it runs out.

A recent example is the collapse of the cod populations on the Newfoundland Grand Banks. When Europeans first became aware of these thriving shoals, they were 'so thicke by the shoare that we heardlie have been able to row a Boate through them' (as John Mason, governor of Newfoundland, recorded in 1620). So long as there was a technological limit on how much each fishing boat could catch, the cod provided an abundant source of food and livelihoods. But technology moved fast in the twentieth century, with the invention of bottom trawling, on-board freezing and larger boats. Fearing to be outdone by their competitors, each fishing boat became better equipped and increased its catch – until, in 1992, the cod population collapsed almost completely, signalling not just an end to the cod but to the entire ecosystem of the local coast. Despite a fishing moratorium, that has reversed the decline, the cod population in this area has still not recovered.

'Ruin is the destination toward which all men rush,' wrote Hardin in his essay, 'each pursuing his own best interest in a society that believes in the freedom of the commons.'

Drift to low performance Also known as the 'boiled frog syndrome',* 'eroding goals' or 'shifting baselines', this trap occurs when a system drifts downhill slowly enough for the actors in the system to forget how much better things used to

---

* Some nineteenth-century scientists suggested that if you drop a frog into boiling water it will jump out, but if you heat the water slowly it won't even notice. The frog will remain in the water and boil to death. Modern scientists refute this. In 1995, Douglas Melton, a biologist at Harvard University, said, 'If you put a frog in boiling water, it won't jump out. It will die. If you put it in cold water, it will jump before it gets hot — they don't sit still for you."

be. Everyone is lulled into lower and lower expectations, lower effort, lower performance. The system requires a balancing feedback mechanism, a burst of energy to raise standards to where they once were. But instead, a reinforcing feedback loop is created as low expectations lead to less corrective action, which leads to continuous degradation of the system.

In the *School Food Plan*, which I co-authored in 2013 (see footnote on p.14), we argued that this is what had happened to the food served in schools, until Jamie Oliver intervened and made everyone realise how bad things had become. Standards are now increasing (albeit much too slowly) as expectations in the system have been raised.

Escalation This happens when the goal of a system is not absolute, but related to another variable in the system. I raise my voice to be heard over you, you yell a bit louder and soon we are both shouting at the top of our voices. There is a reinforcing feedback loop carrying the system into an arms race, a wealth race, escalating loudness, escalating violence.

We can see this in the food system. Humans have evolved to like calorie-dense food. Food companies respond to this innate desire by putting more effort into the development and marketing of calorie-dense food, which increases the consumption of that food, which in turn increases the incentive for companies to make and market it. Increasing sales increases marketing spend, which increases sales. We describe this Junk Food Cycle in greater depth in *Chapter Two*.

Shifting the burden to the intervenor Colloquially known as addiction or dependence. 'Addiction is finding a quick and dirty solution to the symptom of the problem,' wrote Meadows, 'which prevents or distracts one from the harder and longer-term task of solving the real problem.'

Intensive agriculture has an addiction problem. An over-reliance on fertilisers and pesticides has damaged the ecosystem and depleted the soil. This in turn results in increased reliance on fertilisers and pesticides, to make crops grow in such unfertile conditions.

Rule-beating Wherever there are rules, there is likely to be rule-beating. This is when people or institutions take evasive action to get around the rules of a system – abiding by the letter, but not the spirit, of the law. Rule-beating becomes a problem when it leads a system into large distortions, unnatural behaviours that would make no sense at all in the absence of the rules.

In the 1960s, for example, European countries imposed restrictions on imported grains for animal feed, in order to protect prices for their own farmers. Cassava – a good animal feed but not a grain – fell outside the restrictions. So farmers looking for cheap feed replaced corn imports from the USA with cassava imports from Asia. European farmers did not benefit. Regardless of whether you agree with the policy in the first place, it did not achieve its objective.

Seeking the wrong goal If the goals of a system are defined inaccurately or incompletely, the system may work obediently to produce a result that is not really intended.

We have a system of national accounting, for example, that – as the economist Sir Partha Dasgupta points out in his ground-breaking review *The Economics of Biodiversity* – bears no real relation to our national wealth or wellbeing. It counts only the capital from things we produce, and doesn't measure the indicators of 'human capital' (education or health, for example) or of 'natural capital' (the natural resources upon which all life depends). Because these stocks are not written into the system, the system does not value them.

In fact, even on its own terms our system of national accounting doesn't work. GDP (Gross Domestic Product) is not actually a record of our material wealth, but the fever chart of our consumption. It is a measure of the gross addition to stocks – the flows of stuff made and purchased in a year – rather than the stocks themselves: the houses, cars and computers that are in themselves sources of pleasure and indications of wealth.

PART ONE

Our Bodies

CHAPTER ONE

A miracle and a disaster

How solving the last crisis in the food system caused the current one

The food system we have today is both a miracle and a disaster. You could say the miracle caused the disaster. The primary miracle worker was a botanist called Norman Borlaug. In a biopic of his life, Borlaug might have been played by Jimmy Stewart. Born in Iowa in 1914, he was rangy and long-faced, with a strong jaw and all-American teeth. But there has been no biopic. Outside agricultural or academic circles, Borlaug is largely unknown. And yet without the farming system he developed, more than two in three people on this planet could not be fed. Indeed, two-thirds of the people you know might not exist.

Seventy years ago, it was widely assumed that the world was on the brink of running out of food. The global population was rising fast – projected to increase from 2.5 billion to 9 billion over the next century, thanks to improvements in medicine and sanitation. How could all these people be fed?

Throughout history, there had only been one way to increase food production significantly: dig up more land. This is what British farmers had to do during the Second World War, when food security suddenly became a pressing issue. At the start of the war, Britain only produced 30 percent of the food it consumed. The rest was imported from the Empire and beyond. (This still required lots of land to be dug up, of course, but far from home.)

Britain's dependence on food imports was a weakness the Germans were quick to exploit. Nazi U-boats attempted to starve the country into submission by sinking merchant ships carrying food. In every month of the war before May 1943, more merchant ships were destroyed by U-boats in the North Atlantic than could be built. Churchill later said the 'U-boat peril' was the thing that frightened him most during the war. It was farmers who saved the day, with a mass conversion of scrubland to farmland. Under government edict, they grubbed up heather and tore down hedges in order to cultivate every precious inch of land. By the end of the war, British food production had increased from 30 percent to 75 percent of demand.

This correlation – between the number of mouths to feed, the quantity of food produced and the proportion of land used for cultivation – had stayed the same through the course of human history. The graph opposite shows three lines representing those three variables over time. You can see that from the start of the nineteenth century to the early twentieth century they rise together gradually, at an almost identical rate.

By the end of the war, however, most of the world's decent farming land was already taken. With the population explosion under way, it seemed there simply wouldn't be enough land to produce the extra food needed. Mass starvation looked inevitable.

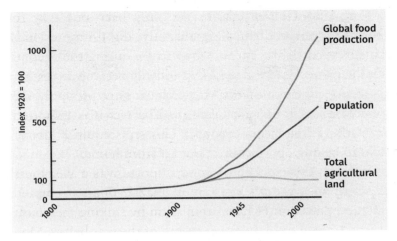

Globally, we now produce 1.7 times more calories per person than in 1945, from a slightly smaller area of land. The result of the so-called Green Revolution, this has enabled us to feed a massively increased global population without digging up a corresponding quantity of land.

Enter Norman Borlaug. Raised on a small farm during the Great Depression, Borlaug had seen starving people begging on the streets and rioting over food. It set him on a mission to fight hunger. Having studied plant pathology, he moved to Mexico in 1944, hoping to develop more productive strains of wheat. The living conditions of the half-starved local population were even worse than the things he had witnessed in his youth. 'These places I've seen have clubbed my mind,' he wrote to his wife, Margaret. 'The earth is so lacking in life force; the plants just cling to existence. They don't really grow; they just fight to stay alive. The levels of nourishment in the soil are so low that wheat plants produce only a few grains ... I don't know what we can do to help, but we've got to do something.'

Borlaug set himself the task of breeding a strain of wheat that would be high yielding, robust enough to thrive in Mexican conditions, and resistant to wheat rust, a fungal disease that could wipe out a harvest. He began by crossbreeding Mexican strains with wheat-rust-resistant American strains. The resulting crop was much higher yielding, but the stems tended to grow lanky and top-heavy. A strong wind could knock down great swathes of crops (a phenomenon known as lodging) and devastate yields.

Borlaug had heard about a shorter stemmed 'dwarf' wheat grown in Japan. He thought that if he could breed his higher-yielding strains so that they developed a stout, stiff, shorter stem he might be able to solve the lodging problem. He managed to source a precious cache

Norman Borlaug, the father of the twentieth century's Green Revolution, displaying his new wheat varietals.

of imported seeds, and started from scratch. Initially the results were not good. The dwarfism of the Japanese wheat was caused by a number of recessive genes, many of which led to undesirable characteristics. But Borlaug was obsessed by the potential of the breed, and he pressed on.

He spent his days in the heat-blasted fields, painstakingly crossbreeding plants. He tweezered off stamen, placed tiny hoods over hundreds of thousands of individual heads of wheat, snipped florets and mingled pollens by hand. Completely absorbed in his work, he often slept on the dirt floor of his research hut. The Mexican farm workers thought he was unhinged.

But his efforts paid off. He managed to breed a rust-resistant, short-stemmed wheat with astonishing yields: over three times the quantity of grain from the same area of land. To overcome the scepticism of local farmers, he gave small bags of his new seed to a select few, knowing that their neighbours would soon be jealous of their yields and eager to try it themselves.

When Borlaug first arrived in Mexico, the country imported 60 percent of its wheat. By the 1960s – thanks to his new strain – Mexico was entirely self-sufficient in wheat. This miracle was subsequently repeated in India and Pakistan, and then across the world. Tougher, higher-yielding breeds of wheat, rice and corn, combined with modern irrigation techniques and industrial fertilisers and pesticides, created a new era of highly productive intensive farming.

As expected, the global population soared. In 1950, the average global life expectancy was 46; today, it is 73. There are 8 billion humans alive today – more than ever before – and yet the threat of mass starvation has receded. Globally, we now produce around 50 percent more calories than we need per head. (Much more than that if you include all the crops that get fed to livestock.) Even when a harvest fails in one part of the planet, supply lines can usually switch to bring in food from another. There have been no famines this century that cannot be attributed to supply-line disruption caused by war or corruption.*

For the first time in history, the increase in food production, and in calories harvested per person, has massively outstripped the additional land being farmed. You can see it happening on the graph. The three lines suddenly peel away from each other, as the global population shoots upwards, but Borlaug's revolution makes it possible to extract more food from the same total area of land. Globally, we produce three times as much food from roughly the same amount of land as we did in 1960. In the UK, average wheat yields have increased from 2 tonnes per hectare at the turn of the twentieth century to around 9 tonnes per hectare today.

This does not mean that wild land is no longer being torn up and turned into farmland. In parts of the world, particularly the tropics, deforestation continues at rapacious speed, making way for palm and soya fields and cattle ranches. Statistically, however, the total area of farmland in use around the globe remains static – even

---

* A country is only considered to be in famine when at least 20 percent of its households are facing an extreme lack of food, at least 30 percent of its children are suffering from acute malnutrition, and two people for every 10,000 are dying every day due to outright starvation or to the interaction of malnutrition and disease. Countries with stable political regimes have, so far this century, managed to avoid famine even in the face of natural disaster. For example, when Niger was hit by both drought and swarms of locusts in 2005, relief provision prevented marked increases in mortality. Both Kenya and Somalia are, at the time of writing, suffering from their worst droughts for forty years, which is causing terrible hardship. But Kenya is not yet close to famine, whereas Somalia – where the government is locked in a destabilising conflict with al-Shabaab, the Salafi jihadist group – is.

falling slightly. This is because vast tracts of farmland have fallen into disuse over the past half-century. In Russia, for example, the amount of land used for farming has fallen by 35 percent since 1990, largely due to the abandonment of Soviet collective farms and the legalisation of private ownership implemented by Gorbachev. The least productive farmland – an area of 426,000 square kilometres, twenty times the size of Wales, to use the time-honoured metric – has been returned to the wild.

By adopting Borlaug's more productive methods, farmers saved billions of people from starvation. This is what became known as the Green Revolution – a title that has since acquired the bitter aftertaste of irony. For we now know something that Borlaug couldn't have.

Every stage of the food production process exacerbates the carbon crisis: the forests cleared to plant crops; the energy-intensive manufacture of fertiliser; the release of carbon from degrading soils; the methane produced by rice paddies and livestock (of which more later); the energy used by manufacturing plants and retail outlets; and the fuel used to power the vehicles in the supply chain. In total, the food system is responsible for an estimated 25–30 percent of total global greenhouse gas emissions.

Modern intensive agriculture, with its crop monocultures and heavy reliance on pesticides and artificial fertiliser, has also led to a global collapse in biodiversity. As the amount of food produced from a given area of land has increased, so the amount of other life occupying that same area of land has decreased. In the UK, where 70 percent of the landmass is occupied by farmland, intensive agriculture has devastated the habitats of many wild animals and insects.

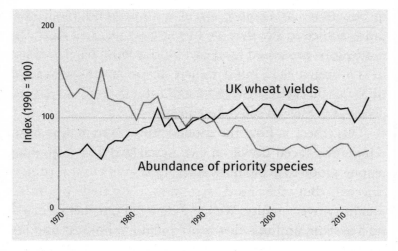

As agricultural production has intensified, biodiversity has declined. This chart shows the changing populations of 224 of the UK's 'priority species' – those deemed to be at risk of extinction – over the past half-century. They include 103 bird species, 24 butterflies, 13 mammals and 84 moths. It is based on data collected by the Joint Nature Conservation Committee, set up to advise the government on nature conservation.

Since 1930, we have lost 97 percent of our wildflower meadows, half our ancient woodland, 56 percent of our heathland and 90 percent of our lowland ponds. Wheat yields in this country doubled from 1970 to today, while the number of farmland birds fell by 54 percent. The UK now sits in last place on the European farmland bird index. More broadly, as the chart above shows, there has been a 60 percent decline in priority UK species since 1970, with a 22 percent decline since 2011.

The effects on human health have been double-edged. On the one hand, there are more of us alive than ever before, because Borlaug's miracle made it possible to feed us. On the other, its side effects are making us seriously ill. Almost one in three adults in England is now clinically obese. We shall examine in detail how modern food production has trapped us in a Junk Food Cycle. For now, suffice to say that we live in a cornucopia of cheap, unhealthy, processed food of a kind we find hard to resist. It is a bizarre fact, but commercially unsurprising, that in the UK you can buy twenty-eight different kinds of KitKat. They are easier to sell than kale.

This, then, is how the modern food system was built. Humanity faced down an existential problem – growing enough food to avoid mass starvation – with extraordinary success. But the food system we created prioritises quantity over quality. We have changed our diet to match this system, and this diet is now making both us and our planet ill.

CHAPTER TWO

Boiling the frog

How did we get so fat?

My youngest child woke me one morning with a question. 'Daddy?' she said, her inquisitive face looming over mine. 'Were you this chubby even when you were young?' It was a bruising start to the day. And the answer, when I tried to locate it, proved elusive.

Throughout my life my weight has oscillated – sometimes gently, sometimes more violently – between the high end of what the NHS would define as normal and the low end of obese. I have tried to flatten out this roller-coaster with exercise and healthy eating regimes. I have done marathons and aquathlons. For a time, I used a fitness programme on my children's Wii Fit console. At the end of each workout, I had to stand on an electronic plate to be weighed. My animated avatar would pump the air in celebration as confetti rained down on screen and a disembodied robot voice offered the faint praise: 'Less. Obese.'

Maintaining a 'healthy' weight has always been a struggle for me, and a puzzle. I cook all my meals from scratch, eat many more than my five portions of fruit and veg a day and almost never have sweets, puddings or ready-meals. On the other hand, I am greedy. I eat too fast, drink wine, and snack on pickled onion Monster Munch when I'm stressed. Maybe it's genetic: my grandfather had the same barrel shape as me. Or maybe I have damaged my metabolism with all this yo-yo asceticism.

People are complicated, and so are the factors that control our weight. Upbringing, culture, financial circumstances and emotional state all influence what and how we eat. A history of dieting, like mine, is a predictor of future obesity. But probably the most significant difference between individuals is genetic.

We inherit our bodies from our parents and grandparents – not just the size of our feet or the colour of our hair, but also our weight. Studies of twins who were adopted at birth into different families suggest that genes account for between 40 and 70 percent of our proclivity to put on weight. This is not, as you might imagine, because people are born with differing metabolisms. It is chiefly about appetite.

In 1999, scientists discovered a gene that is strongly correlated with high bodyweight. They called it – you could get away with this sort of thing back then – the FATSO gene (short for 'fat mass and obesity associated'). Nowadays known, more politely, as the FTO gene, it appears to work by modulating the release of the body's hunger hormones (more on these in the next chapter). In other words, some people are genetically programmed to feel hungrier than others. (Scientists have now identified at least one thousand gene variants that contribute to obesity. Each variant only has a tiny effect but in combination their impact is substantial.)

This sounds to modern ears like a curse (or an excuse), but in evolutionary terms it was a blessing. These robust, well-padded souls could better survive a period of food shortage.

The genetic component does not mean that some people are doomed to get fat. It just means that some of us are wired to want more food than others. It used to be hard work, satisfying a big appetite; there simply wasn't enough food around. Now, we face the opposite problem: highly calorific food is so cheap and ubiquitous that we have a struggle *not* to eat it. Those of us with greedy genes have to work especially hard to resist the powerful current of our appetite.

In 1950, when calorie-dense food was still in relatively modest supply, this genetic variation in appetites across the population produced a distribution of weight that followed the classic bell curve shown below. The solid vertical line on this chart represents a body mass index (BMI – see p.50 for definition) of 25: defined today as overweight. The dotted vertical line represents a BMI of 30: defined today as obese. You can see that the average

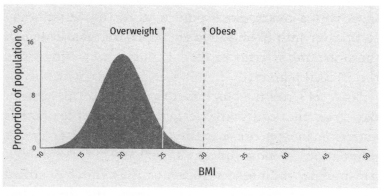

The distribution of people in the UK by weight in 1950. Very few people were obese. A significant number had a BMI of less than 18.5, which is defined today as underweight.

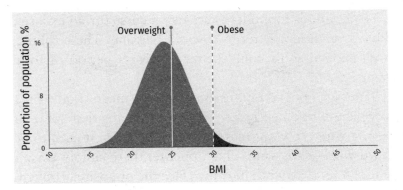

By the 1980s, people in the UK had become on average heavier, meaning the bell curve had moved to the right.

BMI in 1950 was about 20: in today's terms, a little below the 'ideal' BMI (i.e. the number that correlates with the best health outcomes). Evenly distributed either side of that, some people were underweight, some overweight. But hardly anyone was obese.

Let's roll the clock forward to the 1980s (see the chart above). During this time, mass-produced, calorie-dense food became much cheaper and more widely available. As we consumed more of it, we became heavier. Everyone – even the naturally slender – put on some weight, but those with a genetic predisposition to lay down fat began to tip over into obesity. These people are represented by the slope on the right of the bell curve, where it crosses the 30 BMI marker.

Now let's roll the clock forward again to the present day (see the chart overleaf). Although the genetic variation in appetite is still visible, a minority of the population is now at or under the 'ideal' weight. Meanwhile, the obese segment of the slope has grown much longer and thicker, and crossed the dotted line that marks a BMI of 40. A significant chunk of the population is now severely obese.

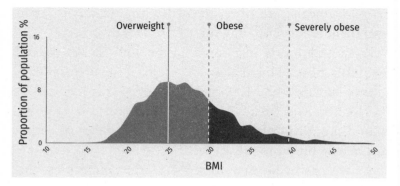

The situation today. Almost one in three adults in the UK are obese or severely obese.

Taken together, these charts illustrate the momentum of our so-called 'obesity epidemic'. It hasn't been a sudden disaster, but more of a slow-moving landslide.

It's not just the abundance of food that has created this landslide. It's also the particular nature of the food. Biologically, we are still hunter-gatherers. If you have to search for everything you eat, it makes sense to look for things that will give you more calories than you expend. Honey, for example, contains six times more energy than an equivalent weight of berries. When we eat honey, our taste buds respond with intense pleasure: a natural feedback mechanism to reward us for finding such a bountiful source of energy.

The same is true of chocolate ice cream. It contains six times as many calories as an equivalent weight of broccoli, and our appetite for it is correspondingly powerful. This craving is strongest when fat and sugar are combined in a ratio of 1 to 2: the ratio found in breast milk. Manufacturers use this formula in products such as ice cream, milk chocolate and biscuits, knowing that we find it irresistible. Even allegedly savoury products, such as ready meals, are often packed with sugar and fat to give them a 'moreish' flavour.

Processed foods also tend to be low in water and insoluble fibre. This is known to slow down the body's satiety signals – the feeling of fullness – so that we eat more of it. And because each mouthful is more calorific than a mouthful of broccoli, the consequences of eating just a little bit more are greater too.

As well as being easy to sell, in larger quantities, this kind of food is cheap to make. The Green Revolution has created an abundance of sugar, flour and vegetable oil. For good commercial reasons, therefore, companies invest a lot of money into researching, developing and promoting foods that chiefly consist of these ingredients. This research is intended not just to capture a bigger slice of the market, but to grow the market itself.

Young marketeers are taught about the 'consumption effect' – meaning that consumers who have more food in their home will eat more of it. In-store promotions such as the classic BOGOF deal ('buy one, get one free') are explicitly designed to persuade shoppers to buy and take home more than they intended when they set out for the supermarket. Research by Public Health England has found that volume promotions such as BOGOFs increase purchases of a product by an average of 15 percent.

Marketeers pore over academic papers with equations showing which promotions are most likely to increase consumption. Chocolate, for example, has an 'expandability' of 93 percent. This means that if you run a BOGOF on chocolate, customers will on average consume almost twice as much as they would have without the promotion.

In systems terms, we have become stuck in a reinforcing feedback loop – a vicious cycle. Let's call it the Junk

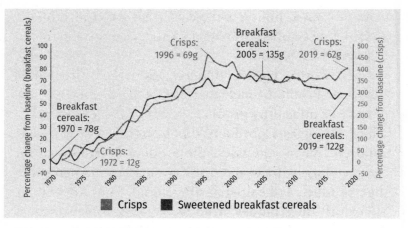

The percentage change in per capita consumption of crisps and breakfast cereals from 1970 to 2020 in the UK.

Food Cycle. We have a predilection for calorie-dense foods, which means food companies invest more time and money creating these foods, which makes us eat more of them and expands the market, which leads to more investment, which makes us eat more.

The average Brit now consumes five times more crisps than in 1972. We also eat 1.5 times the amount of breakfast cereal (and breakfast cereals have become far more sugary). Similar shifts have been repeated across our national diet. In 1980, 57 percent of the average household budget in this country was spent on fresh ingredients to cook at home. This has fallen to 35 percent. We now get 55 percent of our total calories from ultra-processed foods (of which more in *Chapter Five*).

You only have to cast your eye around your local supermarket – where fresh ingredients form a thin coastline around the great landmass of processed, packaged food – to see how the consumer landscape has changed. The fruit and veg market in the UK is now worth a measly £2.2 billion per year, whereas confectionery alone – one small section of the processed food market – is worth £3.9 billion.

The World Health Organization has created a 'Nutrient Profile Model' that can be used to score how healthy or unhealthy products are. It gives a cutoff below which it suggests products should not be advertised to children. When you assess the product portfolios of the eighteen largest food and drink companies, 85 percent of their products fall below this threshold. They are making almost all their money from ice creams, sweets, sugary drinks, crisps, biscuits, cakes and highly calorific, sugary and fatty ready meals and sauces.

Food companies, like consumers, have become trapped in this cycle. What are company bosses supposed to do? If they stop making and selling unhealthy foods, someone else will. They will lose their competitive edge. Behind the scenes, several company bosses have told me they would welcome government legislation designed to reduce junk food sales. They know the food they are selling is terrible for their customers, and they want to do the right thing. But they need a level playing field. They can't act alone. They can't even be honest – at least in public – about what they know. Any CEO who called for stricter government legislation on junk food would be sacked.

Readers of a libertarian bent may be thinking: why the fuss? This is just capitalism doing its job. The purpose of companies is to make money, and successful companies give customers what they want. If a person chooses to spend their hard-earned cash on junk food – even if they keep eating this food until they make themselves

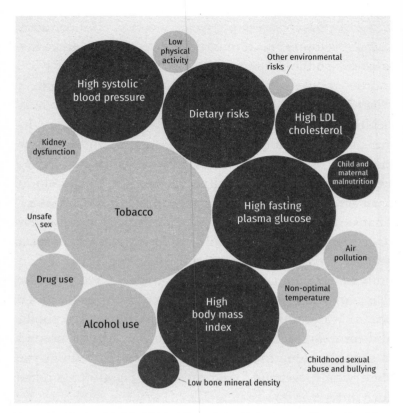

Years lost to avoidable ill health and death by cause. Poor diet (the darker grey circles) is now by far the greatest cause of preventable ill health in the UK. This might explain why, mid-pandemic, England's Chief Medical Officer Chris Whitty took time out to give an online lecture entitled 'What Can We Do About Rising Obesity?'

ill – that is nobody's business but their own. However, very few people who are obese or suffering from diet-related disease are happy with their situation. And even if they were, the State cannot afford to keep picking up the tab.

Sixty percent of adults in this country are now overweight or obese, and by 2060 that proportion is expected to reach 80 percent. The costs of this man-made disaster are hard to overstate. Already, the

OECD (Organisation for Economic Co-operation and Development) estimates that the UK economy loses £74 billion a year in lost workforce productivity, shortened lives and NHS costs because of conditions related to high BMI.

No other avoidable cause of illness – not even smoking – steals so many years of life from us. And before it kills us, it makes us miserable. The side effects of obesity include depression, anxiety, infertility, high blood pressure, painful joints, breathlessness and broken sleep. That's before we even get to the big ones: cancer, dementia, heart failure and type 2 diabetes, which has its own attendant risks of blindness, peripheral neuropathy and limb amputation.

It's extraordinary, really, that there isn't a public uproar about this. Imagine if a novel virus started killing and disabling people on such a scale, and with no end in sight. You don't have to imagine it: we now know the lengths politicians and the public would go to to combat such a threat.

Unlike Covid, however, the plague of diet-related disease has crept up on us stealthily, and under the seductive guise of 'choice'. We appear to have fallen into the 'boiled frog' trap, where a system slides into dysfunction gradually, so that no one panics until it is too late. No matter how bad the headlines get, the British public (and political class) can't seem to muster an appropriate level of fear. Instead, we feel boredom, helplessness, statistical snow-blindness and a kind of instinctive recoil into what we believe to be 'common-sense' solutions. And too often these solutions turn out to be not just wrong, but counter-productive.

CALCULATING BMI

BMI is calculated by dividing your weight by the square of your height in metric measures (kg/m^2). At an individual level, it is an inexact measure, not always reflective of the amount of fat you carry. Muscular athletes, for example, can have a high BMI without any pinchable fat on them. But at a population level BMI is a useful metric, and correlates closely with the risk of diet-related disease. An 18-year-old with a BMI greater than 35 has, on average, a 70 percent chance of developing diabetes at some point in their lifetime. A middle-aged woman with a BMI of 40 costs the NHS, on average, about twice as much as she would with a BMI of 22.

CHAPTER THREE

You can't outrun a bad diet

Exercise will make you healthier,
but it won't cure obesity

Most people in the UK – including the 60 percent who are overweight – believe there is a simple formula for improving dietary health: knowledge, exercise and willpower. Our government should provide information through public health campaigns and product labelling, encourage us to exercise, and leave the rest to individual self-control.

This 'feels' true. Each of us has a body, after all. We know that it grows and shrinks depending on what we put into it. Extrapolating from personal experience, we feel a rush of impatience at the idea of blaming 'the system' for our national weight problem. Surely it is up to each of us to take responsibility for what we eat?

The Sun newspaper made this argument with typical vigour in an editorial attacking proposals to ban junk food adverts before 9pm. Citing flawed data suggesting that such a ban would only trim two calories off a child's daily intake (more on this in *Chapter Eight*), the newspaper

poured scorn on other 'nanny state' interventions such as
the (actually quite successful) Soft Drinks Industry Levy.*
The government, it said, should abandon such 'ludicrous'
measures in favour of the 'common sense' solution: 'Better
education on diet – and exercise.'

The underlying belief here is that we are getting fat and
ill because we are too lazy to take exercise, and too igno-
rant to eat well. If only we were better informed about
healthy eating, and more conscientious about getting up off
our enormous bottoms, the obesity crisis would melt away.

But both these suppositions are demonstrably false.
Numerous studies have shown that the British public
already know what a healthy diet looks like. More than 90
percent of us know we should restrict our intake of foods
that are high in fat, sugar or salt (HFSS), and 99 percent
know we should eat 'five a day' of fruit and vegetables.
There is, admittedly, a serious skills gap when it comes to
cooking from scratch, and a need for much better cookery
lessons in schools. But we really don't need any more
preaching about healthy eating.

The problem is not information, but implementation. In
the next chapter, we will look in detail at why willpower
no longer seems to work. (Spoiler alert: it never did.)

What about exercise? It certainly seems logical to assume
that one of the major causes of the rise in obesity has been a
steep decline in physical activity. At the start of the twentieth
century, 28 percent of Britons worked in manufacturing –
mostly doing manual labour – and 11 percent in agriculture.
They would have used up a huge number of calories just

---

*   The SDIL was announced in 2016 and introduced in 2018. Drinks with
8 grams or more of sugar per 100 millilitres (high tier) are taxed at 24
pence per litre. Drinks with 5 to 8 grams of sugar per 100 millilitres (low
tier) are taxed at 0.18 pence per litre. Drinks with less than 5 grams of
sugar per 100 millilitres are not taxed.

getting through the working day. The Institute for Fiscal Studies has calculated that, to burn the same number of calories as a coal miner, an office worker would have to jog for more than ten hours a week.

By the end of the twentieth century, working patterns had changed dramatically. The proportion of Britons working in manual jobs halved, from four in ten to two in ten. Our domestic lives became more sedentary too. Labour-saving devices such as washing machines and vacuum cleaners have reduced the calorific expenditure required for housework, and cars have made it much easier to get around. The average person in the UK walked 255 miles per year in the mid-1970s, but only 179 miles in 2010. In the new digital age, many people no longer need to leave the house at all to work, play or socialise.

All this amounts to a fundamental change in the way humans interact with the world. We used to do it with muscle power; now we do it with machines. It seems obvious, therefore, that this must be what's making us fat: we are simply burning fewer calories overall than previous generations. The delicate metabolic balance between input and output has been disrupted by technology. But, bizarrely, it turns out that this isn't actually the case.

The average adult man burns about 3,000 calories a day; the average woman, about 2,400. It varies a little, depending on a number of factors, including weight and genetic makeup, but those numbers are the mean.

Broadly speaking, there are two states in which we burn calories: when we are active, and when we are 'resting'. The latter category, which typically accounts for about 60 percent of the calories we burn, is something of a misnomer. We might not appear to be doing much when we are stretched out on the sofa, but our bodies are always busy: breathing, pumping blood around, digesting, working our vital organs, thinking or dreaming (the brain accounts for only 2 percent of the average bodyweight, but approximately 20 percent of our total calorific spend). Some functions are constant, some sporadic, such as thermoregulation (sweating and shivering), the operation of the immune system, growing or menstruating.

When our bodies need energy, they 'burn' the glucose in our blood. This releases carbon dioxide, which is expelled in our breath. In the past, scientists calculated calorific expenditure by measuring the ratio of carbon dioxide in a person's breath, and comparing it to the ratio in the ambient air. But this required the test subject to be strapped into a variety of air-tight hoods, masks and chambers, like some medieval heretic, and could only be done under laboratory conditions.

Measuring carbon dioxide output as a person went about their daily life was impossible until the 1980s, when scientists developed a technique called the doubly labelled water method. This allowed them to calculate exactly how much carbon dioxide a subject breathed out over the course of a day, by getting them to drink water 'labelled' with heavy isotopes of hydrogen and oxygen, and then measuring the changing levels of those isotopes in their urine.

When scientists first started using this technique, they expected to find that each individual would burn a predictable number of calories for their 'resting' functions, and a variable number for their active periods, depending on the intensity of the physical movement. Their total energy expenditure would simply be the sum of these two parts.

This theory, known as the Additive Total Energy Expenditure Model (see the diagram opposite), is how most of us intuitively calculate our daily calorific allowance: the

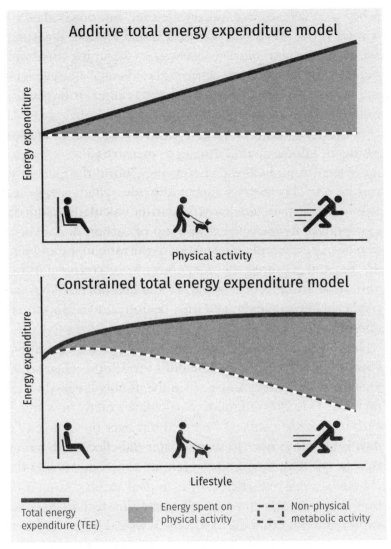

The Additive Total Energy Expenditure Model (top) is how most of us intuitively imagine our bodies work: that our 'resting' metabolism stays constant, whereas we can increase our 'active' metabolism by doing more exercise. In fact, the true model is the one below: the *Constrained Total Energy Expenditure Model*. When we increase our physical activity, the body fights back by reducing the energy it spends on the resting metabolism. This is why it is so hard to lose weight through exercise alone.

more we exercise, the more we burn. But once scientists started using the doubly labelled water method a weirdly counterintuitive pattern emerged. The daily energy expenditure of very physically active populations turned out to be almost the same as that of more sedentary, industrialised populations.

A study of Hadza hunter-gatherers in Tanzania, for example, showed they burned on average the same number of calories per day as urban-dwelling Americans. Another study showed that children of the indigenous Shuar people of Amazonian Ecuador burned the same number of calories regardless of whether they moved into towns and adopted a more sedentary lifestyle or lived like their parents as foraging horticulturalists. Women in rural farming populations in Nigeria have been shown to have similar calorie expenditures to women in metropolitan Chicago. And a global meta-study found that, across the board, people in less developed, more physically active populations have the same daily calorie expenditures as their more sedentary counterparts in rich countries.

How is this possible? To answer that question, we have to answer another, deeper question. What are we here for?

One answer, which will not appeal to the romantics among you, is that humans, in common with all species, are merely machines for converting energy into copies of ourselves. As the evolutionary anthropologist Herman Pontzer puts it in his book *Burn*: 'What is a fly, after all, except a little machine that builds baby flies out of rotten meat?' For any species, the key to success is to evolve a unique strategy for securing and converting this energy. To find a niche, however subtly different, in which you can be more efficient than other species. 'There are as many winning strategies in the game of life as there are species on the planet,' says Pontzer.

Early in his career, Pontzer was the first scientist to use the doubly labelled water method on various apes. His first subject was the orangutan, which he and his team were amazed to discover burned fewer calories each day than humans. 'The difference was huge. Azy, the 250-pound male, burned 2,050 kilocalories per day – the same as a 65-pound, nine-year-old human boy.'

Orangutans eat fruit or, when there is no fruit available, they strip bark from trees: a meagre diet but one they can cope with by moving slowly and spending very little energy on reproduction. Orangutans typically don't have their first child until they are 15, and only give birth about once every eight years – the longest interval between births of any mammal.

Pontzer went on to measure the energy expenditures of as many primates as he could, and discovered that all four great ape genera (chimpanzees and bonobos, gorillas, orangutans and humans) had evolved distinct daily energy expenditures. Humans have the highest, burning about 20 percent more than chimpanzees and bonobos, about 40 percent more than gorillas, and about 60 percent more than orangutans (after accounting for differences in body size).

This high-energy evolutionary strategy is what has made us so successful. Once we began to develop large, energy-hungry brains, we learnt how to find and cook food from many different sources. Cooking our food helped reduce the amount of energy required for digestion, freeing up more energy for our growing brains. A reinforcing feedback loop.

Humans are also – biologically, at least – extreme endurance athletes, designed to wear down our prey through sheer stamina. 'Our VO_2 max, a common measure of peak aerobic power, is at least four times that of chimpanzees.' says Pontzer. 'We have a much greater proportion of fatigue-resistant 'slow twitch' muscles. Our blood holds more haemoglobin to ferry oxygen to working muscle. And our naked, sweaty skin (by far the sweatiest on the planet) keeps us cool, protecting us from overheating even when exercising in hot conditions.'

It may well be this high-energy strategy that has led to our problems with diet-related disease. If you need a lot of calories to survive, you are obviously at greater risk of running short of food. To protect against starvation, therefore, we lay down fat in reserves. On average, humans lay down twice as much fat as other primates, and there appears to be no upper limit to this survival strategy. Captive apes – who have plentiful food, and are less physically active than in the wild – don't get obese. Their bodies convert the extra calories into lean tissue and bigger muscles and organs, but not much fat. Well-fed zoo apes tend to weigh much more than wild apes, but they remain lean. Nor do they suffer from heart disease, diabetes and the other consequences of a sedentary lifestyle in humans.

In order to maintain our high-energy survival strategy, humans have developed complex systems of biological feedback loops to control both energy intake (appetite) and expenditure (metabolism).

Let's look at expenditure first. How it possible that sedentary office workers expend, on average, roughly the same number of daily calories as hunter-gatherers? Clearly, our biological feedback loops must be working hard to keep us within a narrow range of energy use. It is as if we have a set budget for calorific expenditure.

When we exercise in the hope of losing weight, we are unconsciously using the Additive Total Energy Expenditure Model. We can't do anything to increase our 'resting' expenditure, but by springing up from the sofa and running a 10K, we hope to dramatically increase our overall total expenditure. And, at first, this is exactly what happens. In 2015, researchers used the doubly labelled water method to measure the daily energy expenditure of marathon runners in the Race Across the USA. The athletes had signed up to run 4,957 kilometres (3,080 miles) over twenty weeks: that is approximately one marathon per day, six days per week.

For the first few days, their daily energy expenditure was what you would expect: the sum of their resting metabolism (which researchers had measured in advance), plus the massive new energy outlay created by their daily marathons. But, after a week, their metabolisms showed signs of resistance. Their total energy expenditures began to drop back down, even though they were still running a marathon a day. By the end of the race, their total energy expenditure was down 600 kcal from the peak of those early days. Somehow, even as they carried on running, their bodies had found a way to limit the amount of energy they were spending.

There are two theories about how this metabolic balancing act might be achieved. The first is that our bodies simply compensate for increased exercise. When we consciously increase our exercise levels – by going for a run, say – we then unconsciously limit our physical activity for the rest of the day. We may fidget less, for example, or drive to the shops instead of walking.

The second theory, proposed by Pontzer and others, is that our bodies manage the fluctuations in our active energy use by allocating more or less energy to the functions powered by our 'resting' metabolism.

In evolutionary terms, argues Pontzer, our bodies are still designed for a hunter-gatherer's unpredictable life. It makes sense to be able to 'steal' energy from our resting metabolism at times when we need to move faster and longer. But it also makes sense, in quieter times, to invest any spare calories into the functions of our resting metabolism – particularly our reproductive and immune systems. The biological imperative is to stay healthy long enough to mate. Live fast, pass on your genes, die in a hunting accident.

Pontzer suggests this might explain why diseases of the immune and reproductive systems, such as breast cancer, Crohn's disease and IBS, have become so common in developed societies. We move so little that to maintain our total energy expenditure, our bodies invest too much energy into the systems governed by our resting metabolism. This leads to chronic inflammation, stress and reproductive cancers in industrialised populations.

It is possible, of course, that both explanations are true; the body has almost certainly evolved multiple methods for conserving energy.

What is clear, from study after study, is that exercise is not a good way to lose weight. If you increase your exercise level, your body will gradually adapt to moderate your energy output. You may burn slightly more calories than before – especially at first – but the effect will soon become much smaller than you would expect it to be. And even that is likely to be further compromised by increased appetite. Our body's feedback mechanisms work hard to stop us losing weight (of which more in the next chapter). One meta-analysis of exercise-only weight loss programmes showed that, on average, participants only lost 2kg after a year.

The idea that exercise is a good way to lose weight is not just incorrect it is actively harmful. Every January, people take out gym memberships in droves, hoping to lose weight. When the scales don't budge, they become disheartened and give up. But there are so many other benefits to exercising. It improves your posture and muscle tone, making you look good. It lowers blood pressure, reduces the risks of cancer, diabetes and osteoporosis, boosts the immune system and is great for your mental health. Building up muscle has been shown to help stabilise blood sugar, improve bone strength and protect against heart disease.

It is also the case that – for reasons scientists have not yet fully understood – exercise is very effective at helping people maintain a healthy BMI once they have lost weight. (See box below.)

Exercise benefits everyone, regardless of weight. If it could be prescribed it would be one of our most powerful and multi-disciplinary drugs. But in the public imagination it is associated almost exclusively with weight loss. And because it doesn't work well for that purpose, people get disillusioned and give up. The amazing things that exercise can do are eclipsed by the one thing it can't.

KEEPING THE WEIGHT OFF

While exercise is a lousy way to lose weight, it does appear to be useful in keeping it off. In 1989, researchers from the Boston University Medical Center conducted an experiment with 160 obese Boston police officers.

For eight weeks, all the officers were put on a 1,000-calorie diet. Half were asked to attend a 90-minute exercise session three times a week, while the other half continued as normal, without any additional exercise. The participants were then contacted six and eighteen

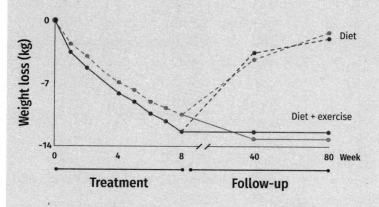

months after the end of the weight loss phase. They were weighed and asked questions about their ongoing eating and exercise habits.

The police officers who had done the additional exercise had only lost a small amount of extra weight. However, those who continued to do the extra exercise *after the weight loss phase had ended* proved much more successful at keeping the weight off. Those who didn't continue to exercise put it all back on.

We do not yet understand exactly what accounts for this. We know that people who have recently lost weight have a reduced resting energy expenditure, as their bodies strive to restore a safe metabolic equilibrium. One 2018 study, which used the doubly labelled water method, suggested that increased exercise might bring the body's total energy expenditure back to its pre-diet level. Because it recognises this as a safe level of expenditure, the body does not fight against it.

Whatever the exact mechanism, this is another reason to incorporate regular exercise into our lives.

CHAPTER FOUR

Appetite

*Our ancient biology can't cope
with the modern environment*

**In 1972, a plane carrying a team of Chilean rugby players,
their families and supporters, crashed in the Andes.** There
were only twenty-nine survivors. They salvaged what food
they could from the wreckage: a tin of mussels and another
of almonds; three jars of jam; some dates, sweets and dried
plums; eight chocolate bars; and several bottles of wine.
They eked out these meagre rations as best they could, but
within a week their supplies ran out. They tried to eat parts
of the plane – leather and cotton from the seats. But these
made them sick.

Faced with almost certain death, they decided, collectively,
to eat the corpses. They cut the flesh from the frozen bodies
with shards of glass from the plane's windscreen, drying it
in the sun and swallowing it raw. At first, they only ate the
skin, muscle and fat, but as stocks dwindled they moved
onto the hearts, lungs and brains. Another 13 passengers
died, from starvation (some refused to eat the human flesh),
exposure and an avalanche. But the remaining 16 lived
for 72 days, until an expeditionary party summoned help.
Their decision to eat the bodies of their friends and family
kept them alive. Their powerful appetites saved them.

At its most elemental, this is what appetite is: a biological system that compels us to seek out food. It isn't just greed – although greed can certainly be a by-product of appetite. It is a survival mechanism, hard-wired into our nervous system.

Under extreme conditions, our appetite can make us do almost anything. Getting sufficient water and food is always the body's top priority. If we are deprived of either, our other primary instincts quickly fall away. We become less alert to sudden threats, and lose interest in what would otherwise be the chief purpose of any species: reproduction. Appetite is the single most powerful driver of human behaviour. It is clearly not a system that you want to go wrong.

How does this system work?

The centre of appetite control in the body is a pea-sized area of the brain called the hypothalamus. This is one of the oldest parts of the brain, with evolutionary origins going all the way back to our worm-like marine ancestors. It controls our most basic, instinctive functions. The outer parts of the hypothalamus appear to be in charge of making us start eating, while the inner parts prompt us to stop. Mice lose their appetites completely if the outer hypothalamus is damaged – they refuse to eat even when there is tempting food right in front of them – whereas damage to the inner hypothalamus makes them gorge unstoppably, until they become obese.

The activity of the hypothalamus is determined by feedback signals from all over the body. These signals can be stimulated by the senses (the smell of a hot stew, or the look of a glossy ice-cream sundae); or by external events (adrenaline blocks appetite, because there's no time to stop and eat if you are in danger); or by internal mechanisms (for example, when your blood sugar is low, you will get hungry).

All sorts of different hormones carry this feedback to the hypothalamus, but there are four that seem to have a primary role in regulating appetite. These are leptin, peptide tyrosine tyrosine (PYY), glucagon-like peptide-1 (GLP-1) and ghrelin.* Each does a slightly different job. It is worth noting that all hormones perform multiple functions. Leptin, for example, also appears to have some role in how much energy we spend on reproduction and growth. Ghrelin affects memory and the sleep cycle. GLP-1 appears to be a particularly hard worker, helping to regulate activity in the brain, heart, tongue, muscles, bones, kidneys, liver and lungs. Our hormonal feedback loops have evolved by random mutation and selection. They act on the body in complex ways. This makes it difficult to devise hormone-based medical interventions without risking unwanted side effects.

Leptin takes its name from *leptos*, the ancient Greek for 'thin'. First discovered in 1994, its primary function is to regulate the amount of fat we lay down. Fat is a wonderful thing: it is light, stores lots of energy and keeps us warm. It acts both as a petrol tank and as insulation. We all need some fat on our bodies. But too much of it makes us less mobile, liable to overheating and prone to all sorts of physical malfunctions.

Leptin is mostly released by fat cells: the more fat cells you have, the more leptin you produce. In a well-functioning body, this should have the effect of putting a natural break on appetite. Once a body has laid down an optimal number

---

* Other hormones that influence our appetite include cholecystokinin, insulin, amylin, cortisol, melatonin, glucose-dependent insulinotropic polypeptide and pancreatic polypeptide. We are only beginning to understand this complex system.

of fat cells, those cells should release enough leptin to reduce overall hunger levels.

For a brief moment in 1997, it was thought that leptin injections might be the cure for obesity. Two morbidly obese children – an 8-year-old girl weighing 86kg (13st 8lb) and her 2-year-old male cousin who weighed 29kg (4st 8lb) – were being treated at a Cambridge hospital. They had a rare genetic disorder which meant they could not produce leptin. As a result, their hypothalamus always thought their petrol tanks were empty, regardless of how fat they got. From early infancy both children had been constantly hungry and begging for food. The girl had already undergone corrective limb surgery and liposuction to try to improve her mobility.

As soon as these children received leptin replacement injections, their appetites corrected themselves and they started to lose weight. Excited by this transformation, researchers began running trials of leptin injections on volunteers. But they quickly discovered that, in obese people without the genetic disorder, the injections had no effect. Their bodies were already producing plenty of leptin; it just wasn't doing its job. It seemed that, in the course of becoming obese, these volunteers had developed some form of leptin resistance.

If leptin is a long-term appetite suppressant, PYY and GLP-1 are the short-term versions. They make us feel full after eating. Both hormones are released from the cells of the intestine as food passes through it, signalling to the hypothalamus to dial down the hunger now that the belly is full. Fat and protein stimulate particularly high levels of PYY production. One theory as to why salty snacks are so moreish is that they are often coated in monosodium glutamate (MSG), which is typically present in high-protein dishes. Detected by the 'umami' sensors on our tongues,

MSG plays a trick on our appetite. (Our tastebuds can detect five main flavours: salt, sweet, sour, bitter and 'umami' – the savoury flavour found in foods such as cooked meat, mushrooms, cheese and soy sauce.) We want lots of protein, so we gobble down the snack; but when it hits the stomach, it doesn't unleash as much PYY as our body is expecting. So we keep eating, waiting for the feeling of satisfaction that should accompany a protein hit. Once we pop, we can't stop.

The fourth significant hormone connected to appetite is ghrelin: the 'hunger hormone'. This is predominantly produced in the stomach when it is empty. It not only stimulates our hypothalamus to make us hungry, but excites the pleasure areas in our brain to make food taste better. It increases both the desire to find food and the reward we get for finding it. As most of us know from experience, ghrelin can be a tyrannical master. When your brain is flooded with ghrelin, it is impossible to think about anything but food. When we say we are feeling 'mad with hunger', we are hardly exaggerating.*

Over the years, doctors have devised extreme measures to help overweight people resist their own hunger. The bariatric surgeon Andrew Jenkinson describes some of these in his book *Why We Eat (Too Much)*. The brutal-looking practice of jaw-wiring requires a dentist to fix metal brackets to the top and bottom teeth and then screw them shut, leaving only a tiny gap through which to push morsels of food. More recent inventions include the gastric band – a plastic ring placed at the top of the stomach that restricts

* There is still much debate about how people with anorexia succeed in living with hunger. One thing researchers know is that, once the human body goes below a certain weight, strange things can start to happen to hormones. Ghrelin levels appear to become suppressed. When a person with anorexia starts trying to put weight back on, leptin comes flooding back, sooner than it should and in larger quantities. This means they feel satiated quickly, which makes it a struggle to keep eating.

how fast you can eat – and an intra-gastric balloon, which is inflated inside the stomach to reduce its capacity.

All these techniques have been shown to have poor long-term outcomes, with most patients eventually putting back on any weight they lose – but not before they have endured something close to psychological torture. The dramatic reduction in food intake means that ghrelin levels soar. The patient's rational mind – which wants to lose weight, so badly that they signed up for this drastic intervention – is overpowered by its own hormonal feedback. Patients with wired jaws often end up sating their hunger by slurping sugary milkshakes through a straw. Those with gastric bands or balloons may eat lots of small but ultra-high-calorie snacks. A slice of chocolate cake provides enough calories to switch off the ghrelin (at least temporarily), while taking up less stomach capacity than a proper, high-fibre meal.

Patients know this is 'cheating', and they feel awful about it. They know they are undermining themselves, and disappointing everyone who has tried to help them. Often they are stricken with guilt that the NHS spent all this money on them, and they are still too 'weak' to resist.*

Crash diets, in all their forms, make us ravenous – and not just in the weight loss phase. They increase our ghrelin levels even after we have started eating normally again. For months afterwards, ghrelin levels remain high, making us hungrier than we were before we tried to lose weight.

In November 1944, the American physiologist Ancel Keyes gathered thirty-six volunteers at the University

---

* Newer forms of bariatric surgery have proved much more manageable and effective, precisely because they disrupt the hormones associated with appetite. More on these in *Chapter Nine*.

of Minnesota to conduct what was to become an iconic study into the psychological and physiological effects of starvation. His motives were benign: all across war-stricken Europe people were starving, and Keyes wanted to work out how best to rehabilitate them. The volunteers were selected from 400 conscientious objectors, who saw it as an opportunity to make a peaceful contribution to a better future. Marshall Sutton, a 26-year-old Quaker who took part in the study, later recalled: 'I wanted to identify with the suffering in the world at that time. I wanted to do something for society. I wanted to put myself in a little danger.'

Keyes divided the study into three phases. The first, lasting three months, was 'Controlled Feeding'. The men were fed normally (about 3,200 calories per day), exercised regularly and took a weekly fitness test on an enormous treadmill that could accommodate up to six men at a time.

The second phase, 'Starvation', lasted six months. The men were fed about 1,500 calories a day. The food was designed to be the kind of thin, bland fare that war survivors might have been forced to live on: watery soup, turnips, swede, potatoes, macaroni. No meat. During this phase they had to walk 22 miles (35 km) a week and continue the weekly treadmill test.

In the final three-month 'Rehabilitation' phase, the men's diet was gradually increased, and then they were allowed to eat as they wished.

During the starvation phase, as you would expect, the men's physiology changed significantly. They lost, on average, 25 percent of their weight. Their resting metabolisms decreased by 40 percent, as their bodies tried to slow the weight loss and hang onto what little energy they had. Sutton coped by trying his utmost not to think about food. He spent as little time as possible in the canteen. 'I ate what I had in about three minutes and got out of there.

Minnesota hunger project volunteers relax in the sun. Left to right: Gerald Wilsnack, Marshall Sutton and Jasper Garner.

I didn't want to stay,' he recalled. 'There were some in the experiment who lingered over that food for 20 minutes. Some fellows were reading cookbooks all the time.'

'Food became the one central and only thing really in one's life,' reported Harold Blickenstaff, another participant. 'I mean, if you went to a movie, you weren't particularly interested in the love scenes, but you noticed every time they ate and what they ate.'

When the men were allowed to eat again, they quickly returned to their old weights – and more. On average, they put on an extra 10 percent above their pre-starvation weight, with a greater proportion of fat to muscle. Their bodies, having experienced an interruption in the food supply, were determined to build up bigger fat reserves.

For years after the study finished, most of the volunteers were still above their pre-study weight, and with a higher proportion of body fat. Three of the men remained overweight for the rest of their lives.

The same phenomenon has now been reported in many different studies. When we undereat, the body activates its emergency protocol: first by massively restricting energy expenditure, and then by increasing our appetite, so that once food is available again we put on more weight. A buffer against future famine.

In fact, the physiological impact of severe calorie restriction can extend across generations. In the winter of 1944 to 1945, German blockades caused a famine in Holland. Known to us as the Dutch Famine, the Dutch call it *Hongerwinter* ('Hunger Winter'). Because the healthcare system remained intact, we can track what happened to the babies who were in the womb during this period of starvation. Children of the *Hongerwinter* were 30 percent more likely to be obese in later life. Their siblings, born before and after the famine, were not affected.

What we see here is metabolism and appetite working hand in hand to adapt to the calorific environment. If food supply reduces, we reduce energy expenditure and obsess about food. When food is plentiful again, our appetite increases to ensure we have sufficient fat reserves to survive the next famine.

As a survival mechanism, it makes perfect sense. But it means that people who want to lose weight often find themselves trapped in a vicious circle. Determined to take control of their weight, they go on a diet. The first day or two might not be too bad: their liver uses up its glycogen stores first, so they don't feel too hungry. They weigh themselves and find they have lost a few pounds. This is going well. But as they continue the diet, their body starts to fight back, increasing ghrelin output and reducing the resting metabolism. Progress slows. But perhaps, if they are determined enough, they manage to hit their target weight.

Within a year they find that they have not only regained the weight, but added more. So they try another diet – and get fatter still. Over a lifetime, they end up more overweight than if they had never started dieting at all.

One of the ironies of this cycle of failure is that it has created an enormous marketplace for new diets, and diet-related products. The very fact that dieting doesn't work means there are always plenty of consumers looking for something that might help them lose weight.

Food manufacturers have responded to this demand with products that are marketed as 'healthy' or 'slimming', when usually they are nothing of the sort. Food packaging is littered with claims that, if not quite lies, are at least wilfully misleading. 'Low fat' tends to mean high in sugar or starch, but it never says so. The words 'free from' are sprinkled around without context. A snack that is sickly with concentrated fruit sugars can still carry the pious boast: 'Free from added sugar'. Nutritional values – calories, salt, sugar, etc. – are given 'per portion', even when a portion bears no resemblance to the quantity of food on offer.

Consumers are easily confused, in part because much of the food on offer today is hard to understand. Largely composed of additives and ingredients that most people have never heard of, let alone seen or touched, it carries very little intuitive meaning. It bears little resemblance, in fact, to food.

CHAPTER FIVE

Anatomy of an egg sandwich

Ultra-processed food and the gut microbiome

On the train from the Lake District to London, I bought an egg mayonnaise sandwich from the buffet car. The front of the packet carried the proud boast 'handmade'. Sceptically, I turned it over to read the ingredients.

1. Flour
2. Water
3. Malted wheat grain
4. Yeast
5. Wheat gluten
6. Barley malt flour
7. Toasted wheat
8. Salt
9. Dextrose
10. Soya flour
11. Sugar
12. Buckwheat flour
13. Monoglycerides of fatty acids
14. Diglycerides of fatty acids
15. Diacetyl tartaric acid
16. Esters of monoglycerides of fatty acids
17. Esters of diglycerides of fatty acids
18. Calcium propionate
19. Vegetable oil
20. Vegetable fat
21. L-ascorbic acid
22. Eggs
23. Rapeseed oil
24. Pasteurised egg yolk
25. Spirit vinegar
26. Mustard
27. Xanthan gum
28. Black pepper
29. Whey powder
30. Potassium sorbate
31. Citric acid
32. Carotenes

The word 'handmade' is intended to conjure up images of wholesome domesticity: fresh food made with familiar ingredients in a recognisable kitchen by a skilled cook. No doubt my sandwich was to some degree 'handmade' – in the literal sense that human hands did some of the work of assembling it. Even now, there is a limit to what robots can do. But really, it wasn't made by anyone: it was processed. And this is true not just of the sandwich, but of all its constituent parts.

Let's take one of the more natural-sounding ingredients on that list: rapeseed oil. This is made from the tiny black seeds of the bright yellow rapeseed flowers that give the British countryside a technicolour splash every spring. It is possible to extract rapeseed oil simply by squeezing it out of the seeds. But cold-pressed rapeseed oil is a yellowy colour, with a distinctive – to my nose fishy, but some say cabbagey – aroma. This won't do for large-scale commercial use, so the vast majority of rapeseed oil goes through extensive industrial processing.

Typically, the seeds are first separated from debris in an enormous vibrating sieve. The chaff that is left behind is sold off as cattle feed. The seeds then fall past a powerful electric magnet, which removes any tiny metal fragments, and are crushed into thin flakes between steel rollers. These flakes are 'cooked' in steam to rupture the cell walls, before being squeesed at high pressure by a screw press, which forces out about 75 percent of the oil.

The remaining oil is still trapped in the hard 'cake' of pressed seed. To remove it, the cake is dissolved in a heated chamber containing hexane: a cheap industrial solvent produced when crude oil is refined. Hexane is used, elsewhere, as a solvent for glues and as an industrial de-greaser in the printing industry. The oil in the cake dissolves into the hexane to create a solution known as miscella. This miscella is then separated from the cake (which is again sold as animal feed). Finally, the hexane is distilled out of the miscella with steam, and the resulting oil is added to the first batch, in steel silos.

I say 'finally', but actually this is only the end of the first step. The oil now enters the 'refining' phase of its production. Depending on the chosen methods of each factory, this process might start with a 20-minute steam-powered wash in caustic soda (sodium hydroxide), which reacts with fatty acids in the oil and turns them into soap. This is done in a centrifuge, so the soap (and other impurities) are spun off at high speed. The soap is sold on to soap manufacturers.

However, the oil is still yellow and contains natural waxes which make it look cloudy. So next it is cooled to 5 °C (this process is sometimes known as winterisation), at which point the waxes solidify and can be filtered out. The waxes are used to produce vegetable shortening.

Water and organic acids may be used to remove lipids, gums, free fatty acids and fine meal particles. The oil is then 'bleached', by passing it through a mixture of clay and synthetic silica (similar to the filters used in First World War gas masks) and then heated to about 100 °C. Once the oil is no longer yellow, its distinctive odour is removed by passing steam through layers of oil held in trays and heating them to 180–240 °C in a high-pressure boiler.

The product that emerges from all this processing might be called rapeseed oil (or canola oil in America), but chemically it is completely different from the yellow, pungent cold-pressed stuff. And something similar could be said of almost every ingredient in that egg mayo sandwich.

It is unnerving to realise you don't actually know what the food you are eating is; that its true provenance and composition is virtually unknowable, however hard you scrutinise the ingredients list. Modern industrial food processing is so high-tech and multi-layered as to be mysterious to almost everyone. But does that actually matter? All sorts of wonderful modern inventions, including life-saving medicine, are too scientifically complex for the lay person to understand. As long as a food product is tasty and safe to eat, what does it matter how it was made?

The idea that there is something inherently bad about industrially manufactured food is not exactly new. When I was a child, the worry was all about 'E-numbers' (chemical food additives, which had been newly classified by the EU). That worry turned out be at least partly justified: several E-numbers, especially food colourants, were found to cause problems such as hyperactivity or anaemia, and have since been banned.

Today, the debate is about 'ultra-processed' food: a term coined by the Brazilian physician Carlos Monteiro, who has spent his working life studying what different manufacturing methods do to food. In 2009, Monteiro published a new categorisation system for food. Known as NOVA, it divided all commercially available edible products into four groups:

1. *Unprocessed or minimally processed foods.* This group includes anything from a tomato to a bunch of mint, a pork chop to a walnut. They are obtained

directly from plants or animals and go through minimal processing (such as cleaning or freezing) before reaching our kitchens.

2. *Processed culinary ingredients.* This includes things like butter, sugar and honey. They are extracted from nature by processes such as pressing, grinding, crushing, pulverising and refining. They are often used sparingly to make other foods delicious.

3. *Processed foods.* These contain elements from groups 1 or 2, processed by manufacturers – often salted, fermented or pickled. They include bacon, cheeses, canned fruit and vegetables, smoked salmon and traditionally made bread.

4. *Ultra-processed foods.* These are quite different from the other groups. They tend to contain the sugars, oils and starches from group 2, but instead of being used sparingly these ingredients make up the bulk of the dish. Ultra-processed foods also contain ingredients unfamiliar to domestic kitchens, such as soy protein isolates or dextrose. Colourings, emulsifiers, flavourings and other additives are added to make the products better-looking, tastier, more stable and longer-lasting. This makes them extremely 'moreish' – or 'hyper-palatable', in Monteiro's jargon. Foods in this group include most shop-bought biscuits and cakes, mass-produced bread, reconstituted meat products, mass-produced desserts, some vegan sausages and burgers, and many ready meals.

Based on these definitions, the British eat more ultra-processed food than any other European country. It comprises 57 percent of our diet, according to the *British Medical Journal*. This compares to 46 percent for Germany,

14 percent for France and 13 percent for Italy. So what is this ultra-processed diet doing to our bodies?

Rats and mice have many of the same metabolic quirks as humans. Some are born with a disorder that prevents them producing leptin. Like the children mentioned on page 66, they become severely obese and exhibit constantly ravenous behaviour. But researchers have found that even rats who produce a normal amount of leptin react strangely to ultra-processed food. They seem to develop a resistance to their own leptin, and become obese. Once they are put back on a diet of natural foods, they lose that weight again.

Monteiro argues that a similar thing happens in humans. Ultra-processed food is known to have a disproportionate effect on weight and health, compared to equivalent food cooked from scratch. Studies have shown that an incremental 10 percent increase in the proportion of ultra-processed foods in a person's diet is correlated with a 12 percent increase in cancers, a 21 percent increase in depressive symptoms and a 12 percent increase in cardiovascular disease risk.

Sceptics – including some distinguished academics, as well as large food manufacturers – argue that Monteiro has created a straw man. 'Ultra-processed', they say, is just a new piece of jargon. What it actually describes is food that is sugary or fatty or salty, or all of these at once. We already know that, taken in excess, these ingredients are not good for us. Why blame the degree of processing, rather than the contents?

Dr Kevin Hall started out as one of these sceptics. A senior researcher at the US National Institute of Diabetes and Digestive and Kidney Diseases, he ran a clinically controlled trial in 2019, in an attempt to settle the argument once and for all. Hall gathered ten men and ten women at a clinic just outside Washington, DC. Over a four-week residential stay, they were fed two different diets under controlled conditions. For two weeks, the participants ate mostly ultra-processed meals, such as turkey sandwiches with crisps, and then for another two weeks they ate mostly unprocessed food, such as spinach omelette with sweet potato hash. The diets were carefully matched for fat, sugar, calories and fibre. The researchers also worked hard to design both sets of meals to be tasty and familiar to all participants. When participants were asked to rate the food for pleasure, there was little difference.

Blood tests showed that, when the participants were on the unprocessed diet, their levels of the appetite-suppressing hormone PYY increased in comparison to when they were on the processed diet. Levels of the hunger hormone ghrelin, by contrast, fell. In other words, they felt less hungry and got full more easily when they were eating freshly cooked, unprocessed food. Not surprisingly, they lost weight: an average of 0.9kg.

When they were on the ultra-processed diet, the participants ate an average of 500 calories more per day than on the unprocessed diet, and gained an average of 0.9kg. These are big differences – easily enough to explain massive weight gain across a population.

It is still not clear exactly why ultra-processed food has this effect on appetite. Kevin Hall has been running further studies, which so far suggest there may be two interlinked factors: calorific density and so-called 'hyper-palatability'. This phrase is used to describe foods that we perceive as extra-delicious because they contain specific ratios of nutrients – fat and salt; fat and sugar; and salt and carbohydrates – that do not appear in unprocessed food. Hall's experiments have found that people find it much harder to manage their intake of 'hyper-palatable' foods.

Chicago-based physicist Albert-László Barabási has his own theory about ultra-processed foods. Barabási is a pioneer in the science of 'complex systems'. In his book *Linked*, he argues that, until now, scientists have tried to understand nature by disassembling it – for example, breaking matter down into elements and then into electrons, neutrons and protons. The science of nutrition has mostly consisted of studying food through its component parts – vitamins, minerals, proteins, fibre and so on – rather than considering how all the different components interact.

This, he says, is a fundamental misunderstanding of how complex systems work. The hubs and spokes within any network, from the internet to the food chain, can produce different effects depending on how they are arranged, and even the smallest change in the topography of a network can radically alter its behaviour. 'In complex systems,' he writes, 'the components can fit together in so many ways that it would take billions of years for us to try them all. Yet nature assembles the pieces with a grace and precision honed over millions of years.'

Having already mapped the complex reactions between different proteins inside human cells, Barabási turned his attention to food. Scientists, he notes, have recorded more than 26,000 distinct biochemicals* across the entire range of food eaten by humans. Yet most nutritional research is centred on the 150 key nutritional components tracked and catalogued by the USDA (United States Department of Agriculture). Some of this research has been extremely important, transforming our understanding of the role of

---

* A recent estimate suggests there may be over 50,000.

calories, sugar, fat, vitamins and other nutrients. But without studying how the thousands of micronutrients within any given food interact, how can we properly understand their impact on health?

Consider garlic, a key ingredient of the Mediterranean diet. The USDA lists sixty-seven nutritional components in raw garlic, but each clove actually contains at least 2,306 distinct chemical components. Two examples are allicin, an organosulfur compound responsible for the distinct aroma of the freshly crushed clove, and luteolin, a colourless crystalline compound with reported protective effects in cardiovascular disease.

In one of his laboratory studies, Barabási compared the chemical composition of a range of ultra-processed foods with similar home-cooked dishes. He found that, even where the macronutrient profiles looked similar – same levels of protein, carbohydrates, fat, etc. – the micronutrients in ultra-processed foods were different in quantity and type. The reason for this is still unclear. Is it the processing itself that causes the difference, is it the recipes, or is it an interaction between the specific ingredients that go into this kind of food?

Barabási has now created a machine-learning tool which can search and draw from all the academic papers written in every country in every language. In this way, he hopes to build a digital catalogue of every nutritional biochemical, along with all the research done on each so far, to better understand how they react with each other and with our bodies to make us healthy or sick. He calls this a study of 'the dark matter of nutrition'.

What Barabási's work shows us is how much we don't yet know. Not just about the array of biochemicals in our food, but about how they might work together. Nutrition has long been the Cinderella of medical research, even though – or perhaps because – its effects are so dauntingly widespread.

The British scientist Tim Spector conducted an experiment that elegantly proved this point. As a genetic epidemiologist, specialising in the study of twins, Spector has spent much of his career trying to untangle the influences of nature and nurture on various medical conditions. This led him to an interest in nutrition, and then the gut microbiome, where he now focuses most of his research.

Spector's team sent out a survey to thirteen professors of nutrition at prestigious institutions, asking them how they would rate 105 different common foods in terms of how healthy they were. For half the foods, the professors were in broad agreement. Most fruits and vegetables were considered beneficial; and most processed foods, savoury snacks, sugary foods and drinks and cheap fried foods were not. But for the other half of the foods – including lots of dairy products, lean meat, artificially sweetened drinks and dried fruits – there was no consensus.

Spector argues, like Barabási, that nutritional science is still struggling to grasp the inherent complexity of our bodies and their reactions to food. The average person, globally, eats 35 tonnes of food over a lifetime. Americans eat more than twice that amount – and we Brits are not far behind. This torrent of food doesn't just pass through us; it becomes us. It is used to make new cells, blood and tissue and bone.

If we don't put in the right fuel, our cells struggle to function properly. This can manifest itself in any number of diseases: not just diabetes and coronary heart disease, but strokes, cancer, depression, and arthritis. In this sense, we really are what we eat.

What is true for our cells is also true for our gut biome.

We each have around 37 trillion cells in our body, every one of which runs off the energy provided by the food we eat. But these are marginally outnumbered by the 40 trillion bacteria in our guts – our microbiome* – which feed off the same food. We are just beginning to understand how important these bacteria are to the functioning of our bodies. In his book *Food for Life*, Spector says it is best to think of this collection of foreign bodies as 'little chemical factories or pharmacies'. While the cells in our gut wall can produce about twenty enzymes to digest our food, our microbiome can produce thousands of chemicals that play a part in digestion. This is just one of the services our microbiome provides. We know that it also helps protect against other disease-causing bacteria, produces vitamins such as B6, and has a close relationship with our immune system. In laboratory experiments, mice reared to have no gut biome – or any exposure to microbes at all – lack a properly functioning immune system.**

We also know that, even in identical twins, individual biomes can be very different, populated by different kinds of bacteria in varying numbers – and that this difference is connected to diet. The greater the variety of vegetables you eat, for example, the greater the diversity of your biome.

Understanding what food does to the complex systems of the human body should be a top priority for scientists

* A microbiome is simply a community of microscopic organisms (such as bacteria, fungi and viruses) that inhabit a particular environment – in this case, our guts.
** The focus of research is currently on bacteria, but our gut is also teeming with fungi, parasites and viruses. Spector recently discovered that he was one of 25 percent of adults in the UK (and 4 percent in the USA) that has a parasite called *Blastocystis* living inside him. Hosts to this parasite tend to be thinner and produce less internal fat.

and doctors – especially now that our health services are so clearly sinking under the landslide of diet-related illness. Yet in a recent survey of UK doctors and medical students, over 70 percent said they had less than two hours of nutritional training while at medical school. 'Nothing is considered more of a pussy move, in health care, than nutritional intervention,' says Dr Casey Means, an American physician who gave up practising in despair when she realised that almost all her patients – although presenting with very different symptoms – were suffering from diseases related to poor diet.

Means, who now runs a tech company that helps people monitor their own blood sugar, points out that big food manufacturers spend a fortune on scientific research to make us eat more of their products. 'Food technologists', for example, develop and refine techniques for improving 'mouth feel' – the way a food crunches, melts or oozes in the mouth – and actively look for ways to hijack our satiety hormones, so that it takes longer to feel full.

'Food designers' are in charge of making sure the shape, colour and texture of the product is appetising, both in and out of the packet. There are food chemists, sensory scientists, food consultants and food marketers, all paid to find ways of making processed food irresistible. Yet nutritional medicine remains a chronically underfunded area of health research, and something that many doctors don't really know how to treat.

We have spent 'trillions of research dollars' taking nature apart 'like a child taking apart his favourite toy', writes Barabási. 'Now we are close to knowing just about everything there is to know about the pieces. But we are as far as we have ever been from understanding nature as a whole.'

CHAPTER SIX

Inequality

Eating well is much harder if you are poor

In his youth, the TV presenter Andrew Marr was a devout Marxist – dubbed 'Red Andy' by his fellow Cambridge students. Asked about this at a book festival, Marr explained that in later life he had come to appreciate the power of the free market – albeit with reservations. 'The market is something we live in all the time,' he said. 'It's almost the water we swim in, and it gives us all the things we take for granted about ourselves. It's a great machine for inventiveness and ingenuity, but it presents two really serious problems. One is dirt: it produces filth and pollution. The second is that it produces huge and unacceptable levels of inequality. For me, the job of politics is to remove the dirt, and reduce inequality.'

Much of this book is about the 'dirt' – or externalities, in economics jargon – created by the food system. But in this chapter I want to focus on inequality.

It isn't just capitalism that creates inequality. Throughout human history inequality has been a defining feature of our species, regardless of the political structure we use to govern ourselves. In *The Great Leveller*, the Stanford-based historian Walter Scheidel showed how inequality always increases over time, from the Stone Age to the present day, thriving in both communist dictatorships and capitalist democracies. Only the 'Four Horsemen' of social levelling – mass-mobilisation warfare, transformative revolutions, state collapse and catastrophic plagues – have ever significantly reduced inequality. And it never goes peacefully.

In modern Britain, the way we eat is one of the clearest markers of inequality. You can actually see it with the naked eye. A diet of cheap junk food has the peculiar quality that it can make you simultaneously overweight and undernourished. Children in the poorest areas of England are both fatter and significantly shorter than those in the richest areas at age 10–11. (This is a big enough problem to have an impact at an international level. The average 5-year-old in the UK is shorter than their peers in nearly all other high-income countries.)

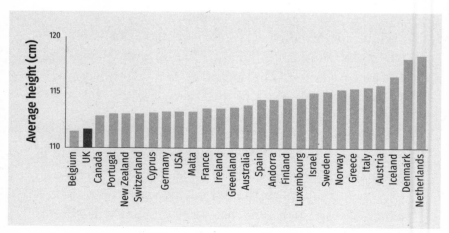

Average height of girls in high-income Western countries, 2019. British girls are the second shortest in the wealthy world. British boys are the shortest.

In recent years, GPs in the poorest areas have reported an extraordinary resurgence of 'Victorian' diseases such as rickets and scurvy, which are largely caused by nutritional deficiencies. Analysis of the annual National Diet and Nutrition Survey shows that children from the least well off 20 percent of families consume around a third less fruit and veg, 75 percent less oily fish, and a fifth less fibre than children from the most well off 20 percent.

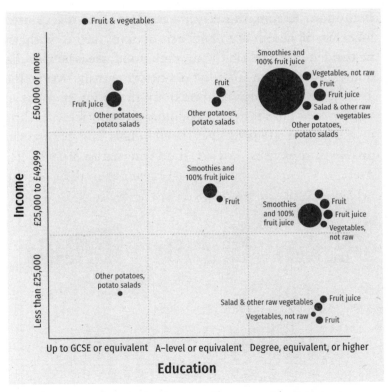

There is a strong correlation between income, educational attainment, and fruit and vegetable consumption. The circles on this chart show where each group consumes more than the population average. They represent foods that stand out on a statistical basis, not the total diet of that economic group. The size of the circle is the difference between consumption in the demographic and the population as a whole.

The consequences of this are captured in dreadful statistics. Children in the most deprived decile are three times more likely to have tooth decay at age 5, compared to those in the richest decile, and nearly twice as likely to be overweight or obese at age 11. Their parents are almost twice as likely to die from a diet-related condition. They are, on average, 2.1 times more likely to die from preventable cardiovascular (heart) disease (CVD) and 1.7 times more likely to die from 'preventable' cancers (those that are chiefly associated with environmental or lifestyle factors).

Dietary ill health is a major reason why, at the height of the pandemic, people in the most deprived areas were twice as likely to die from Covid. Even before then, however, the upward trajectory of life expectancy in the UK had begun to slow – and, in some areas, go into reverse. Women in the most deprived 10 percent of neighbourhoods in England now die 3.6 months younger than they did in 2010. Their

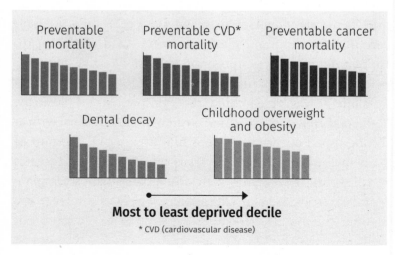

People on low incomes are more likely to suffer, and die, from diet-related conditions. The bars on each chart show the relative risk of suffering from each condition, moving from the 10 percent least affluent postcodes on the left, across to the most prosperous on the right.

life expectancy is 7.7 years shorter than that of women in the richest areas. The differential for men is 9.5 years. For 'healthy life expectancy' – i.e. the number of years a person spends in good health – there is an even greater disparity, with a gap of nineteen years between rich and poor.

The same households that struggle to eat well may sometimes find themselves unable to eat at all. Data collected by the Department of Work and Pensions in 2019 (before the pandemic or the cost of living crisis, both of which have pushed many more households into poverty) found that 4 percent of UK families were already having to cut back on food due to a lack of resources (the government calls this 'very low food security'.) Among those on Universal Credit, this proportion rose to 26 percent.

By now some readers may be writhing irritably, wondering whatever happened to personal responsibility. The wartime generation managed to survive on scraps, through careful budgeting and menu planning. Lentils are cheap. Isn't eating badly a symptom of laziness, or at best incompetence, rather than just poverty?

While I was researching the National Food Strategy, I got embroiled in an email argument about this with a distinguished economist. I sent him a paper by a group of academics from Oxford University which estimated the cost of following the Eatwell Plate (the government's template for a balanced diet) at £5.99 per day. This was similar to the amount the average UK citizen spends daily on food, but well above the average of £3.60 spent by those in the poorest decile of the population. He emailed me this response:

I remain unconvinced that food that is bad for you is cheaper than food that is good for you. What evidence is there for this proposition? Veg is very cheap. Asda will sell you peas for 68p a kg, which is cheaper than their cheapest oven chips.

Asda have a special offer on cheese and tomato pizza today – 70p. That is about as low as a prepared ready meal goes. For 70p, I can get a jacket potato (200g, 13p), 10g of butter (5p), one chicken drumstick (125g gross, 72g net, 23p), 80g of peas (5p), and 240g of broccoli, carrots and cauliflower mix (24p).

My meal would fill you up much more: it weighs 600g rather than 330g, and it has 488 kcal rather than 391. It is really hard to find a cheaper thing than veg.

I was poor once, but it was a long time ago. My mum tried very hard not to cry when I lost a pair of new school shoes, coming back from a cross country race. She succeeded but it was so obvious that she was trying that the victory was Pyrrhic. It is tough being poor. You are tired most of the time. The lure of the chippy is real. But the problem – I think – is poverty and exhaustion, not the price of bread, yoghurt or vegetables.

The economist has a point. It is indeed possible to assemble a healthy meal for 70p. But the practicalities are not straightforward. Let's take it step by step.

First, you have to find your raw ingredients. The poorer you are, the harder this is likely to be. In wealthy areas, it is still possible to find butchers, fishmongers and even greengrocers on the high street – along with well-stocked convenience stores and mini-supermarkets. But in low-income areas the streets have been colonised by fast food joints. There are almost twice as many fast food outlets in the most deprived areas of England compared to the least (see the chart opposite). In one area of the north-west,

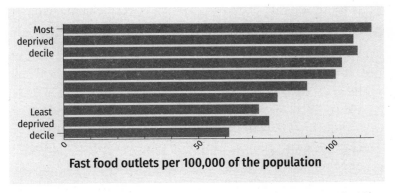

Fast food outlets per 100,000 of the population

The poorer you are, the more likely you are to be surrounded by fast food. The most deprived areas of the UK have nearly twice as many fast food outlets per capita as the richest.

there are 230 fast food outlets for every 100,000 people, compared to an England-wide average of 96.

In these so-called 'food swamps', it can be impossible to find non-processed food. Roughly 3.3 million people in the UK live in areas where there are no shops selling fresh ingredients within 15 minutes by public transport. Since 40 percent of the lowest-income households lack access to a car – almost twice the national average – the practicalities of 'healthy' shopping can be daunting. You need to find the time and energy (and the fare) for a long bus journey to a supermarket, followed by a return journey lugging heavy shopping bags.

Once you do get to the supermarket, your tiny budget makes it hard to shop economically. You can't buy supermarket ingredients in the way our economist suggests: a single chicken drumstick, a handful of peas, a knob of butter. You have to buy a pack of drumsticks and a bag of frozen peas and a block of butter, which would immediately take you well over the 70p threshold.

If, somehow, you could scrabble together enough money to pay for it all, you could cook in bulk and store the extra food for future meals. But only if you have a big enough freezer. Or any freezer at all. Cooking requires technology, even at the most basic level. There are currently 1.9 million people in the UK living without a cooker, 2.8 million people without a freezer and 900,000 people without a fridge. Many more households have the relevant white goods in place, but not enough money to run them.

And then there's the final – for some the biggest – hurdle. Cooking from scratch requires time, knowledge and confidence. Kitchen skills have diminished across every social class since convenience food became widely available. Several generations have now been raised in households where no one ever cooked. They have never seen their parents whisk an egg or peel a potato, let alone boil a carcass to make cheap stock. As one generation after another grows up without seeing or trying cookery at home, the national level of culinary skill keeps diminishing. (This is another example of a reinforcing feedback loop.)

The tighter your budget, the smaller your margin for error. You can't afford to learn how to cook by trying things out and making mistakes. Naomi Eisenstadt, an expert on child poverty who launched the Sure Start programme in 1999, told me: 'The women that I worked with knew what a healthy diet was. But they couldn't afford to say to their children, "Well, try it – if you don't like it you can have something else." Instead, poorer mothers fed their children the less healthy stuff that was certain to be eagerly received.'

The plain fact is that unhealthy processed food is cheaper per calorie than fresh food, and that's before you factor in the valuable time spent shopping and cooking from scratch, or the risk that your amateur cooking goes to waste. If you're tired and short of time – and especially if you're not a confident cook – it makes perfect economic sense to buy a box of chicken and chips instead of toiling at the stove.

I met Daisy Stemple, a single mother of two young girls, through a food bank in Thanet. She later agreed to sit on the advisory panel for the National Food Strategy, and helped make the argument to government for funding hot meals and activities for children during school holidays. (Known as the 'Holiday Activities and Food', or HAF programme, this has now been rolled out to all schools in England.) I have reproduced Daisy's testimony below, as it answers my economist friend more eloquently than I ever could.

> I think one of the main things I'd like people to know is that when you're poor your food budget has to be flexible. It's not always a priority. My girls can't walk around with shoes that don't fit, or no coat in the cold weather, but they can eat beans or egg on toast multiple times a week. So if there is an unexpected expense like shoes, or an unusually high heating bill, my food budget will be the first to take a cut.
>
> It's this that makes school dinners so important to me. If you know your child has had a big, healthy meal at school, it takes the pressure off at home. Which is why during school holidays my food costs increase dramatically. This summer I was really lucky to have the Summer Kitchen at my girls' school. Three evenings a week we could go and eat for free in the school canteen, and sometimes there would be extra fruit or veg or tins to take home. This was a huge help to us, and the girls really enjoyed it, as there was sports equipment and craft stuff out in the school field at the same time.

In September I went on to Universal Credit, which meant for five weeks I had no income at all.* Having the Summer Kitchen in August meant I could save up as much as possible and give us a bit of a cushion for when September hit – with two lots of uniforms to buy!

Another point I'd like to get across is the fact that it *is* cheaper and easier to eat less healthy food. I work three jobs, and cooking from scratch around them is very hard indeed. I also have a *tiny* kitchen, so I don't have the storage space to bulk-buy or batch-cook. Healthy Start vouchers, which were fantastic, ended when each of my girls turned 4, so I don't have as much to spend on fresh fruit and veg, and don't have the freezer space for much frozen. But it's true that these are all choices I make. I could (and do) cook from scratch if I really put the effort in every day. It's just more effort than more-well-off people need to make.

It's not just fruit and veg, though. To illustrate my point, I'll give you some examples. Peanut butter with palm oil and sugar added is a third of the price of the good stuff that's just squashed peanuts. Yoghurts with sweeteners are a quarter of the price of organic no-added-sugar ones. White bread that has an ingredient list full of chemicals is a quarter of the price of a store-baked wholemeal loaf. A bottle of squash is cheaper than juice. I could go on and on.

Feeding my kids nutritious food is such an enormous priority for me and most of the mums I know who are in the same position. I would rather keep my heating turned off and go without three meals a day myself if

---

* This was a common problem when Universal Credit was first rolled out. Like many other recipients, Daisy did not take up the offer of an advance to cover the five-week wait, because she was afraid of getting into debt.

it means buying better quality food for them, but I just think there must be a better way. I live in an area surrounded by farms and the sea; why is it cheaper and easier for me to feed my family powdered mash and sausages with a 5 percent meat content (we're actually vegetarian, but looking at my friend's shopping was an eye-opener) than local veg and decent food? I know a sack of potatoes from my local farm shop is cheap and good quality, but I can't get there without a car.

One last point is that an awful lot of the women my age I know don't have a clue how to cook. This is an area of multi-generational poverty. When I was little, I didn't know any adults who weren't on the dole, the majority of my peers grew up eating crap, or very simply indeed. We've lost the skills our nans had. Women like me don't make toad in the hole any more, 'cos Yorkshire pudding is a cheap way to bulk out a dinner. We buy frozen Aunt Bessie ones, 'cos they're £1 at Iceland. The only reason I'm any different is because my mum's a hippy and I know how to cook.

CHAPTER SEVEN

Should Nanny tell us what to eat?

The argument for state intervention

North Karelia doesn't look like the kind of place you'd expect to find a crisis of ill health. A remote province of Finland, thickly forested and sparkling with more than two thousand lakes, it is celebrated these days as a holiday destination for outdoorsy types. But fifty years ago, the men of the region were dying in their 40s and 50s. They had the highest mortality rate from heart failure ever measured anywhere in the world: 30 percent higher than their peers in Mediterranean countries.

This gave North Karelia an unhappy fame. 'Researchers would come here year after year, ask us questions, poke us with needles, and tell us we were the most unhealthy people in the world,' recalled Esa Timonen, the former governor of the region. 'At a certain point we said, "Enough!"' And so, in 1972, Timonen arranged for a 27-year-old doctor with an MA in Social Sciences to lead a public health project. Legend has it that Pekka Puska was chosen not because of anything especially dazzling in his CV, but simply because he was young. North Karelia's health problems were so big and entrenched they were bound to take a long time to solve.

Puska turned out to be an inspired choice. Over the next three decades, he devised and led a regional health programme that reduced heart disease by 80 percent among the men of North Karelia. His work also rewrote the rules of what is possible in public health.

Until the Second World War, the people of North Karelia had been pretty healthy. The men were mostly lumberjacks, so their jobs provided plenty of physical exercise, which we know protects against heart disease. The local diet consisted chiefly of berries, fish and hunting game, such as venison and elk. But after the war, as part of their compensation package, veterans were given their own little plots of land to tend. Not having the skills required for arable farming, they mostly used the land to rear pigs and cows. This led to a dramatic increase in the amount of red meat and animal fat in their diets.

After the scarcities of war, this abundance of high-protein, high-fat food must have seemed like manna from heaven. Butter found its way into every recipe. There was pork or beef at every meal, fried in butter and accompanied by a glass of milk and a slab of buttered bread. The question of whether animal fats are especially bad for coronary health is still hotly debated by scientists, but there's no doubt that the North Karelian diet was exceedingly high in fat, salt and preserved meats such as sausages and bacon, which are known to increase the risk of strokes and heart attacks. Critically, it was also very low in vegetables, which were regarded as food for the animals. A typical North Karelian stew had three main ingredients: water, fatty pork and salt.

This change of diet was accompanied by a new habit picked up by soldiers during the war. By the time Puska arrived in North Karelia, around 60 percent of men in the region smoked.

Existing public health policy was no match for the scale of the problem. Doctors could dish out medication to patients who were already on the brink of heart failure, but they could not stop people getting so ill in the first place. Puska quickly realised that he needed to address the habits of the entire population, not just those most immediately at risk. He had to make it easy to be healthy.

'The whole environment had to change,' Puska told me. 'The food industry, restaurants, cafeterias, supermarkets. We had to make sure that the healthy choices became the easy choices.' There wasn't much definitive evidence on which interventions would work best, so Puska resolved to try them all. 'We decided you have to do as many of the things that might work at the same time. You need to get stuck in. Get your boots deep in the mud.'

Puska assembled a small team, and together they set up a smorgasbord of different initiatives. All were designed to remove obstacles – subconscious and conscious – that might get in the way of healthy behaviour. They cleared snow from footpaths, built new bike paths and gave free tractioned shoe clamps to the elderly so they could walk in winter. They persuaded the local government to ban tobacco advertising and encourage smoke-free offices. To improve year-round fruit consumption, they set up cooperatives to pick and freeze berries in summer and distribute them in winter. They devised a recipe book that added vegetables to traditional dishes, and gave out copies to North Karelian housewives. (One such adaptation, which added swedes, carrots and potatoes to a meaty classic, became known as 'Puska's Stew'.)

Puska's team also lobbied food companies to reduce the fat and salt levels in their products. They persuaded a local sausage manufacturer to add mushrooms to the mix, an innovation so delicious that sales went up. And they worked with schools to improve the quality of their lunches. (Finland has long provided free school meals to every pupil.) 'The free school meal was essential. If we were to change our national diet, it was critical that this started in schools,' Puska told me. 'All of the evidence shows that a childhood habit for healthy eating is likely to stay with you for life.'

Within five years, deaths from heart disease started to fall dramatically. Puska was asked to roll out his project – or rather, portfolio of projects – across the country. His team also created an *X-Factor*-style TV show where Finns competed to see who was healthiest. It was a smash hit, watched by around a third of the population.

By 2009 the annual mortality rate from heart disease in men had fallen by 85 percent in North Karelia, and by 80 percent across the whole of Finland. Thanks to Puska's work, average life expectancy in Finland rose by seven years for men and six years for women.

This isn't just a parable about the power of so-called 'nudge theory'. Although Puska's methods were various and often subtle, it is the scale of his ambition that is most striking. That, and the way both local and national governments got behind it. Once Finland's politicians understood what he was trying to do, they were not afraid to intervene on a grand scale.

It is difficult, alas, to imagine the government in this country acting so decisively. This is partly because the British have yet to settle one of the fundamental questions of political philosophy: what role should the State play in the private lives of its citizens?

The term 'nanny state' was coined in this country, by a ruling class of men raised by nannies. It conveys mixed feelings – a similar jumble of security and dread, perhaps, to that inspired by the old-fashioned matriarchs of the nursery. Libertarians and statists are always squabbling about how much we should let Nanny boss us about. Neither has yet won, or lost, decisively.

The Institute of Economic Affairs – a free-market think tank very much on the libertarian side of the spectrum – publishes a biannual series called the Nanny State Index. The title is intended to sound disapproving. The latest edition has Finland coming third of the 30 countries assessed, after Norway and Lithuania. The UK comes in tenth. Germany is 30th.

In other words, we are not a very libertarian country, or a very statist one. Nanny holds quite a lot of sway in the UK, but our obedience is variable and sometimes grudging. By and large, those on the political left are comfortable with lots of state intervention, while those on the right are more libertarian. This means that differences of opinion on issues such as obesity – which ought to have nothing whatsoever to do with political dogma – are easily hijacked by partisans in the culture wars.

Devout libertarians are offended by the very idea of the state interfering in what we eat. Any attempt by central government to change how food is manufactured, marketed or sold in this country is seen as an assault on choice, personal responsibility and the free market.

I am not unsympathetic to the libertarian position. I don't like being bossed about myself, least of all by distant policymakers. When I was running Leon, I had many a tense moment with visiting officials from the 'Department of Tables and Chairs Licensing'. The usefulness of state intervention should always be weighed against the inconvenience it may cause to individuals or organisations.

In the case of diet-related illness, however, the libertarian argument is exhausted. For one thing, it does not offer any hope of change. Libertarians always fall back on that same tired refrain – *Education! Exercise! Willpower!* – which we know to be utterly ineffective. Since 1992, UK governments have tried 689 different anti-obesity schemes, with no success. That is because these schemes are almost all concerned with individual responsibility – trying to help people resist the temptations of an obesogenic environment* – rather than changing the environment itself.

The mantra of 'choice', beloved of free marketeers, is similarly deluded. How much choice do consumers really have? Certainly we can choose from a profusion of sugary, fatty, heavily processed convenience foods. Anyone within walking distance of a corner shop can 'choose' from hundreds of such products. But real sustenance is more expensive and much harder to find. As we saw in the last chapter, for those living on the lowest incomes it can be dauntingly difficult to 'choose' to eat well.

Companies don't have as much choice as libertarians seem to imagine, either. The financial feedback loops within the food system reward one kind of business model: use cheap ingredients to make cheap products that hijack our evolutionary cravings. Trying to make money out of nutritious food – freshly cooked, carefully composed, with a wide variety of fresh ingredients and no chemical additives – is extremely difficult. This is what we tried to do at Leon. It took us almost a decade just to break even. Everything is more expensive when you try to make good food, from

---

* This term, now commonly used in public health, simply means a social and commercial environment that is conducive to weight gain.

the raw materials to the skilled labour. You have to charge more for your products – thus pricing yourself out of the mass market – while also resigning yourselves to a smaller profit margin on each product. It's not an attractive 'choice' for many entrepreneurs, which is why so few attempt it.

It is, in fact, lack of choice that has led us into our current predicament. One kind of food has come to dominate the consumer landscape. The toll this is taking – in terms of illness, premature death and the costs to the Treasury and the wider economy – is becoming unsustainable. The State intervened successfully to bring down tobacco consumption; now it must do the same with the Junk Food Cycle.

The alternative is to resign ourselves to a future of waning health and productivity. Andy Haldane – a former chief economist to the Bank of England – warned recently that the poor physical condition of our population is leading to workforce shortages and a slowing economy: 'Health is now serving as a brake in the rise of growth,' he observed. Ill people are less able to work. The OECD estimates that the combined cost of food-related disease, in lost workforce productivity, low educational outcomes and NHS funds, is £74 billion every year in the UK. This is equivalent to cutting the country's GDP by 3.4 percent. To cover these costs, each person in the United Kingdom pays on average an extra £409 in taxes per year.

I don't want to pretend that there are any obvious, off-the-peg solutions to get us out of our predicament. Ploughing through the thicket of studies on dietary health and government initiatives, one thing soon becomes clear: it is extremely hard ever to be certain that intervention X will lead to outcome Y. The problem of modern dietary ill health is so complex and multi-faceted that there is no simple, one-size-fits-all solution.

So how should the government go about changing things? One approach is to pull lots of levers at the same time and hope for the best – the Puska approach. The other is to pull one lever at a time and see what works. If it doesn't work, drop it. The problem with the latter method is that societal change does not work like a sausage machine: inputs followed by outputs. It's more like an ecology. The success of any single policy might depend on how and when it is implemented and how it interacts with other policies. Human beings are complicated and often react in unpredictable ways.

Over the past 30 years, there has been much emphasis on the importance of 'evidence-based policymaking'. This sounds eminently sensible; indeed, you might think it the minimum one should strive for. But it has given birth to a new science of 'policy evaluation' which often leads, inadvertently, to political cowardice. It creates a Catch-22 situation. You can't bring in a policy until you have the evidence to show it works; but you can't get the evidence without first introducing the policy. If you don't have supporting data, because you can't do the policy that would produce the data, you're stuck. It's all too easy to end up doing nothing rather than risk unintended consequences.

Moreover, the threshold for what can reasonably be considered 'evidence' tends to be set high. Again, that might sound like a sensible precaution. But small adjustments in a system can eventually lead to big changes – if they are allowed sufficient time to work, or combined with other interventions.

There are sceptics, for example, who argue that the tax on sugary drinks has not yet produced any directly measurable reduction in obesity across the UK population.

But it has led to large-scale reformulation of soft drink recipes, taking 45,000 tonnes of sugar out of our annual consumption of soft drinks. Given time, and in combination with other anti-obesity strategies, that could snowball into something eminently measurable.

When Pekka Puska was rolling out his projects in Finland, some academics criticised his scattergun approach. Because he was doing so many different interventions at once, he couldn't say for sure which worked best or in what combination. But the point is they worked.

Not knowing for sure is a hazard of most ambitious enterprises. In the private sector, lack of certainty is overcome by a lot of trial and error. You go with your gut instinct, supported by as much evidence as you can find, and if it's not working you try something else. But you have to be brave. You can't afford to wait around.

A better model for state intervention would be 'evidence-informed policymaking'. That is, introduce policies where you can anticipate the likely effects, and where the existing evidence suggests they will not be harmful. You also have to build into each intervention a method for measuring its effects. It is important to watch closely as a policy begins to take effect, and be prepared to change course if it proves ineffective or counterproductive.

We expect politicians to be cautious when introducing new laws, or allocating taxpayers' money. But caution should not be an excuse for inaction.

CHAPTER EIGHT

Hacking the system

How to legislate to break the Junk Food Cycle

We are fat and ill because we live in a world full of food that makes us fat and ill. Our biology is completely unsuited to the obesogenic environment we have built for ourselves. In order to break free of the Junk Food Cycle, therefore, we must either change our environment, or change our biology.

Bizarrely, the first option is turning out to be harder than the second – not because it can't be done, but because it requires political determination. In the next chapter we will see how medical innovations are enabling desperate individuals to alter their own appetites. But drugs and surgery are always risky, and often expensive. Besides, diet-related disease is a systemic problem. Why should individuals have to fight it alone?

The recommendations we made in the National Food Strategy were all designed to create changes, big and small, within the food environment. I hope it doesn't sound boastful to say that we worked on them extremely hard. We studied policy ideas from around the world, as well as hundreds of proposals that were submitted to our public 'call for evidence'. We narrowed these down to a few dozen ideas, which we then analysed in detail, modelling their potential impact and cost, consulting our advisory panel along with other experts and stakeholders, and testing the most challenging ideas in focus groups and with citizens at the 'deliberative dialogues'* we held around the country. Only then did we settle on our recommendations to government. (You can find the National Food Strategy online, with detailed evidence for each of the recommendations.)

The National Food Strategy was published on Thursday 15 July 2021. The prime minister at the time, Boris Johnson, was due to make a key speech on levelling up in the West Midlands. But the morning news was dominated by our recommendations – in particular, our suggestion that the government should introduce a tax on the salt and sugar used in processed food. The usual suspects – food companies, some newspaper columnists and free-market think tanks – rushed to denounce this idea, explaining that what was actually needed was exercise and education. However, we got support from some unexpected quarters. 'Snack Tax to Fight Fat Crisis', announced the front page of the *Daily Mail*. As well as endorsing our recommendations, it sent its star columnist, Liz Jones, out in public wearing a fat suit, so that she could report back on 'The Hell of Being 20st for One Day'.

---

* A deliberative dialogue is similar to a focus group, but longer and more in depth. The goal is to understand what matters to the participants, what they want to see in the future and what interventions they would accept to achieve this. We convened 180 citizens in five groups drawn from each of five regions of England, demographically balanced to be representative of each region. We held multiple workshops with each group, first exploring their attitudes to the food system; then bringing in experts to explain the various workings of the system, and answer their questions; and finally debating possible mechanisms to improve the system.

Even more surreal, to me at least, was the endorsement of Mick Jagger. Under the headline 'No Brown Sugar! Mick rolls up to back levy,' he was reported as tweeting: 'This report by @food_strategy has some interesting and far-reaching ideas that could mean a big change for the better in our food system and make us all healthier. I hope that these plans will be taken up by government.'

No such luck. Arriving in Coventry to make his speech, Johnson was asked by the press what he thought about the tax idea. He admitted that he had not yet read the National Food Strategy, but gave his instinctive reaction: 'I'm not, I must say, attracted to the idea of extra taxes on hardworking people.'

'Neither am I!' I found myself shouting at the radio.

The point of our proposed Sugar and Salt Reformulation Tax – as the name suggests – was to make food companies change their recipes, rather than raising prices. The tax would only apply to sugar and salt bought in bulk for food processing, not the stuff sold in shops. It was, in fact, designed to shift the onus away from 'hardworking people' (or even lazy ones) and onto the manufacturers who make what we eat.

Most food manufacturers use an awful lot of sugar and salt in their products – much more than you would ever dream of adding to a home-cooked dish. Sugar and salt can give a moreish kick to products that would otherwise taste horribly bland because they don't contain many fresh, flavoursome ingredients.

Over the decades, the abundance of salt and sugar in processed foods has retrained our palates, so that we now expect it in everything we eat. Adults in this country consume an average of 50 grams of sugar a day. That's 20

grams over the recommended limit. Children aged 11–18
eat even more: an average of 55 grams a day. This means
they're getting 12 percent of their daily calories in the form
of sugar. And it almost all comes from one source: processed
food. Of the sugar sold in this country, 85 percent is used
in manufacturing, as is 75 percent of salt.

A company that is producing ready meals to sell at 80p
per meal, or ice cream at 10p a scoop, is very sensitive to
the cost of ingredients. They don't want to have to shrink
their profit margins, but nor do they want to risk losing
customers by putting up prices. So if sugar became more
expensive, manufacturers would use less of it.

This is exactly what happened when the Soft Drinks
Industry Levy was introduced in 2018. The makers of
sugary drinks reformulated their products – reducing
sugar content by 29 percent across the market – rather
than increasing their prices. And they did so without
consumers even noticing the difference.

We know that taxes work. When petrol is more
expensive, people drive more carefully and buy more
fuel-efficient cars. Cigarette consumption fell when prices
rose. Taxing the added sugar in processed food would be
no different. When we modelled the effect this tax would
have on calorie consumption, we found it would reduce
the average daily intake per head by 15–38 kcal. You may
not think that sounds like a lot, but it is. The UK's expert
group on calorie reduction has calculated that an average
reduction of 24 kcal per person per day would halt weight
gain at a population level completely. To put it another
way, that would save the UK population from putting on
118,000 tonnes of extra fat every year.

This would obviously be great for the overall health and
economy of the nation. But it would also provide a new,
and much-needed, source of tax revenue. The Sugar and

Salt Reformulation Tax could raise £2.9–3.4 billion per year for the Treasury. Some of this money could be used to help those who face the biggest struggle to eat well. Our recommendations included:

1. Expanding eligibility for free school meals (at the time of writing, the eligibility threshold is a household income of less than £7,400 before benefits).
2. Rolling out the Holiday, Activities and Food programme (HAF) in schools, which provides children with hot meals, cookery lessons, sport and activities during the holidays.
3. Expanding the Healthy Start programme (which gives money to pregnant women and parents of young children in poverty to spend on healthy food, including milk, vitamins and fruit and veg).

These last two recommendations have now been implemented by the government, thanks in large part to the campaigning of the footballer Marcus Rashford. But the government says it can't afford to increase free school meals eligibility. At the same time, it refuses even to consider introducing a tax that – on top of improving the nation's health – would more than cover the cost of extending free school meals to every child.

Why wouldn't politicians take up such a win–win proposition? Chiefly, from an abundance of caution. It is, by the modest standards of past anti-obesity interventions, a big move. Politicians are understandably nervous about seeming to interfere in matters as personal as what we eat. They especially don't want to be accused of taxing the pleasures of the poor (who eat more sugar than the rich), even though the poor would reap the biggest health benefits of reformulation. Politicians are also anxious not to do anything that might make food companies in this country less competitive, or put any kind of drag on the economy. This is a perfectly legitimate concern. But it does mean that they are susceptible to scaremongering from industry lobbyists, who fight hard to maintain the multi-billion-pound status quo of the food system.

One of the recommendations we didn't make in the National Food Strategy – because we thought it was already in the bag – was to introduce restrictions on in-store promotions of unhealthy food, and on the advertising of junk food to children. The government had already agreed, in 2020, to bring in legislation to this effect. It would have introduced a 9pm TV watershed for junk food adverts, and banned such adverts online, as well as putting paid to junk food BOGOFs.

I should have sensed it was too good to be true. One of the first meetings I had after starting work on the National Food Strategy was with a group of executives from ITV. They wanted to make the case against introducing a TV watershed for junk food adverts. It was a masterclass in the kind of lobbying that ministers are constantly subjected to: a mix of spurious argument, obfuscation and the sowing of doubt.

The meeting was held in a tiny glass-walled room at Defra. The ITV executives made three arguments:

1.   That such a ban would cut off a significant revenue stream for ITV, and thus imperil a public service broadcaster.
2.   That it would force junk food advertising onto less-well-regulated online platforms.
3.   That it wouldn't even make much difference to people's eating habits.

Each of these arguments falls apart on examination. It is true that a lot of advertising money – about £215 million per year – is currently spent on pre-watershed ads for HFSS (high in fat, sugar or salt) food. But introducing a pre-watershed ban would not wipe out this revenue stream. Many companies would move to later advertising slots, or advertise different products before 9pm, or even – ideally – adjust the ingredients in their products so that they no longer fell foul of the watershed. In 2007, junk food adverts were banned from the breaks in children's TV shows. But junk food advertising, as a proportion of all TV advertising, remained stable. Food companies just advertised those products in different slots.

The second argument against the watershed – that it would push advertising onto online platforms, which are harder to regulate – also cuts no mustard. It only means we should ban junk food adverts online as well, and improve online regulation. It is not an excuse for inaction.

As for the final argument – that junk food adverts don't actually influence what a child eats – this is the strangest proposition of all. Why do companies spend so much money on advertising if it doesn't work? What is the point of advertising (and advertising executives) if not to alter consumer behaviour?

Proponents of this baffling logic sometimes refer for evidence to a study published in 2018 by the UCL Great Ormond Street Institute of Child Health. This analysed data from a compendium of sources, including twenty-five research experiments. It found that children exposed to HFSS advertising on TV and in online games consumed an average of an extra 13.6 kcal (equivalent to three Smarties) for each minute of advertising they watched, compared to children who were not exposed to the advertising. Children who were already obese increased their consumption by almost half as much again, to 20.9 kcal (or four Smarties) per minute of advertising watched. That is easily enough to have a significant long-term impact on weight.

However, some children spend a lot more time looking at screens than others. To work out how many calories a 9pm watershed would save overall, government statisticians calculated the average number of minutes spent watching HFSS adverts across the entire population of children, and then used that relatively modest figure to deduce the average calorie increase. The grand total at the end of all that was just 2.28 kcal a day, or roughly half a Smartie.

Such is the diluting effect of averages. The truth – that advertising does have a significant effect on some children, and especially those who are most in danger of putting on weight – can be flattened out by maths. So the study gave critics of the watershed a perfect visual image – half a measly Smartie! – with which to make the argument that advertising restrictions aren't worth the bother.

Few politicians or commentators would think to question the sums, or the methodology, behind the half-Smartie. Parents, on the other hand, know very well that advertising does work. This is why 83 percent of the British public want the government to restrict junk food adverts. But, under pressure from food companies, advertisers and free-market ideologists, the government appears to have lost its nerve. The legislation on junk food advertising and in-store promotions has been delayed three times, and continues to languish in the long grass.

It's a familiar pattern. Politicians resolve to do the right thing, but balk when they run up against the inevitable wall of resistance. John Hegarty, advertising grandee and a founder of the agency Bartle Bogle Hegarty, told me his own industry is always ready to fight new legislation. Yet it adapts nimbly enough when change does come. 'First it was cigarettes, and that was followed by cigars, alcohol, gambling and other categories. Advertising always fills those gaps with new categories that in themselves become more dynamic.'

Hegarty was dismayed by the fight over the watershed. For him, it was a matter of conscience. 'Advertising junk food to children is no longer a decent thing to do,' he told me. 'No one is against profit – but profiting from illness and misery is not a sustainable business model. On commercial grounds, if nothing else, the advertising industry must do the right thing.'

CHAPTER NINE

Hacking the body

If politicians don't act, drug companies will

What if we could undo hundreds of thousands of years of evolution? What if we could change the way our appetites work, so that food becomes less enjoyable, less tempting? We could break the Junk Food Cycle without putting governments through all the bother of regulation.

An old friend (let's call her Lucy) came round for dinner recently. I hadn't seen her for ages, and at first – stupidly – I couldn't work out why she looked so different. 'I've had a gastric bypass!' she laughed, rolling her eyes at my slowness. 'I've lost seven and a half stone [48kg]!'

I had never thought of Lucy as obese. But her whole life, she told me, she had been struggling with her weight. Coming, she said, from a long line of 'short, fat ancestors', she had inherited a big appetite, and the psychological burden of always trying to curtail it. Dieting only made her fatter and more miserable. Her weight crept up and up until, on the day of her surgery, she weighed 17 stone (108kg).

The most amazing thing about having lost so much weight, she said, was not the physical change (although she did feel much healthier). It was the psychological lightness that came with it. She couldn't believe how effortless the weight loss had been.

As noted in *Chapter Four*, early forms of bariatric surgery tended to have poor long-term results. Although they restricted the amount of food a patient could comfortably eat in one go, they did nothing to reduce their levels of hunger. More recent surgical innovations – the gastric sleeve and the gastric bypass – are proving much more effective, because they interrupt the hormonal feedback that governs appetite. A gastric sleeve, shown on the left below, removes the bottom part of the stomach, which is where the hunger hormone, ghrelin, is chiefly produced. A gastric bypass, shown on the right, bypasses the stomach altogether. This means food reaches the small intestine faster, leading to the early release of the satiety hormones GLP-1 and PYY. For reasons that are not yet

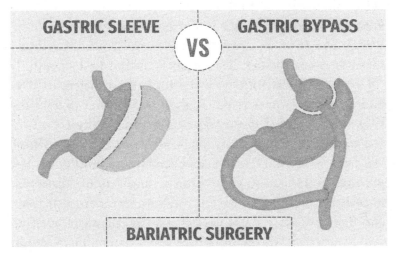

The two most common forms of modern bariatric surgery are the gastric sleeve which removes the lower section of the stomach, and the gastric bypass, where the surgeon removes most of your stomach and the first part of your small intestine, and then reconnects a small, newly created stomach pouch to the remaining small intestine.

fully understood, this procedure also suppresses ghrelin production, even though the stomach remains intact.

Lucy's gastric bypass means that she is no longer besieged by hunger hormones. For the first time in her life, she told me, she just isn't that interested in food. 'It is such a relief,' she says, 'and it has freed up so much time. I only now realise how much mental energy worrying about food and my weight took up.'

Having a large organ all but removed from your body is a pretty extreme way to escape the Junk Food Cycle. But if we can't (or won't) act as a society to change our obesogenic environment, what options remain? Increasingly, I believe, people will resort to drastic medical interventions to free themselves from this trap of our own creation.

Stomach surgery isn't for everyone. Going under the knife is always risky (although less risky than being morbidly obese), and the side effects of gastric surgery can include vomiting, malnutrition, stomach ulcers and leaky guts.

For those who want a less brutal intervention, there are drugs. In recent years, a new family of weight loss drugs has emerged almost by accident. The best known is semaglutide, created by the Danish drugmaker Novo Nordisk. Most commonly sold under the brand names Ozempic and Wegovy, semaglutide was originally designed to tackle type 2 diabetes. It mimics the effects of the GLP-1 hormone, which, as well as suppressing appetite, encourages the pancreas to produce more insulin. Natural GLP-1 only lasts in the blood for a matter of minutes, but its synthetic replicant is engineered to last longer in the body, so that patients can inject it weekly.

As soon as they started prescribing semaglutide to diabetics, medics noticed that it was extremely effective at helping patients lose weight. Doctors in America began to prescribe semaglutides 'off-label' for weight loss. Soon, the phrase 'post-Ozempic body' started popping up on social media, with users posting 'before' shots of them injecting the drug into their love handles, followed by 'after' shots of their newly concave bellies. Elon Musk revealed that he had used Wegovy – a higher-dose semaglutide – to help him lose weight.

In February 2022, the National Institute for Clinical Excellence (NICE) gave the go-ahead for NHS doctors to prescribe semaglutide to people with a BMI over 35 and with at least one weight-related medical condition. But private doctors can, and do, prescribe the drug to people with less severe weight problems. The rich have always been better equipped to free themselves from the Junk Food Cycle, and now they have a new tool at their disposal. If you have the money, you can inject your way out of trouble.

Another friend of mine (let's call her Kate) has been taking semaglutide for three years, and has lost about three stone. She injects herself in the stomach once a week – sometimes less often, if she feels she doesn't need the extra boost to her self-control. The drug inhibits her hunger hormones and stabilises her blood sugar, smoothing out the highs and lows that previously had her reaching for a sugary snack. It costs her £110 per month.

Kate says semaglutide makes food less enjoyable. Eating is no longer an indulgence for her; merely a process of refuelling. To me, this sounds like too big a sacrifice. I get so much pleasure from dreaming up recipes, cooking and eating, and from the social rituals of food. But for Kate it's a price worth paying. Before semaglutide, she had been pre-diabetic and exhausted by the difficulty of losing weight. Now, she feels liberated from that lifelong battle.

Semaglutide is not a 'miracle drug', however. I am always amused by the way American adverts for pharmaceuticals combine images of physical perfection (handsome, white-toothed grandfathers playing golf with their ageless wives) with a narrator reading out a list of gruesome contra-indications. The Ozempic advert is a classic of the genre. A series of wholesome all-American actors twirl and grin in celebration of their supposed weight loss, while the narrator intones: 'Do not take Ozempic if you have a personal or family history of medullary thyroid cancer [or] multiple endocrine neoplasia type 2 syndrome. Stop taking Ozempic and get medical help right away if you get a lump or swelling in your neck, severe stomach pain, itching, rash or trouble breathing. Serious side effects may happen, including pancreatitis. Tell your doctor if you have diabetic retinopathy or vision changes. Common side effects are nausea, vomiting, diarrhoea, stomach pain or constipation.'

On top of these physical dangers, there are wider concerns. Semaglutide is a quick medical fix for a long-term social problem. Solving obesity with drugs may divert us from the more important (and harder) job of addressing the causes of diet-related disease. This applies at a personal, as well as societal, level. People who get very overweight often have other problems that coexist with, and exacerbate, poor eating habits. These may include stress, depression and poverty – none of which can be cured by semaglutide.

Because semaglutide is so new, and because it was not intended to be used for weight loss, no one knows yet what the long-term effects might be on non-diabetic patients. Severe side effects appear to be rare – but if large numbers of people start taking it, as seems likely, those rare occurrences will happen more often, and may start to make the news. We saw with the Covid vaccines how even statistically minute risks can undermine public trust in a medicine.

One obvious drawback of semaglutide is that, in order to maintain their weight loss, patients have to stay on it forever. As soon as they stop taking the drug, the old hunger returns. This is great news for pharmaceutical companies. Less so for paying customers.

On the other hand, obesity is costly too. If semaglutide were widely available on the NHS, it could stop many diet-related illnesses in their tracks. As well as making people eat less, it also seems to steer them towards healthier, less processed food. This could have benefits far beyond weight loss.

If such an intervention were rolled out on a large enough scale, it would rebalance the whole food economy. Processed food would become less profitable, and drug companies more so. Economies of scale would almost certainly bring down the price of semaglutides, in which case the NHS could end up saving money by treating us all with drugs, rather than treating diet-related diseases.

If that sounds to you like a dystopian future, I tend to agree. But our present situation isn't much better. If governments won't intervene to improve the food system, pharmaceuticals may be our best option. It seems to me that we face a choice between two types of intervention: public or private. We can try to improve the food environment for everyone, through legislation and financial incentives. Or we can leave it to individuals to hack their own biology, with the help of modern medicine.

'I have been miserable, uncomfortable and overweight all my life, living in an obesogenic environment,' says Kate. 'Why shouldn't I take a drug that stops me being obese?' She draws a comparison with anti-depressants. 'We live in a depressing world, and lots of people take drugs to help them cope with that,' she points out. 'It has completely changed my life for the better. You should try it!'

PART TWO

Our Land

CHAPTER TEN

How humanity ate the world

*The food system is the greatest cause
of environmental destruction*

Worried about biodiversity loss? Focus on food.
Worried about freshwater supply and quality? Focus on food.
Worried about deforestation? Focus on food.
Worried about overfishing? Focus on food.
Worried about climate change? Focus on energy, and food.

RICHARD WAITE, WORLD RESOURCES INSTITUTE, APRIL 2021

**October, in a normal year, is the start of the snow crab
fishing season in Alaska.** Around 60 boats head out into
the gale force winds and heaving waters of the Bering
Sea, to empty and relaunch the crab pots that (again, in a
normal year) come up laden with pale, long-limbed crabs,
perfect for the restaurant table.

This is one of the most dangerous jobs in the world –
famously so, thanks to the hit TV series *Deadliest Catch*,
which follows various crews as they struggle to bring in
the catch while skidding about on an icy deck in violent
storms. The mortality rate for Alaskan fishermen is higher

than in any other US industry. But they are fiercely proud of their work. Many of the boats are family-owned, with crews that have fished the Bering Sea for generations. It is part of their identity, and part of Alaska's identity: the state supplies 60 percent of all the seafood eaten in America.

In the winter of 2022, however, there was no snow crab season. For the first time ever, the Alaskan government banned all commercial snow crab fishing, in an effort to halt a catastrophic decline in numbers. An estimated 8 billion snow crabs had vanished from the Bering Sea over the previous four years. Just in the two years between 2019 and 2021, the population fell by 90 percent.

Climate change is the likely culprit. Snow crab younglings mature in cold-water 'nurseries' at the bottom of the sea, fed by melting sea ice which keeps the temperature below 2 °C. But in recent years Alaska – the fastest-warming state in America – has experienced a series of 'marine heatwaves'. The sea ice is melting too fast, and the waters becoming too warm, to sustain the younglings.

It may also be that the shrinking of the cold-water grounds has forced more crabs – not just the younglings – into a smaller area, leading to starvation and the spread of parasitic diseases. Scientists are investigating all these possibilities, hoping to avert further calamity. But in the meantime, the effects are already being felt on land.

Unable to cover the fixed costs of their boats and licences, many Alaskan fishermen are facing bankruptcy. One missed season means a loss of around $500 million for the crab fishing industry, but around $1 billion for the state's economy, once you include the ripple effects into subsidiary jobs. The city of St Paul, Alaska – the heart of the crab fishing industry – projected in late 2022 that it would lose 90 percent of its tax revenue as a result.

The fate of the snow crab is a stark warning for the food system. The effects of environmental degradation can be sudden and dramatic, taking whole industries by surprise. The collapse of one species or crop can have ramifications across multiple systems, both natural and man-made. While the residents of Alaska struggle with the human cost of losing such a big chunk of their economy, at the bottom of the Bering Sea a bountiful food source for predators has abruptly disappeared. This means that crab predators will have to find a different food source, or starve. Either way, this will create new problems elsewhere in the ecosystem.

In terms of the human food chain, snow crab is a luxury item. But climate change also poses a growing threat to many of our staple foods. The hot, dry summer of 2022 produced dismal grain harvests in Europe, with French maize crops around 28 percent below expected forecasts. In Italy, the worst drought for seventy years led to a drop of around 45 percent in corn and animal feed yields, while fruit harvests fell by 15 percent and milk yields by 20 percent. The EU only managed to keep supply pressures under control by increasing its food imports from Ukraine.

There is an awful circularity to this predicament. Environmental disruption – particularly climate change – is the single biggest threat to our current food system. And yet our food system is the single biggest cause of environmental disruption. It is the number one cause of soil degradation, water pollution, drought, deforestation and biodiversity collapse. After the fossil fuel industry, it is the biggest contributor to climate change. Globally, the food system is responsible for up to one third of all greenhouse gases. In the UK, our domestic food production alone (ignoring the emissions embedded in the food we import) accounts for 20 percent of our greenhouse gas emissions. The way we eat is imperilling the way we eat.

The chart below, produced by the UN Food and Agricultural Organization, forecasts how climate change is likely to affect crop yields globally. The darker shading shows where harvests are expected to increase; the lighter where they are expected to decrease. It paints a picture of extreme global inequality. Notwithstanding droughts and floods, wheat yields in the northern hemisphere are forecast to increase, with productivity boosted by warmer weather

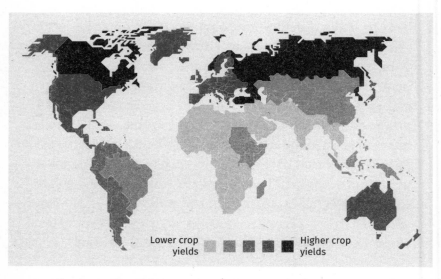

Lower crop yields ▢ ▢ ▢ ▢ Higher crop yields

Studies by NASA and the UN's Food and Agriculture Organization both predict that climate change will lead to higher wheat yields in the global north and some of the southern hemisphere, while in countries closer to the Equator, fierce heat will reduce yields of maize and rice. However, climate change is inherently destabilising, and there may be other food perils ahead – including for the global north. For example, if melting glaciers caused the Gulf Stream to slow to a standstill, UK temperatures and rainfall would fall abruptly, which could dramatically reduce harvests.

and higher CO_2 (carbon dioxide) levels. In the global south, however, rice and maize yields are expected to fall. Some of these losses could be disastrous. Vietnam, for example, is currently the world's second largest rice exporter. Half of its rice is grown in the Mekong Delta, but half of the Mekong Delta will be submerged under water if sea levels rise by 1 m – a very plausible scenario. Whenever I look at this chart, I see global unrest, famine, mass migration and war.

Later, we will look in detail at how the food system has become such a powerful engine of climate change. But for now I want to widen the aperture, to take in the other 'biogeochemical cycles' that have been radically disrupted by the food system. These are systems in which nature recycles non-living things. The three most important are the water, nitrogen and carbon cycles. Each of these cycles is vital to maintaining the delicate balance of life on Earth. Our food system both depends upon and threatens them all.

We all learnt about the water cycle at school. Water enters our atmosphere largely through the evaporation of sea water. Then, when warm air hits cold air, it condenses and falls out of the sky as rain, snow or hail. Fresh water makes up only 3 percent of the world's water and yet is essential to life for almost all land-based creatures.

Farming uses 70 percent of all the fresh water on Earth. The impacts of this – ranging from water shortages to drought, harvest failure, famine and war – are less apparent in the wet, temperate climate of the UK than in much of the world, although we contribute to the problem by importing foods from drier regions. But even in this country, the pumping of ground water to irrigate fields is a key contributor to droughts during hot summers.

The nitrogen cycle is less familiar to many of us. Plants need certain forms of nitrogen – chiefly nitrates and nitrites – to perform many of their critical functions. Bacteria in the soil, and attached to the roots of some plants, convert nitrogen from the atmosphere and turn it into nitrates and nitrites, which are then absorbed by plants. When the plant dies (or is eaten) and returns to the soil, a different set of 'denitrifying' bacteria convert these chemicals back into nitrogen gas, and release it into the atmosphere. Intensive farming has played havoc with this cycle.

At the start of the twentieth century, two German scientists, Fritz Haber and Carl Bosch, devised a new method for creating fertiliser out of thin air. Using intense heat and pressure, they managed to combine nitrogen from the atmosphere with hydrogen, to create ammonia – which in turn can be used to make nitrogen-based fertiliser. This proved to be one of the most important inventions in modern history. After the First World War, the victorious Allies made it a condition of the Treaty of Versailles that Germany should release the details of the Haber–Bosch process. Artificial fertiliser has since become an essential tool in industrial agriculture. Without it, an estimated 30–50 percent of the current global harvest would be lost.

But the environmental impact of man-made fertiliser is dire. The energy required for the Haber–Bosch process releases masses of carbon in itself: about 1 percent of all global greenhouse gas emissions. Once on the soil, artificial fertilisers tend to leach into our watercourses. (As does the manure and slurry from livestock farming.) Nitrogen run-off from farms is leading to high levels of 'eutrophication': excessive plant and algal blooms in both fresh and sea water. These blooms stop light penetrating the water, plunging entire ecosystems into darkness. Plants can't grow, which means animals can't eat them. Aquatic predators cannot see to hunt, so they starve. Eutrophication can also raise the pH of water, making it unhabitable for many species. When the algal blooms eventually die, their decomposing cells suck oxygen out of the water, creating hypoxic or anoxic 'dead zones' in lakes and oceans. (Hypoxic refers to a partial lack of oxygen; anoxic means a total lack.)

Run-off from farmland causes more than three-quarters of global eutrophication. In England, just 16 percent of our surface and ground waters meet the criteria for 'good ecological status', and none of our lakes or rivers meet the criteria for 'good chemical status'. We have some of the most polluted waters in Europe. Poor water quality – along with over-fishing and global warming – is one reason why our traditional salmon rivers are becoming desolate places. In 2022, wild salmon numbers in England and Wales were the lowest on record.

Our careless husbandry of the earth is having awful consequences for all forms of biodiversity: wild plants, animals, insects and fish. A quarter of all remaining mammal species are currently threatened with extinction, as their natural habitats are converted to food production. In this country, we have lost 20 percent of our wild bird population since 1966. That is 44 million birds: a breeding pair lost every minute.

The state of our oceans is no less desperate. In its 2022 report on the state of the oceans, the UN found that over a third of global stocks were being fished at unsustainable levels: a three-fold increase since 1974.

No form of fishing has caused more harm than bottom trawling: the practice of dragging a large, weighted net along the ocean floor. This is useful for catching deep-sea fish, but it can leave a trail of devastation in its wake:

churning up the seabed, pulling plants out by their roots, damaging coral and other marine habitats, and catching turtles, invertebrates and juvenile fish in the net. Recent research suggests that, by stirring up the seabed, bottom trawling also releases large quantities of so-called 'blue carbon'* from marine sediments, which would otherwise remain locked away in the seabed.

Since the 1890s, when fossil-fuel-powered bottom trawling began, there has been a staggering decline in overall fish abundance. Cod landings have declined by 87 percent; hake, by 95 percent. For halibut, the figure is a near-terminal 99.8 percent. In the 1830s, small sailing vessels around the Dogger Bank could catch 1 tonne of halibut per day. Today, all fishing across the entire Dogger Bank lands less than 2 tonnes of halibut a year.

The global collapse in natural abundance has consequences far beyond those we can measure statistically. As the American biologist Edward O. Wilson explained in his seminal work *The Diversity of Life*, it is impossible to put a true value on genetic diversity, because we cannot know its worth to future generations. Wilson gave the example of Madagascar's rosy periwinkle (*Catharanthus roseus*). In the 1950s, this pretty herbaceous flower was found to produce two alkaloids that cure most victims of two deadly cancers – Hodgkin's disease, prevalent in young adults; and acute lymphocytic leukaemia, which used to be a death sentence for children. By the 1990s, income from the manufacture of these two substances exceeded $180 million.

---

* 'Blue carbon' refers to any carbon sequestered in marine habitats. This includes coastal mangroves and all other marine plants, fish stocks and plankton.

Over 40 percent of modern medicines are extracted from plants, micro-organisms or animals. Yet, as Wilson noted, 99 percent of all of the species that ever lived are now extinct. Who knows what medicinal potential has vanished with them?

Another utilitarian argument for genetic diversity is that it could future-proof the food system. Currently, while 300,000 species of plant have edible parts, just twenty species account for 90 percent of the world's food; and three – wheat, maize and rice – supply more than half. To be so heavily reliant on a tiny handful of crops puts humanity in a precarious position. 'This thin cushion of diversity', writes Wilson, 'is biased toward cooler climates, and in most parts of the world is sown in monocultures sensitive to disease and attacks from insects and nematode worms ... Modern agriculture is only a sliver of what it could be. Waiting in the wings are tens of thousands of unused plants.' These alternative crops could be farmed as they are, or their traits bred into other plants to increase the resilience of the food system as our climate changes.

Beyond the utilitarian arguments, there is the intrinsic – to some sacred – value of nature. 'Wilderness settles peace on the soul because it needs no help; it is beyond human contrivance,' as Wilson puts it.

Being in nature, having access to wild spaces, enriches the human spirit. It raises the quality of human life. And leaving humans out of the equation altogether, the natural world is precious in and of itself. The precise motive doesn't matter as much as the shared imperative: to halt the destruction of nature, and restore it to abundance. 'The stewardship of environment', Wilson concludes, 'is a domain on the nearside of metaphysics where all reflective persons can surely find common ground.'

CHAPTER ELEVEN

The invisibility of nature

What does our food really cost?

For all our inventiveness, the human race remains utterly dependent on the natural world for our survival. You would expect us, therefore, to value nature highly. Yet in almost all the data we use to measure our own security and success the so-called 'natural capital' of our planet is conspicuous by its absence.

Nature doesn't sit in bank accounts or wallets, waiting to be counted. It goes about its business in ways that are not easily captured on a spreadsheet. Much of the natural world is silent, invisible or mobile. Microscopic bacteria in the soil quietly break down matter to make nutrients accessible to plants. Populations of deep-water fish rise and fall unseen on the ocean floor. Winds blow, rivers flow, oceans circulate, and insects and birds flutter across national borders, belonging to no one but the Earth.

In *The Economics of Biodiversity*, Sir Partha Dasgupta's formidable review for the UK Treasury, the Cambridge economist points out that nature is not extraneous to the economy, as we often seem to think. On the contrary, the economy sits squarely within it. Without the materials and services that nature provides, human industry could not function. Dasgupta argues that wealth should be measured in three different forms of capital: *produced capital* (the things we make); *human capital* (the health, education and skills of our population); and *natural capital*. This last category includes not only the materials – such as wood – that nature provides, but also the services it performs, from filtering rainwater and pollinating our plants to providing places of leisure and beauty.

Because we systematically measure only produced capital, we undervalue human and natural capital. The natural world is treated as carelessly as if it were a limitless resource. Dasgupta points out that between 1992 and 2014, produced capital per person doubled, while human capital per person increased by an estimated 13 percent globally. But the stock of natural capital per person is thought to have declined by nearly 40 percent. If this trend continues, the mathematical conclusion is mass extinction.

What we don't notice, we don't tend to appreciate. It is no surprise that the most eye-catching parts of nature – charismatic megafauna, such as giant pandas – get more attention than the biodiversity of life in our soil. And if carbon dioxide smelled bad, you can be certain we would have done more about cutting down on greenhouse gas emissions.

Crucially, the global economy does not place any financial value on nature. Environmental destruction and climate change create enormous (and growing) costs for governments, and thus taxpayers. Yet none of this is factored into the GDP with which we measure a nation's health. Nor is it felt in the pockets of those who cause it.

Suppose a farmer has a potato contract with a supermarket and, in growing the crop, pollutes a nearby watercourse with fertiliser. The cost of that bad practice falls on us, the public, because our environment is polluted. If neither the farmer nor the supermarket (nor indeed the end consumer) is forced to cover the cost of cleaning up the watercourse, there is no market incentive to avoid such destructive practices.

These kinds of hidden costs – consequences of commercial activity not reflected in the price of that activity – are known by economists as 'negative externalities'. Precisely because they are external, because their cost is not incorporated into the transactions of the free market, they are often allowed to run rampant. No one picks up the cost, but everyone pays the price.

Every economist since Adam Smith has recognised that the incentives of the free market do not work properly if negative externalities are not priced into the system. Yet this insight is almost never applied in practice. The food system is riddled with negative externalities: polluted water and air, greenhouse gas emissions, antibiotic resistance, zoonotic disease, soil erosion, biodiversity loss, diet-related illness. All of these are costs imposed on a third party – the citizens of the world – by businesses within the food system.

In theory, these externalities should be costed into the price of the relevant goods. But they are not even measured. There is no government department in the UK that has any idea, or has even been tasked with finding out, what the true costs of food production are.

The fact that nature doesn't feature in the financial calculations that shape governmental and commercial decisions leaves it extremely vulnerable to bad ideas. We treat Earth's resources as if they were both costless and infinite. Actually, no – it is worse than that. Our political systems actively encourage the destruction of nature. Dasgupta calculated that governments around the world spend around $500 billion every year subsidising practices that destroy nature, such as intensive agriculture, fisheries, fossil-fuel mining and fertiliser manufacture. These subsidies, he estimates, cause $4-6 trillion of environmental damage every year. In economic terms, we don't just undervalue nature – we actually give it a negative value. We pay people and businesses to destroy it.

As Dasgupta's review makes plain, we are currently living way beyond the Earth's means. Unless we make dramatic changes to our agricultural, industrial and consumer patterns, we will destroy the lives of future generations. Once ecosystems are lost, it is extremely expensive – and often impossible – to rebuild them.

The world is slowly (too slowly) waking up to this reality. Farmers are increasingly paid by governments to deliver environmental benefits as well as food. But these interventions are tiny compared to the scale of the problem. For example, only 4 percent of payments to EU farmers under the Common Agricultural Policy go towards supporting low-carbon, environmentally friendly farming.

In 2012, the UK government set up a Natural Capital Committee (NCC), a team of economists and environmental academics, to work out how to become 'the first generation to leave the environment in a better state than it inherited'. The NCC's 2020 report set out three 'guiding principles':

1. *Net environmental gain.* It is not enough to stop destroying nature; we need to start rebuilding it.

2. *Public money for public goods.* The government should spend taxpayers' money on things that benefit everyone in society. For a farmer, this might include creating habitats that foster biodiversity, or which capture water to prevent floods, or which are simply beautiful places to visit. By definition, public goods are non-excludable (their benefits cannot be confined just to those who have paid for them) and non-rivalrous (consumption by one person does not restrict consumption by others).

3. *The polluter pays.* Any individual or organisation that destroys the natural habitat must be made to pay to restore the harm they have done.

These are good principles. But enforcing them is difficult. We don't have any internationally (or even locally) agreed metrics by which to measure all the different elements of the natural world, let alone put a financial value on them.

A UK-based organisation called the Global Farm Metric Coalition (GFMC) has been trying to solve this part of the puzzle. A collaboration between farmers, food producers, supermarkets, environmental NGOs, banks and investors, the GFMC wants to create an international set of indicators for assessing the sustainability of any farm: the Global Farm Metric. That is the limit of their scope – just agreeing on the indicators, not assigning any value to them – much as the International Bureau of Weights and Measures in Paris defines the metrics used in science and engineering (the precise length of a metre, for example).

The graphic opposite, a work in progress, shows the many factors the GFMC currently believe should be measured in order to understand the impact of a farm – not only on nature, but also on society. These range from water quality to soil structure to animal welfare and the skills of the human workforce. For each of these elements, and more, the GFMC is devising a metric of measurement.

This is easier in some cases than others. The methods for quantifying greenhouse gas emissions are already well rehearsed (although, even now, not universally agreed). But the science of measuring, say, carbon sequestration

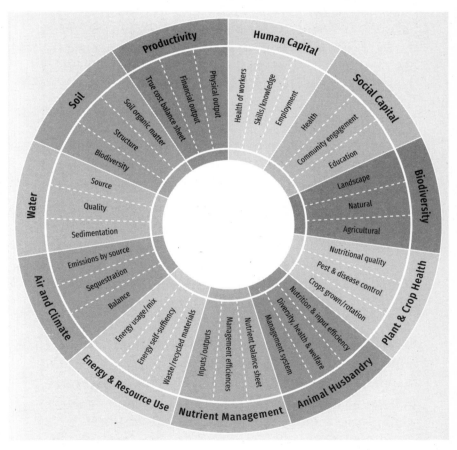

The Global Farm Metric is an attempt to agree an international set of rules by which to measure the social and environmental impact of a farm. As this graphic shows, there are a lot of different aspects to measure – and that's before you even get to the question of how to measure them and assess their relative importance.

has a long way to go. No one has yet worked out how to measure the carbon stored in soils or plants systematically over large areas. And we are only just beginning to think about how to quantify other elements of nature, such as biodiversity.

Realistically, we cannot afford to wait until all these questions are settled before we act to protect our most important global asset: the natural world. We need to re-balance the financial incentives and disincentives within the food system, so that we no longer actively reward the destruction of nature. And we need to do it fast, using the best knowledge available to us now.

An annual £2.4 billion of payments will be distributed to English farmers in place of the Common Agricultural Policy. In devising this new scheme, the government has pledged only to subsidise public goods, such as flood management, biodiversity restoration, carbon capture or preserving historic environments. (Not the production of food, which – on top of being a moneymaking enterprise in itself – is both excludable and rivalrous. I can stop you eating my apple; and, once I have eaten it, you can't.)

This new payment system, dubbed the Environmental Land Management schemes (ELMs), could be a big step in the right direction. If implemented well, it will make the UK a global leader in sustainable land management. But again, it isn't simple. How should the government weigh various public goods against one another? What is a beautiful view of pasture and dry-stone walls worth, compared to a biodiverse riparian woodland along a stream, or a flood-preventing wetland? It will take time (and almost certainly error) to devise a new system of payments that creates maximum environmental returns

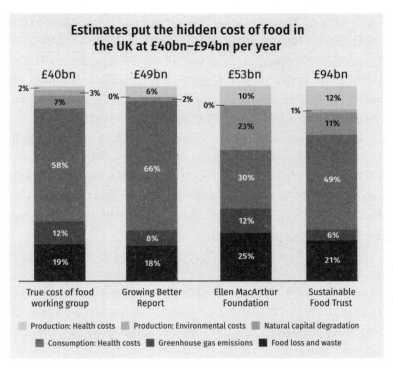

Estimates put the hidden cost of food in the UK at £40bn–£94bn per year

	£40bn	£49bn	£53bn	£94bn
	2%	0%		1%
	3%	6%	10%	12%
	7%	2%	23%	11%
	58%	66%	0%	
			30%	49%
	12%	8%	12%	6%
	19%	18%	25%	21%
	True cost of food working group	Growing Better Report	Ellen MacArthur Foundation	Sustainable Food Trust

Production: Health costs · Production: Environmental costs · Natural capital degradation
Consumption: Health costs · Greenhouse gas emissions · Food loss and waste

Several recent studies have attempted to measure the hidden cost of our food – that is, the negative externalities (to health and the environment) that are not factored into the price at the till. As you can see above, their estimates have ranged from £40 billion to £94 billion per year, on top of the £100 billion we already spend on food. When I first read these studies, I thought the true cost would probably be at the lower end of the scale. But the more we dug into the data, the more I came to believe that all these studies probably underestimate the hidden costs of food, particularly the harm to the environment.

for taxpayers' money. And it won't be enough on its own. As well as incentivising good practice, we will have to start disincentivising destruction.

There is, still, intense debate over exactly how one makes the polluter pay. In 1920, the British economist Arthur Pigou proposed that externalities should be dealt with by simply levelling taxes on the relevant goods. (The externalities that troubled Pigou were of their time. They included smoke from factory chimneys, 'for this smoke in large towns inflicts a heavy uncharged loss on the community, in injury to buildings and vegetables, expenses for washing clothes and cleaning rooms, expenses for the provision of extra artificial light, and in many other ways'.)

These 'Pigouvian taxes' should be equal to the cost of the externality – so that the true cost of the product is reflected in its price. In this way, argued Pigou, the free market could be left to work its magic. Producers would have a built-in financial incentive to keep damaging externalities to a minimum.

Imagine, however, the effect of adding Pigouvian taxes to food. A handful of recent studies have calculated the effect this would have in the UK (see the graph on the previous page). They found that if all the externalities of our food system – including the costs to the health service, and to the environment – were factored into the price of our food, the price of the average weekly shop could double. I used to think this was an exaggeration, but I have come to believe it is actually a rather conservative estimate. If the government were to inflict such a drastic price hike on its citizens, there would be riots.

This is one reason why many policy makers and commentators tend to be sceptical, verging on defeatist, about the possibility of radical change in the food system. They see it as a choice between two evils: we can either stick with our damaging but cheap food, or risk civil unrest.

But Pigouvian taxes are a blunt instrument, and not the only one available. In his response to Pigou, *The Problem of Social Cost* (1960), the American economist Ronald Coase pointed out that there are plenty of other methods for encouraging different modes of production, with fewer unintended consequences. Grants and subsidies, legal rights, prohibitions and obligations are all existing tools in the legislator's box. The job of government is to use the most effective tools for any given set of circumstances; the ones that it believes will be most effective and politically acceptable, and least likely to create unintended consequences.

A good example is the UK's transition from fossil fuels to more sustainable forms of energy. A strict Pigouvian approach would have been to slap a whopping carbon tax on everyone's fossil-fuel-powered energy bills. This would undoubtedly have encouraged companies to invest in renewable energy, so that it would soon become cheaper than coal and gas. But the political and social jeopardy of imposing such a big tax would have been prohibitive.

Instead, the UK government chose to introduce subsidies (for wind and solar energy providers), bans (no new coal-fired power stations)* and legal obligations (an air pollution requirement that was almost impossible for coal-fired power stations to meet cost-effectively). As a result of these combined measures, the cost of wind power is now cheaper than the cheapest coal-fired power station. This has been achieved with only the most modest carbon tax.

We should use a similar approach to curtail (and reverse) the damage done by the food system. Rather than suddenly adding the costs of externalities at the till – a burden that would fall hardest on the poorest – we should create a similar portfolio of incentives and restraints to shift the food system to a more sustainable mode of production, without the need for drastic price increases.

---

* In December 2022, the government broke with this commitment by giving a green light to the first new coal mine in thirty years, to be built in Cumbria.

All this would require the government to measure and price these externalities, albeit imperfectly. There are some people – not just red-blooded capitalists – who instinctively dislike this idea. Environmentalists are sometimes wary of putting a price tag on nature. The journalist and campaigner George Monbiot, writing in the *Guardian*, derided the concept of 'natural capital' as 'morally wrong, intellectually vacuous, emotionally alienating and self-defeating'. It 'reinforces the notion that nature has no value unless you can extract cash from it,' he argued. It turns the natural world into just another tradable commodity, subject to the corrosive values of the marketplace.*

Dasgupta's report was criticised along similar lines, often by people who don't appear to have read it. In fact, Dasgupta is keenly aware of the dangers of abandoning the environment to an unregulated free market. 'Markets alone are inadequate for protecting ecosystems from overuse,' he writes. He recognises that the value of some ecosystems may essentially be infinite, either because they have sacred value or because they are close to a tipping point, past which they will be lost forever.

Dasgupta also accepts that often it will be impossible to measure and value the true harm done to a system. We know, for example, that the extraordinary complexity of mycelia, bacteria, protists, archaea, and the vast array of micro-organisms and invertebrates in our soils, are essential to both agriculture and the natural world. But we are a long way from truly understanding this part of our eco-

---

* A contrary view was taken by the environmentalist (and former Friends of the Earth director) Tony Juniper in his 2013 book, *What Has Nature Ever Done For Us?*, which argued strongly in favour of the concept of natural capital – and the importance of putting a financial value on nature's 'services'. Juniper estimated nature as being worth $100 trillion annually to the world economy – nearly double the value of the global GDP.

system, let alone being able to put a price on it. If we just hazard a guess, and mistakenly slap on a price tag that undervalues a vital part of the natural world, we might accelerate its destruction. In many cases, says Dasgupta, it would be simpler and safer to impose legal restrictions to stop people exploiting certain habitats, rather than relying on taxation.

The 'invisibility' of nature is what makes it so acutely vulnerable to human activity. But there is no straightforward way to make it visible. Clumsy reform could easily lead to unintended consequences, which is why both policymakers and campaigners must always be alert to their own fallibility and ready to adjust course. But doing nothing is more dangerous still.

CHAPTER TWELVE

Warming meals

*The many ways in which food production
contributes to climate change*

**In January 1861, the Irish physicist John Tyndall delivered
a lecture at London's Royal Society** with the somewhat
dry title 'On the Action of Gases and Vapours on Radiant
Heat'. The audience, which included Michael Faraday
and Lord Alfred Tennyson, 'heard me with breathless
attention from beginning to end', Tyndall later claimed.

And this may in fact be true – for on stage that day,
Tyndall unravelled one of the mysteries of life on Earth.
How is it that our planet – uniquely, so far as we can
tell, within this solar system – maintains a climate mild
enough for life to survive and thrive?

Tyndall was a lean and dashing figure, with enormous
mutton chops leading into a commanding beard. He
had become addicted to Alpine climbing while studying
in Germany under Robert Bunsen (inventor of the
eponymous burner). During these adventures, Tyndall
became intrigued by the fluctuations of temperature
within mountainous regions. He developed a theory
that it might have something to do with the absorptive
properties of 'perfectly colourless and invisible gases
and vapours' in the atmosphere. He went on to design

and build a sophisticated apparatus which enabled him to measure accurately how gases in the atmosphere – predominantly water vapour – absorb heat.

The Sun washes the Earth with every wavelength of light. Around half of that never reaches ground level: it is either reflected back by clouds or absorbed by airborne water vapour. The remaining half does make it to the Earth's surface, where most of it is absorbed by the land, oceans and vegetation.

The Earth heats up, and then emits this heat back into the atmosphere in the form of infrared light, invisible to the human eye. Some of this energy gets trapped in the atmospheric water vapour, and some makes it back out into space. In total, the water vapour traps just enough heat to make the world warm enough for us to live in, while releasing just enough to ensure we don't overheat. Or as Tyndall put it:

> This aqueous vapour is a blanket more necessary to the vegetable life of England than clothing is to man. Remove for a single summer-night the aqueous vapour from the air which overspreads this country, and you would assuredly destroy every plant capable of being destroyed by a freezing temperature. The warmth of our fields and gardens would pour unrequited into space, and the sun would rise upon an island held fast in the iron grip of frost.

In his experiments, Tyndall had studied the absorptive effects of many different atmospheric gases, including carbon dioxide. But compared to water vapour, these gases appeared in such tiny quantities that it seemed unlikely they could have much bearing on global temperatures. If you were to fill a million balloons with air from the

Earth's atmosphere, the total quantity of water vapour would fill 25,000 balloons. The total amount of carbon dioxide, even today, would only fill 400 balloons.

What we now know, however, is that certain gases trap wavelengths of light that water vapour can't. They also build up in the atmosphere – unlike water vapour, which circles from oceans and lakes to the atmosphere and back again in the never-ending waltz of the water cycle. There are three greenhouse gases responsible for the bulk of man-made climate change: carbon dioxide (CO_2), methane (CH_4), and nitrous oxide (N_2O). Food production is the only field of human activity that emits all three.

In terms of volume, these gases are all bit-part players. To continue with the balloon-filling metaphor, where carbon dioxide would fill 400 balloons, methane would fill less than one and a half balloons, and nitrous oxide just under a quarter of one balloon. However, methane and nitrous oxide are more potent than carbon dioxide. A tonne of methane in the atmosphere absorbs about 100 times as much heat as a tonne of carbon dioxide. Nitrous oxide absorbs 265 times as much as carbon dioxide. This is why, since 1800, relatively small increases in CO_2, CH_4, and N_2O have added 1.1°C to the world's average temperature.

Methane has another, unique, quality: over the course of about twelve years, it gradually transforms into a mixture of water vapour and (much less potent) carbon dioxide. The impermanence of methane sits at the heart of many a furious debate about the impact of meat production on climate change, and we shall return to it in the next chapter.

The food system is responsible for 25–30 percent of global greenhouse gas emissions, if we take into account agriculture, food production, distribution and retail. In the

UK, the food system accounts for 20 percent of domestic emissions – a figure that rises to around 30 percent if we factor in the emissions produced by all the food we import.

There are four major ways in which the food system contributes to climate change:

1. The damage done when wild areas are converted to farmland, or when farmland is prevented from reverting to forest.
2. The release of carbon from farmland soil – particularly peat soils.
3. The use of fossil fuels in every part of the food system.
4. The release of methane and nitrous oxide from agriculture.

Wherever land is converted for farming, it exacts a terrible toll on the environment. The most famous example is the burning of the Amazon rainforest, which – as well as destroying regions of ancient beauty and biodiversity – has released a huge amount of carbon into the atmosphere. During the 2010s, tree burning in the Amazon released more carbon than seven years' worth of UK fossil fuel emissions. And, of course, once a forest has been felled or burnt down, it can no longer absorb carbon from the atmosphere.

In Britain, we destroyed our forests long ago. In 5000 BCE, 75 percent of the UK was covered in wildwoods. But, as human settlements spread and became more sophisticated, trees were chopped down to clear land, build houses and boats, and burn for fuel. By 1086, when the Domesday Book was completed, the proportion of land in England covered by forest had shrunk to 15 percent. It now sits at just 10 percent – up from a low point of 6 percent at the end of the Second World War.

A more recent calamity in this country is the destruction of our peat bogs. Peat is created when plants growing on top of a bog – typically mosses, sedges and reeds – sink into wet, acidic and anaerobic conditions below. Under these conditions they do not fully decay. Instead of rotting and releasing carbon back into the atmosphere, like most dying things, these plants retain their carbon as they sink in layers down into the bog. By this process, a peat bog might gradually sequester 0.4–1.1 tonnes of carbon dioxide per hectare per year. (This compares to 5–40 tonnes for growing woodland, with temperate forests typically sequestering 10–20 tonnes per year.)

It takes thousands of years for a peat bog to form, but a matter of days to plough it up. Over the past couple of centuries, 80 percent of the UK's peatland has been degraded – with peat cut for fuel or compost, or the land repurposed to grow timber, graze animals or plant crops. When peat dries out, the organic matter that has built up for thousands of years begins to be eaten by bacteria in the soil. This process converts the carbon in the peat into carbon dioxide, which is then released into the atmosphere.

Emissions from converted peat bogs can be enormous – each hectare of lowland peat used for crop farming emits an average of 4 tonnes of carbon dioxide equivalent per year. And like a burning forest, this land doesn't just emit carbon; it also loses the ability to sequester more carbon.

Most farming in the UK relies heavily on man-made herbicides, pesticides and, above all, fertilisers. These days most fertiliser is not created from manure or nitrogen-fixing crops but from ammonia, which is produced in vast factories using the energy-intensive Haber–Bosch process (as described in *Chapter Ten*).

Once spread onto the land, any fertiliser that isn't taken up by plants sinks into the soil. From there, it is either washed into our rivers and underground aquifers, contaminating both, or converted by bacteria into nitrous oxide – a greenhouse gas which, as we have seen, is roughly 265 times more potent than carbon dioxide over a 100-year horizon. These effects mean that synthetic fertiliser alone accounts for about 4 percent of global emissions (1 percent from the original manufacture and 3 percent from the nitrous oxide).

Farm machinery and buildings also require a lot of energy to run. And, once the raw ingredients have left the farm, another long chain of energy consumption begins:

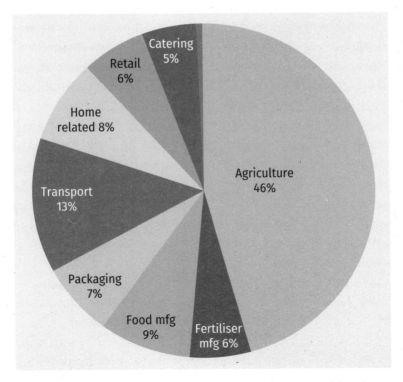

Carbon emissions from agriculture and fertiliser manufacturing (mfg) alone represent half the emissions in the UK.

processing, packaging, transport, retail, cold storage, cooking in homes and restaurants, waste disposal. The good news is that these parts of the food system increasingly benefit from innovations in clean and efficient energy. As renewable energy has begun to replace fossil fuels, many food manufacturers and retailers have been able to cut their carbon footprints dramatically. Nestlé UK and Ireland, for example, has reduced its operational emissions by more than 60 percent since 2007.

The chart on the previous page shows how greenhouse gas (GHG) emissions are distributed across the various parts of the food system. It is worth noting that the transport of food – the famous 'food mile' – actually accounts for only 13 percent of the food system's carbon footprint. Airfreight is a small percentage of that (estimated at under 1 percent of total emissions from food) because so little food is carried by plane these days.* By far the biggest slice of the GHG pie belongs to 'agriculture', meaning the actual farming of crops and animals.

All farming involves some GHG emissions, although there are techniques, both ancient and modern, that can go a long way towards minimising the damage. But there is one kind of farming that, as we shall see in the next chapter, does more damage to the climate than any other. To say as much is to incite bitter arguments on all sides: meat-lovers versus vegans, libertarians versus environmentalists, nostalgics versus progressives. If, like me, you are a meat-eater yourself, it also means having to take a discomfiting tour of your own conscience.

---

* Air transport can turn low carbon food into very high carbon food: the carbon footprint of asparagus, for example, increases by 25 times when it is flown to the UK from South America, rather than grown locally.

CHAPTER THIRTEEN

Peak meat?

Why we need less livestock farming

Imagine a landscape with a herd of cattle grazing on the left, and a coal-powered power station on the right. A warm breeze blows across the pasture as the bullocks graze languidly. They are busy turning grass, which humans cannot digest, into meat, which we can. This is the argument most often invoked in pointless Twitter spats about meat farming. 'That land is no good for anything else,' say the meat lovers. 'Why not stick some cows/sheep on it?'

However, there is more going in our pastoral scene than first meets the eye. To start with, that grass probably hasn't just sprung up unattended. The majority of land used for grazing ruminants in the UK is treated with fertiliser. This makes the grass more lush, so that it fattens up the animals faster.

Once eaten, the grass has to be digested. Cows and other ruminant animals do this by fermenting the plant cellulose until it turns into starches. This process creates methane in their stomachs, which has to come out somehow: burps, mostly, rather than the farts of popular imagination. Ruminant manure also releases methane and nitrous oxide. Taken together, the burping and manure of ruminant animals account for two-thirds of the UK's agricultural greenhouse gas emissions.

Meanwhile, back in our green and pleasant landscape, the power station on the right is belching out carbon dioxide. This is bad too – but differently bad from the belches of the cows. As we touched on in the previous chapter, methane and CO_2 have different qualities. Methane traps more heat than CO_2, making it more dangerous to the climate. However, unlike carbon dioxide or nitrous oxide, both of which linger in the atmosphere for centuries, methane transforms itself. It reacts with hydroxyl radicals (OH) – oxidising chemicals that are abundant in the upper atmosphere – leading to a chain of reactions that transform it into water vapour and carbon dioxide, which traps 100 times less heat than the methane it replaces.

Hydroxyl radicals are sometimes called 'the detergent of the troposphere', because they react with many pollutants to remove them from the upper levels of the atmosphere. In the process, however, they themselves are removed. The increase in methane in the atmosphere is leading to a reduction in hydroxyl radicals, which in turn means the removal of methane from the atmosphere is slowing down. In 1990 it took an average of ten years for a molecule of methane to disappear from the atmosphere. Today it is closer to twelve.

Still, it remains the case that while methane is a more potent gas to emit into the atmosphere, at least it doesn't stick around. The amount of methane put into the atmosphere by a new herd of cows will stabilise after about twelve years, as long as the size of the herd remains the same. New burps will keep going up, but old methane will begin to vanish from the atmosphere.

This is not true of the CO_2 emitted by the power station. Because carbon lingers for hundreds of years, it keeps building up in the atmosphere, trapping more and more heat.

When scientists measure the emissions of different gases, they use something called the Global Warming Potential (GWP) scale. The GWP of each greenhouse gas is calculated over a specific time horizon, commonly twenty or 100 years, and measured against the benchmark gas, carbon dioxide, which is assigned a GWP of 1. Over twenty years, methane has a GWP of 85. But over 100 years its GWP drops to 34, because of its powers of metamorphosis. (Nitrous oxide has a GWP of 265 over both periods.)

Methane's disappearing trick has two implications for climate change. The first is that – as with our imaginary herd – if the number of ruminant animals on the planet does not increase, the methane in the atmosphere will stabilise over twelve years. The existing ruminants will not warm the planet any further than they already have.*

You may think this sounds like wishful thinking. There are currently more animals being reared for food than ever before. Every year around 1.3 billion ruminants are slaughtered for food. However, in recent years the global demand for ruminant meat has begun to tail off. In developed countries, consumption of beef and lamb seems to be in (very modest) decline, perhaps because of perceived health or environmental concerns. Even in developing nations the rate of increase is slowing. Some commentators have suggested the world may be reaching 'peak meat'. If that is the case, it may be possible to cap

---

* For complicated reasons of atmospheric science, the herd would have to reduce in size by 0.3 percent each year for its global warming effect to remain constant.

methane emissions at their current level simply by eating the same number of ruminants as we do today.

But what if we were to go further, and actively reduce the amount of ruminant meat we eat (or the methane produced by each ruminant)? Because of the impermanence of methane, this would have a cooling effect. If all the ruminants on Earth mysteriously vanished tomorrow, it would take roughly twelve years for the methane they had produced in their lifetimes to vanish almost completely. After a couple more decades, the temperature of the planet would have cooled to the same temperature as if those animals had never existed.

Obviously, that particular scenario isn't going to happen. But by reducing livestock farming we can have a direct, and relatively fast, impact on methane levels in the atmosphere. The more we cut back, the bigger the cooling effect. There is no comparable vanishing trick that can be performed with carbon dioxide or nitrous oxide. Cutting back on meat is therefore one of the very few methods by which we could put a rapid brake on climate change before it's too late.

Some people have argued that methane is a less urgent problem than other greenhouse gases, precisely because of its impermanence. Every tonne of carbon that gets released into the atmosphere stays there forever. Stopping carbon emissions should therefore be the priority, to prevent this cumulative effect.

But in truth, we no longer have the luxury of picking one option or the other. We need to cut back on carbon and methane emissions simultaneously. As we can see in the chart on the facing page, cutting methane emissions now could result in a peak global temperature increase 0.25 °C lower than cutting them in 2035. This could mean the difference between climate change that is just about manageable, and a tipping point that leads to runaway

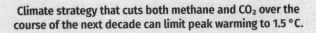

Climate strategy that cuts both methane and CO_2 over the course of the next decade can limit peak warming to 1.5 °C.

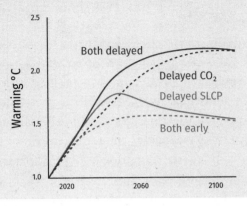

This chart shows why we can't afford to wait to reduce the amount of meat we eat. It was created by Myles Allen, one of the UK's leading climate scientists. 'SLCP' stands for 'short lived climate pollutants', predominantly methane. If we cut both methane and carbon dioxide emissions, we can limit global warming to 1.5 °C. But if we delay the cuts to methane, the global temperature will rise above 1.5 °C, before falling back down. That temporary peak might send us past a tipping point, doing irreversible damage to the environment and climatic systems.

ice melting, ocean current disruption and permanent coral reef death.

Cutting back on meat consumption isn't the only way to reduce methane emissions, although it is by far the most effective. Some farmers are experimenting with rearing ruminants in ways that curtail their emissions – by feeding them supplements that supress methane production in the gut, or by selectively breeding animals that produce less methane. The manufacturing giant Nestlé believes that, by buying milk products from such farms, it can halve the carbon footprint of its dairy products in less than a decade.

There are many factors that make some meat more ecologically damaging than others. The chart opposite shows the greenhouse gas emissions produced in the creation of 100g of protein from various foodstuffs. (These totals include measurements of all the major greenhouse gases, but are recorded, using the aforementioned GWP scale, as carbon dioxide equivalents, or CO_2-eq.) The undulations within each foodstuff occur where they are being farmed or processed in a particular way, with higher or lower resulting emissions.

You can see, predictably, that vegetable proteins hug the left-hand side of the chart, meaning they are low in emissions, while meat and dairy extends much further towards the carbon-heavy right. But you can also see that the picture is complex. Most fish farming, for example, ranks on the left-hand side of the chart. This is one of the lowest-carbon forms of animal protein. But if – as sometimes happens – ponds are left warm and unaerated, the feed and excreta that falls to the bottom can ferment and emit more methane per kilogram of protein than cattle. Hence, the long, thin tail extending towards the right.

Chicken is also a relatively low-carbon protein, but the chart shows a bumpy tail to the right. This is because some methods of chicken farming are much higher in emissions than others. Instinctively, one would expect the culprits to be intensive, indoor farms. Surely it must be more climate-friendly to raise chickens outside in nature, rather than in temperature-controlled, strip-lit warehouses? Alas, no: the more intensively you rear some animals, the more carbon-efficient they tend to be. Leaving aside other important concerns – including animal welfare, the pollution caused by manure run-off, and ammonia emissions into the atmosphere – intensively farmed chicken has a lower carbon footprint than free-range chicken. This is because

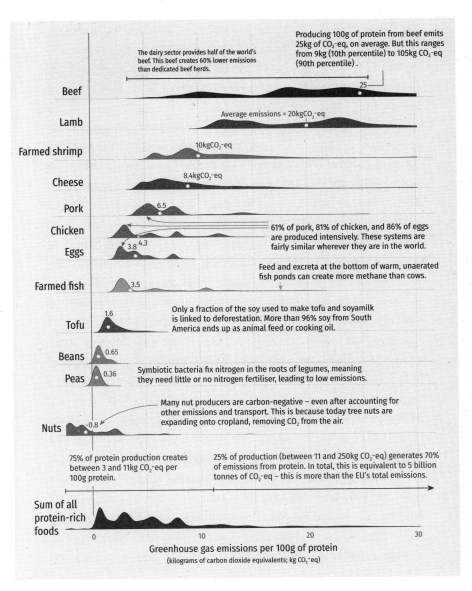

Producing 100g of protein from beef emits 25kg of CO_2-eq, on average. But this ranges from 9kg (10th percentile) to 105kg CO_2-eq (90th percentile).

The dairy sector provides half of the world's beef. This beef creates 60% lower emissions than dedicated beef herds.

Beef 25

Lamb Average emissions = 20kgCO_2-eq

Farmed shrimp 10kgCO_2-eq

Cheese 8.4kgCO_2-eq

Pork 6.5

Chicken 61% of pork, 81% of chicken, and 86% of eggs are produced intensively. These systems are fairly similar wherever they are in the world.

Eggs 3.8 4.3

Feed and excreta at the bottom of warm, unaerated fish ponds can create more methane than cows.

Farmed fish 3.5

Tofu 1.6
Only a fraction of the soy used to make tofu and soyamilk is linked to deforestation. More than 96% soy from South America ends up as animal feed or cooking oil.

Beans 0.65

Peas 0.36
Symbiotic bacteria fix nitrogen in the roots of legumes, meaning they need little or no nitrogen fertiliser, leading to low emissions.

Many nut producers are carbon-negative – even after accounting for other emissions and transport. This is because today tree nuts are expanding onto cropland, removing CO_2 from the air.

Nuts -0.8

75% of protein production creates between 3 and 11kg CO_2-eq per 100g protein.

25% of production (between 11 and 250kg CO_2-eq) generates 70% of emissions from protein. In total, this is equivalent to 5 billion tonnes of CO_2-eq – this is more than the EU's total emissions.

Sum of all protein-rich foods

0   10   20   30

Greenhouse gas emissions per 100g of protein
(kilograms of carbon dioxide equivalents; kg CO_2-eq)

Hannah Ritchie at Our World in Data produced this chart. It shows greenhouse gas emissions per 100g of protein for different food products, based on a sample of 38,700 commercially viable farms in 119 countries. Her conclusion was that 'Less meat is nearly always better than sustainable meat, to reduce your carbon footprint.'

the birds gain weight more quickly when housed indoors, they catch fewer viruses, get sick less often, and fewer die before they are ready to be slaughtered. This higher survival rate means you get more output (a portion of chicken) for less input (bags of chicken feed).

The livestock industry with the biggest variations in emissions is cattle. The chart opposite shows the average kilos of carbon released per kilo of beef in various countries (overlaid with the amount of beef each country produces). The range is huge, with Paraguay emitting over 200kg of carbon per kilo of meat and Denmark emitting less than 15kg. The reasons for this are various. Clearing forest to create pasture – which is still being done in many countries – massively increases emissions. This isn't just a problem in developing countries: 73 percent of all deforestation in Queensland, Australia, is due to beef production. (The chart is somewhat unfair, as it doesn't reflect historic deforestation in the UK and elsewhere. But that damage is a sunk cost.) Other factors include: how intensively the animals are reared; the suitability of the land for pasture (how much carbon-intensive fertiliser must be put on the land to create nutritious grass); and whether dairy cattle are subsequently used for beef, which lowers the overall carbon footprint.

While UK emissions from cattle farming are much lower than the worst producers, they are higher than some OECD countries – including the United States, with its vast and (to most British eyes) dystopian feedlot systems. Once again, intensive livestock rearing has its carbon benefits. Feeding

The chart opposite shows how carbon emissions from beef vary enormously by country. CO_2 emissions per kilo of beef (on the top axis) are shown by the dark grey bars. The light grey bars show the emissions caused by turning rainforest into pasture and land to grow feed crops. The dots show the amount of beef produced by each country in megatonnes per year (on the bottom axis).

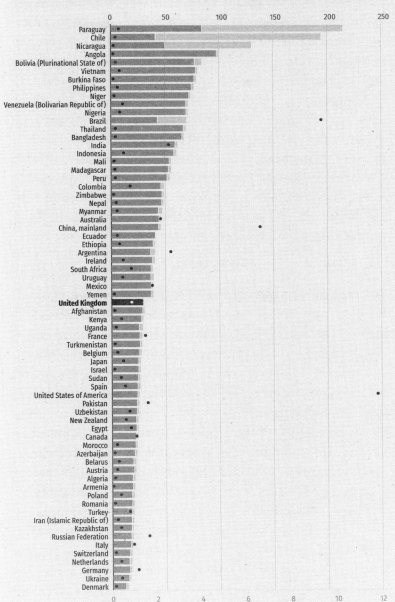

Greenhouse gas footprint (CO$_2$-eq/kg bovine meat, carcass weight)

Bovine meat production (megatonnes/year)

cows on grain (more calorific than grass) and giving them growth hormones means they gain weight more quickly, go to the slaughterhouse younger and therefore have less opportunity to emit methane than cows reared on pasture. It might not be the life you would wish upon any sentient animal, but the methane cost is unquestionably lower.

The countries with the lowest emissions from cattle, such as Denmark, combine intensive farming with an appetite for ex-dairy meat. Because dairy cattle produce protein throughout their lifetimes, in the form of milk, the overall ratio of emissions per kilo of total protein is lower. Ex-dairy beef is a taste we haven't developed in the UK, although on the continent the dense, highly marbled, strongly flavoured meat is considered a delicacy.

The case for and against meat is further complicated by the fact that we get more than just sustenance from our livestock farmers. In Britain, beef, dairy and lamb farming is largely responsible for the appearance of our 'traditional' pastured countryside. These animals are, literally, part of the landscape.

They have their ecological uses, too. Some native breeds of cattle are being used in rewilding projects to create 'pastured woodland'. Where trees and scrub are allowed to spread, the trampling and grazing of small herds of cows creates clearings in the budding forest; places where sunlight can get through and create an abundance of biodiversity.

Some conventional farmers, too, are reintroducing cows and sheep as part of a crop rotation system. This traditional practice, of allowing animals to graze on fallow land, fell out of favour after the Green Revolution. But growing numbers of farmers are now realising that it can improve soil quality, eliminate some plant diseases and reduce the need for expensive fertilisers and pesticides. In the right circumstances, and used in the right way, some people believe that cattle might even be able to effectively sequester carbon (see box below).

It is important to encourage this kind of imaginative, ecological livestock farming. Realistically, however, it could never produce enough meat to cater to our current appetites. We simply cannot reduce greenhouse gas emissions to a safe level without cutting back on meat consumption.

CARBON COWBOYS

Could cattle, instead of being a contributor to climate change, become a cure? This is the claim made by some proponents of Adaptive Multi-Paddock (AMP) grazing, a form of mob grazing. This new – or rather, deliberately ancient – method of cattle grazing is designed to mimic the way herds of wild bison would once have roamed across native grasslands. Instead of leaving cattle to graze in the same place for long periods, AMP grazers move their herds continuously, sometimes more than once a day, between small paddocks (created, in most cases, with easily movable electric fences). The grass in these paddocks is allowed to rest and regrow between grazing, which means taller stems, more photosynthesis (turning carbon into plant matter) and deeper roots (which access more nutrients in the soil). As the cattle move through each paddock, they eat much of the grass and trample a good deal into the ground, which creates a protective shield against heat and evaporation. And before moving on, they deposit their manure. AMP grazers don't need to use man-made nitrogen to grow lush grass: the cattle fertilise their own pastures.

The film-maker Peter Byck, whose 2014 documentary *Soil Carbon Cowboys* helped bring AMP grazing to a wider audience, has been coordinating academic research on five pairs of neighbouring cattle farms in south-east America. In each of these pairs, one farm has been AMP grazing for at least ten years, while the other has maintained a conventional approach. Biodiversity is much greater on the AMP farms. They have, on average, four times the number of grassland birds on their land, compared to the conventional farms, and a third more insect species. The soil on AMP farms contains an average of 25 percent more microbes, and, despite the absence of man-made fertiliser, 9 percent more available nitrogen. The better soil quality also makes it more absorbent, holding three times the volume of rainwater per hour. This makes the AMP farms less prone to flooding, soil erosion and watercourse pollution. And crucially, for the farmers, these AMP farms are making bigger profits. AMP grazing has allowed them to rear larger herds and spend less on hay and fertiliser.

Byck also says he has new evidence, currently unpublished, that AMP-grazed pastures can sequester significant amounts of carbon. Cow manure, he argues, forms a new layer of organic matter on the soil, some of which gradually becomes new soil, locking away the carbon it contains. Could AMP grazing be a major new tool to combat climate change?

Most soil and climate experts are extremely doubtful on this point. AMP grazing, they agree, might have significant environmental benefits. On the right soils and in the right climatic conditions it has been shown to sequester carbon, even when you take into account the methane emissions of the cattle. But it does not sequester as much carbon as other forms of land use. A recent review in *Science* magazine concluded that, on average, you could take ten to twenty times more carbon out of the atmosphere by restoring pasture to nature. And, if all beef were AMP grazed, and not more intensively produced, there is also no way we could satisfy our current demand for meat. AMP grazing may turn out to be the best possible way to rear cattle, kind to the environment and kinder to the climate. But we will still need to reduce our overall meat consumption to have any hope of reaching net zero.

CHAPTER FOURTEEN

Sentient food

The miseries of intensive farming

When opining on the environmental rights and wrongs of meat, it is all too easy to forget what meat actually is. It isn't merely a product, or an ingredient. It is (or was) the flesh of a sentient* animal.

If we were to measure the success of a species by the volume of DNA it reproduces, farm animals could claim to be some of evolution's biggest winners. There are currently around 80 billion animals on this planet being reared for food. But what kind of success is this? What lives do these animals enjoy – or rather endure – before they get bundled into lorries and taken to the slaughterhouse?

From a commercial point of view, it is cheaper to be ruthless in livestock farming. Pack as many animals as possible into the smallest space; keep disease under control with massive doses of antibiotics (which also promote rapid growth, because the animals don't have to expend

---

* The dictionary definition of 'sentient' is able to 'perceive through the senses'. This may range from the perception of physical pain to sophisticated emotional or intellectual consciousness.

energy on their immune systems); grow them fast and kill them young.

'Forget the pig is an animal — treat him just like a machine in a factory,' *Hog Farm Management* advised US farmers in 1976. Not a single federal law on animal welfare has been passed since then, and life remains bleak for the American pig. Farmers in the US are still allowed to keep sows in tight 'gestation crates' for their entire pregnancies, so confined that they cannot even turn around. Almost all male piglets are castrated to prevent 'boar taint': a change to the smell or taste of pork caused by male sex hormones. This procedure – which involves slicing the piglet's scrotum open, pulling out the testes and cutting them off – is not a uniquely American practice. Around 80 percent of male piglets on EU farms are castrated, generally without pain relief.

In China – the world's largest consumer and producer of pork – pigs are increasingly reared in giant, multi-storey indoor farms, where millions of animals pass their lives in metal stalls without ever feeling sun or rain, or earth under their feet. One recently opened farm in Hubei province has 26 storeys, and is expected to produce and slaughter 1.2 million pigs a year. (The whole of the UK only produces 4 million pigs a year.) When mass culls are necessary – for example, to contain the spread of African swine fever – Chinese pig farmers have been known to herd their animals into giant pits and bury them alive.

Better, perhaps, than being cooked alive, which was the fate of millions of American pigs during the Covid pandemic. Staff shortages created long backlogs in slaughterhouses and processing plants, so farmers needed to get rid of the mature livestock on their already overcrowded farms. They converted barns into giant ovens by fitting them with heaters and steam generators. Then they herded the pigs inside and locked the doors. This was judged by the

An intensive 12-storey pig production unit near Guigang in southern China. The inset shows one of the inmates of this unit.

American Veterinary Medical Association to be 'humane', because all the animals died within an hour.

The UK has much tougher rules on animal welfare than most countries. Still, all intensive livestock farming involves a degree of suffering. It is an unavoidable side effect of packing animals together in close confinement, away from their natural environment, and then killing them with maximum efficiency.

Chickens, for example, are prone to pecking each other savagely when they are forced to live in close proximity. To prevent this, they have parts of their acutely sensitive beaks cut off. When they are ready for slaughter, most chickens are strung up by their feet on a conveyor belt and dunked head first into electrocuted water before being decapitated. Billions of fish die through suffocation, freezing or crushing; pigs are gassed to death. All these are considered 'humane' practices, chiefly because the alternatives are worse.

It is awful to contemplate the misery we inflict on animals before we eat them – which is why, on the whole, we prefer not to think about it. Ironically, this squeamishness is itself a by-product of the food system. If we hadn't learnt to cook and eat other species, we would never have developed our big, complex brains. And without those brains we would not be able to comprehend the moral consequences of what we have done. But neither would we have the intellectual muscle required to put right our mistakes.

In the early 1830s, one of the founding members of the RSPCA took a stroll around the city of Bath. By then in his 70s, William Wilberforce was a 'little dwarfish figure, twisted in a strange conformation', according to his biographer, John Colquhoun. He was puffing his way up a particularly steep street when he came across two men driving a horse-drawn cart laden with coal.

One of the horses lost its footing and fell. The larger of the two carters, a giant of a man, flew into a rage and started kicking and beating the exhausted animal. But Wilberforce, who was little more than five feet tall, rushed forward to stop him, and poured upon the assailant 'a torrent of elegant rebuke'. The burly carter, we are told, 'stood with his face like a thundercloud, as if meditating to turn his stroke on the puny elf who appeared before him'. Luckily, the other carter recognised the elf. He whispered to his colleague not to punch the great anti-slavery campaigner and Parliamentarian. 'In an instant,' we are told, 'the lowering face cleared; and from rage and sullen hatred, the look passed into one of reverence.'

This anecdote shows not only the prestige Wilberforce had attained by the end of his life, but also that the abolition of slavery was not his only life's work. In 1787, at the age of 28, Wilberforce had written in his diary: 'God Almighty has placed before me two great objects: the suppression of the Slave Trade and the Reformation of Manners.' To modern ears this second object might sound a bit quaint, but in this context manners meant morals. And for Wilberforce, a devout Christian, the morality of the British nation was compromised by many of the barbaric practices that were inflicted on both humans and animals at the time.

To take one example, Wilberforce fulminated against the 'sport' of bull-baiting. Typically, a bull would be paraded through a town or village before being tethered to a stake. The bulldogs of the time were specially bred for this public spectacle, with huge heads, powerful jaws and small bodies, to make it hard for a bull to shake them off. The dogs, flattening themselves to the ground, would attempt to creep up on the bull, while the bull tried to knock them back with its horns. Eventually a dog would succeed in clamping itself onto the bull's face or nose, tearing its skin to shreds, while the bull tried to throw it off. Often the dog would be hurled high into the air. If it didn't break its neck on landing, it would crawl back to attack the bull again.

At the time, Wilberforce's campaign to reform such 'manners' was dismissed by many critics as po-faced and needless interference. He was accused of being motivated by 'fussy disapproval of the lusty joys' of the working classes: a libertarian burn that sounds like it could have come from Georgian Twitter.

In 1822, Britain became the first country in the world to introduce legislation to protect animal welfare: the 'Act to Prevent the Cruel and Improper Treatment of Cattle'. Amazingly, however, bull-baiting was exempt. Wilberforce then joined forces with other campaigners to set up the 'Society for the Prevention of Cruelty to Animals'. Thanks partly to lobbying by the Society, bull-baiting was finally banned in 1835, two years after Wilberforce's death. In 1840, Queen Victoria allowed the society to add 'Royal' to its name.

Wilberforce's concern for animal welfare was informed by his Christianity. Like most pious citizens of the time, he believed that God had, in the words of Genesis 1:26, given man 'dominion over the fish of the sea, and over the fowl of the air, and over the cattle, and over all the earth, and over every creeping thing that creepeth upon the earth'. But in exercising this sovereignty, Wilberforce believed, humanity must take care not to be wantonly cruel or thoughtless. To behave unkindly towards animals was a failing in itself, but also a corruption of our divinely exalted soul.

This is similar to the position taken by some modern-day humanists. They, too, regard humanity as a uniquely moral species, alone among the animals in having the rights and obligations that come with extreme sentience. It is this uniqueness, they argue, that means we have a duty to treat animals with compassion, sparing them unnecessary suffering. (The word 'unnecessary' does a lot of heavy lifting here.)

Cartoon of Charles Darwin published in the satirical *Hornet* magazine, in 1871, entitled: 'A Venerable Orang-Outang. A contribution to unnatural history.'

But what if humans are not as special as we like to think? As far back as Aristotle, philosophers recognised that the so-called 'higher animals' experience some of the same emotions as humans. Charles Darwin went further still, arguing that 'there is no fundamental difference between man and higher animals in their mental faculties', and that even the lower animals 'manifestly feel pleasure and pain, happiness and misery'. 'Natura non facit saltum' was how he put it in his *Origin of Species* – 'Nature does not make leaps.'

Darwin was mocked for this view, which was very much in the minority among his fellow scientists. It is only in recent decades that more detailed research into animal sentience has begun to vindicate him. Even the so-called 'lower animals', it seems, have more complex inner lives than most scientists previously imagined.

In the 1990s, a young neuroscientist called Robert Elwood was sitting in his local pub when he spotted the seafood chef Rick Stein having a pint. The two men started chatting and when Stein learned that Elwood was studying crustaceans, he asked him for a definitive answer to a question that has troubled many a restaurant chef. Can lobsters feel pain? Elwood replied that it was impossible to know for certain, because the neurobiology of the lobster is so far removed from our own. But, unsatisfied by his own answer, he went away determined to find out.

The received wisdom at the time was that invertebrates cannot feel pain. Although they recoil from painful things, such as hot or sharp objects, this was assumed to be purely reflexive: an automatic instinct to avoid injury. Elwood began experimenting on shore crabs, the kind you see children hoiking out of the water and plonking into buckets at the seaside. He painted a mild irritant onto their antennae to see if they showed signs of pain. The crabs rubbed their antennae against the glass of their tank, apparently trying to rub off the irritant. When Elwood applied an anaesthetic over the area, they stopped rubbing. This is behaviour that suggests they could feel pain.

In subsequent experiments, Elwood established that crustaceans will learn to avoid certain areas of a tank if they experience an electric shock there. This suggests a capacity not just for feeling pain, but for remembering it and learning from it. They also guard wounded limbs, as if to protect themselves from further pain. (You should know that Elwood is not a fan of boiling lobsters alive. He says it is quicker and kinder to stab them through the head.)

Elwood and other scientists are rapidly expanding our understanding of what the 'lower animals' can feel and do. Bees, for example, have been shown to display signs of nervousness, and can quickly learn to avoid unpleasant experiences. Fish turn out to have rather good memories, and can be trained to perform simple tasks in return for rewards. They can also plan ahead, solve problems and even play.

There are still sceptics who argue that all this is fuzzy anthropomorphism. They point out that some of these animals don't have the brain structures that enable humans to feel pain. But the fact that some species may experience the world through very different neural pathways to us is not proof that they don't feel at all. In fact, it is precisely our anthropomorphic tendency – our insistence on interpreting the whole animal kingdom in relation to ourselves – that has made us so dismissive of the lives of other species. 'If a lion could talk,' said the philosopher Ludwig Wittgenstein, 'we would not understand him.'

Most animals are sufficiently different from us to be pretty baffling, and this alien quality enables us to turn a blind eye to their suffering when it suits us to do so. Nevertheless, we have all had moments when we look into the eyes of one of the 'higher' animals – in my case, my cat Ronnie – and feel a current of understanding pass between us. This too used to be dismissed as mere sentimentality, but recent scientific research suggests that, once again, we have underestimated the sophistication of our fellow beasts.

Take dairy cows. For at least 10,000 years, humans have been rearing cows for milk. On modern dairy farms, cows are inseminated so that they become pregnant, give birth and start producing milk. Their calves are usually removed from them within twenty-four hours of birth and reared separately so that the mother can be milked commercially. The distress this separation causes for both cow and calf is now well-documented. The cow bellows for her lost calf, sometimes for days. The calf, separated from its mother, goes on to develop similar behaviours to those observed in children who grow up without a strong attachment figure. When introduced into a herd, they appear withdrawn, anti-social and sometimes disruptive. Calves that are raised with their mothers have been shown to be more playful and curious, and better at navigating the social rules of the herd.

Even chickens appear to demonstrate maternal instincts. When researchers disturbed hen's chicks with annoying puffs of air, the mothers clucked in protest. Their heart rate increased more than when they were subjected to the same treatment, suggesting that they cared more about the comfort of their young than about themselves.

As our understanding of animal sentience grows, it will become harder and harder to justify the relationship we have built with the animal kingdom. The roots of human exceptionalism look increasingly shallow. And even if you still believe that humans should have dominion over all the creeping things, can you honestly say that we are exerting that power kindly? I believe it is quite possible that in 200 years' time we will look back at industrial livestock farming with some of the horror that we feel for bull-baiting now.

In his book *How to Love Animals*, the writer Henry Mance neatly sums up our predicament: 'If we lived in a vegan world,' he writes, 'and someone said there was an alternative which involved breeding and killing billions of animals, and denuding much of the world's surface of wildlife, I'm pretty sure that Silicon Valley's venture capitalists would pass.'

The problem is, we do not live in that world. We live in a world where a strong appetite for meat is hard-wired into most of our genes, and where the eating and preparation of meat has for centuries been central to our self-image and social rituals. We British are famed as a nation of animal lovers. Yet we are also proud carnivores. Once nicknamed 'les rosbifs' by the French because of our appetite for red meat, we still seem to believe there is something culturally sacred about the Englishman's God-given right to a slab of flesh on our plate.

Mance calls this the 'meat paradox': a feat of cognitive dissonance that enables us to care about animal welfare while eating farmed animals. Studies have shown that the very act of eating meat changes our perspective on animal sentience. If you give someone a beef snack and ask them whether cows suffer pain, they are less likely to say 'Yes' than if you had given them nuts. As Mance puts it, 'we don't want to eat animals because we underplay their suffering; we underplay their suffering because we want to eat them'.

Most people who eat meat would be aghast if they saw what goes on in its production. Workers on industrial livestock farms often become inured to the distress of the animals – they have to, in order to do their job. A friend who worked on an intensive pig farm as a youth (and who is still a meat-eater) described the experience to me. 'You quickly get used to ignoring the horrible bits to get the job done,' he said. 'The job is to make cheap bacon. From dragging dead pigs from filthy overcrowded stalls to smoking cigarettes with your fingers covered in fresh shit. It's just habit. I became callous very quickly.'

'That which can be done only by a callous person, ought not to be done,' wrote the late philosopher Roger Scruton in his essay *Animal Rights and Wrongs*. Scruton was a meat-eater himself (and a keen fox hunter), and believed humans had a 'duty' to keep eating farm animals, in order to maintain their populations on Earth. He argued that meat-eating was justified – even virtuous – provided we rear the animals in natural, happy conditions.

Probably the happiest of the animals that we rear to eat are the sheep and cows who are allowed to roam and graze outdoors. But ruminants, as we have already seen, produce dangerous quantities of methane. And even if they didn't, it would be impossible to rear enough meat for our current needs in such high-welfare conditions.

And then there's the inescapable fact that in order to eat meat we have to sanction the mass slaughter of animals.
Even the most well-run slaughterhouses are disturbing for the conscientious meat-eater. I have visited quite a few clean, orderly, welfare-conscious abattoirs, but always come away feeling slightly mad. Partly, this is because you have to walk through an abattoir in reverse. To preserve food hygiene, you start at the end of the butchering process, where it is cleanest, and then proceed backwards through the various stages of dismemberment and death.

In a beef abattoir, the tour begins in a giant walk-in fridge full of cellophaned packs of steak or mince, labelled and ready for the supermarket shelves. It is very cold and quiet and odourless here. Then you proceed to the butchery zone, where lines of white-clad workers make quick, deft movements with their knives. Next is a room where animal carcasses – skinned, decapitated, sawn in half lengthways and strung up on a slow-moving conveyor belt – are graded on the quality of their meat. After that, you push through a door into a hot, red cacophony of smell and noise. This is where animals get turned into carcasses.

Just outside the room, the live cow walks into a narrow metal box. It gets a squirt of water on its forehead, to conduct electricity, and a metal apparatus descends from above to touch its heart and head. A strong electrical current is passed through this device and, eyes swivelling, the beast drops unconscious. The metal box then tips sideways into the processing room, where a worker ties a chain around the cow's back feet, hoists it up onto the conveyor belt and slits its throat. Blood gushes noisily through grates in the floor.*

From there, the body is carried by the conveyor belt to one worker after another, each with a different dismembering task. One slits open the belly and removes the guts. One makes circular incisions around the feet and attaches chains to the skin, which is then pulled off in one go, like a jumper. At the side of the room, a man (I have only seen men do this) stands on a moving platform, wearing an enormous circular saw, so heavy that it has to be strapped to his torso. As each carcass reaches him, he rises up and down on his lift, sawing the body in two. The noise is appalling.

I should say that beyond this room, at the point where the animals are herded towards their death, the scene is less awful than you might expect. In this country most

* As might be expected for such a particular profession, abattoirs develop distinctive cultures. I went to one which had been built on two floors. Lamb was slaughtered on the first floor, whereas the beef slaughter, described above, took place on the ground floor. The 'lamb' and 'beef' teams worked independently and if, as rarely happened, a member of the 'lamb' team ventured onto the ground floor, those slaughtering beef would all 'baaaaa' loudly at them.

abattoirs use carefully devised systems, such as the curved ramps designed by the American animal behaviourist Dr Temple Grandin, that help keep the animals calm. Even so, it is impossible to walk away from an industrial-scale abattoir without feeling somewhat queasy.

I don't wish to guilt-trip or berate meat-eaters. Despite everything I have seen, I still suffer from the meat paradox myself. I love the taste of liver and kidneys; the technical challenge of smoking a beef rib for twelve hours until it is falling succulently off the bone; the social ritual of the barbecue and the roast dinner. Although I have cut back hard on my meat consumption, I have yet to muster the will to go full vegetarian.

But it is important to be honest with ourselves about where meat comes from. We must take responsibility for the harms our appetites cause – not just to the planet, crucial though that is, but to our fellow creatures. In the coming chapters, I will return to the environmental arguments for eating less meat. The compassionate argument is, at the very least, an added incentive. As the most sentient of the animals (so far as we know), humans have the curse and the privilege of a conscience. We should not be afraid to listen to it.

ANTIMICROBIAL RESISTANCE AND ZOONOTIC DISEASE

Livestock farming, particularly the intensive kind, is not just bad for the animals farmed. When chickens, pigs or cows are forced to live in crowded conditions – sometimes by the tens of thousands – disease is inevitable. This has led to the widespread use, and overuse, of antimicrobial drugs (which include antibiotics) in farming. In some countries, antibiotics are routinely added to livestock feed, regardless of the health of the animals, because it can make them grow faster – immune systems that aren't fighting off infections use less energy, leaving more for growth.

But the microbes have fought back, becoming resistant to many antimicrobial drugs – including some that are used to treat humans. Intensive farming of pigs and chickens is thought to be a major cause of antimicrobial resistance worldwide. In some parts of the world, microbes have already evolved to resist 80 percent of the antimicrobials used on animals. Drug-resistant infections could eventually make surgeries (including caesarean sections) and cancer treatments too dangerous to perform.

Alongside the threat of antibiotic resistance, we must contend with the emergence of new zoonotic diseases – those that jump between species. When forests and wild areas are cleared to make way for livestock farming, the animals that manage to survive the clearance tend to be rats and bats. Both animals carry viruses that can infect other species. Once such a virus passes into a livestock population, it can incubate and mutate until it is capable of infecting people.

Intensively reared animals, which are selectively bred to have nearly identical genomes, act as vast replication vessels for viruses.

We have recently seen how a new infectious disease – even one with a relatively low mortality rate – can devastate our health, economies and wellbeing.

CHAPTER FIFTEEN

Making the most of our land

For our own self-interest, we need to make more space for nature

Land in Britain is a precious resource, and we don't always use it wisely. The map opposite shows how land is used in the UK – not geographically, but as proportions of the whole. The hexagons to the right, drawn to the same scale, represent agricultural land abroad that is used to cater for the UK market (including the land used to grow animal feed for UK livestock).

A few things immediately catch the eye. Agriculture as a whole takes up 70 percent of the UK's landmass. The built-up areas combined are only fractionally bigger than the area we use for dairy farming. And an astonishing 85 percent of the farmland that feeds us, here and abroad, is used for rearing livestock – either as pasture or to grow crops for animal feed.

This is wildly inefficient. Meat, dairy and eggs provide only 32 percent of the calories we eat. By contrast, the 15 percent of farmland (half in the UK, half overseas) used to grow plants for human consumption provides 68 percent of our calories. The extravagance of this – using most of our land to get such a small portion of our food – is all the more obvious when you consider how many other things we could be doing with it.

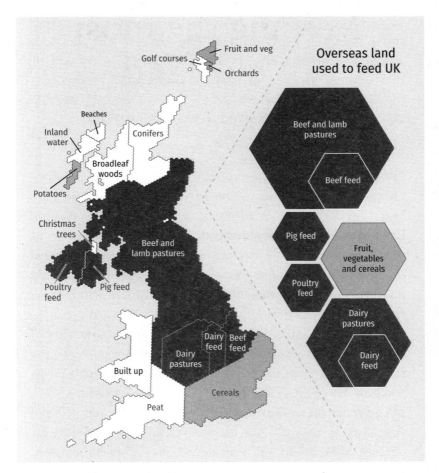

The land we use to feed ourselves, both here and (in the hexagons on the right) abroad. 85 percent of agricultural land, shaded dark grey, is used to graze animals or grow crops to feed to animals. Only 15 percent of agricultural land, shaded light grey, grows crops for human consumption. The remaining land is a combination of built-up areas, peat bogs, woodland, beaches, lakes and golf courses (five times as much land as orchards).

The UK is a relatively small country (smaller than the US state of Oregon), with a big population (61 million, compared to Oregon's 3.8 million). We ask a lot of our land: we live and work on it, farm it, use its resources for energy production and manufacturing. We want some areas to be suitable for holidays and leisure, and expect those areas to be beautiful. The government has also pledged to protect 30 percent of UK land 'for nature' by 2030, in an effort to restore the diminished biodiversity of our countryside. On top of all this, we urgently need to start using more of our land to sequester carbon.

The word 'sequester' has appeared a few times in previous chapters, and is about to be sprinkled around like corn seed. So let's take a moment to properly understand its meaning. The dictionary definition is 'to remove or separate, to retire or to requisition'. It's not the same as offsetting carbon emissions (paying for services that balance your emissions). It is about *actually removing it from the atmosphere.*

At the 2015 Paris Agreement, the UK – along with 192 other countries – signed a pledge to limit global warming to 1.5 °C. To some extent this is an arbitrary figure: every fraction of a degree makes a difference, and 1.5 °C is already an alarming proposition. But scientists predict that this is roughly the threshold after which climate change will inflict such extreme and chaotic damage on our planet that human ingenuity will not be able to mitigate it.

For example, at 1.5 °C, there's still a chance of preventing the total collapse of the Greenland and West Antarctic ice sheet, limiting the extent of sea level rises. At 2 °C, however, we could expect vast swathes of inhabited land to disappear under the waves, leaving behind a much smaller global landmass, new coastlines and hundreds of millions of displaced people.

Without man-made global warming, extreme heatwaves would be a once-a-decade phenomenon. A rise of 1.5 °C – which now looks all but inevitable – is expected to increase the frequency to 4.1 times per decade. A rise of 2 °C would push that up to 5.6 times per decade. With much of our cultivatable land under water, and droughts or floods afflicting the rest, how will humanity feed itself?

There are two ways to limit global warming: decrease the amount of greenhouse gases we put into the atmosphere, or increase the amount we take out. Or better still, do both. In 2019, the UK government passed a law committing itself to the goal of reaching 'net zero' by 2050. In other words, within less than three decades we need to be removing at least as much carbon dioxide, methane and nitrous oxide as we emit.

Technology alone cannot save us. Although great strides have been made in the production of renewable energy, removing existing greenhouse gases from the atmosphere is much harder. The various man-made technologies for carbon capture are expensive and hard to scale up to anywhere near the capacity required. So, at least for now, we remain largely dependent on nature: the most effective carbon sponge imaginable.

There are innumerable systems through which nature removes carbon dioxide from the atmosphere and locks it away within forests, oceans and the soil. Photosynthesis is the most obvious of these: as a plant grows, it converts carbon dioxide from the air into sugars to sustain itself. CO_2 thus becomes sequestered within the body of the plant. Earth's forests absorb around 7.6 billion metric tonnes of carbon annually, or one third of annual global emissions. Our oceans absorb an estimated 2.5 billion metric tonnes.

But that still leaves a lot of excess CO_2 going into the atmosphere. Although renewable energy is now overtaking fossil fuels in many spheres, there are some industries that will remain heavily dependent on gas, coal or oil for the foreseeable future. Most steel production, for example, currently requires hotter temperatures than green energy can provide. Aeroplanes still need petrol-based fuels to get them off the ground. Like it or not (and many don't), these industries are not about to disappear. We need to find ways to mop up their dirt, and using land to sequester carbon is the only large-scale method we have.*

Every nation needs to free up more land to perform this vital work. And we must act quickly. It takes around ten years for trees to grow big enough to sequester significant levels of carbon. The UK Climate Change Committee, which advises the government on how to reach net zero, has said that we need to create new woodlands covering an area the size of East Anglia.

* The climate expert Myles Allen, professor of geosystems science at the University of Oxford, takes a harder line. In a paper published in 2023, with scientists from Oxford, the US and the Netherlands, Allen proposed that companies profiting from fossil fuels (oil, gas and coal producers) should be obliged to pay for an equivalent amount of CO_2 to be captured and stored as a condition of operating. He points out that, although carbon capture technology is still expensive, the profits made by fossil fuel companies are even bigger. Using the 'polluter pays' principle, they should be forced to clean up their own mess. The cost of doing so would, at current prices, halve their profits. But it would also concentrate their minds on improving the technology which in turn would help bring down its cost. Allen argues that, although it is also vital to free up land for sequestering carbon, this should be done in addition to, rather than instead of, building carbon capture plants.

Unless we are to give up all hope of reaching net zero, we need to use our farmland more wisely, to free some up for environmental purposes.

Luckily, not all farmland is created equal. Some is too rocky, exposed or lacking in nutrients for growing plant crops. The least productive 20 percent of our farmland produces just 3 percent of the calories we consume – chiefly in the form of meat. Most of this land is currently used for grazing sheep and cows.

'We have an excellent climate for growing grass' is a common refrain. But the pasture in Britain, even in the rolling uplands, usually has to be treated with fertiliser just to make it grassy enough to sustain cattle and sheep. And although ruminants are experts at turning grass into delicious meat, that is not the most useful purpose this land could serve.

Upland areas also provide bountiful opportunities for carbon sequestration. Most contain some peat bogs, which could be rewetted to prevent them releasing carbon into the air, as well as areas that would be ideal for growing trees and shrubs. Many upland areas, such as Dartmoor, were once covered in temperate rainforests. A few fragile remnants of these rainforests still survive – beautiful places, verdant and twisted and mossy, dense with plant and animal life. But most of the uplands have been grazed almost bare. Sheep nibble very close to the ground, making it difficult for tree saplings to grow.

Globally, as we can see in the chart overleaf, the biggest carbon benefit of eating less meat would not actually come from the reduction in methane emissions – fantastic and future-changing though that would be. The biggest win would actually come from repurposing pasture, handing it back to nature so that it can be used to sequester carbon. This is why goats and sheep, both of which roam over large areas and have a taste for tree saplings, are the most environmentally costly form of agriculture, in terms of lost potential for carbon sequestration.

Reclaiming some land for natural carbon capture also presents an opportunity to create new habitats for

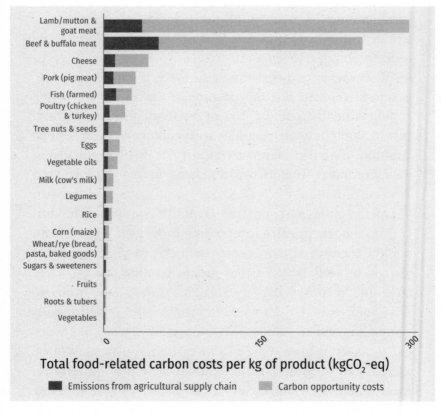

Total food-related carbon costs per kg of product (kgCO₂-eq)

■ Emissions from agricultural supply chain   ■ Carbon opportunity costs

The biggest potential carbon benefit of eating less meat is the opportunity to repurpose land to sequester carbon (and restore biodiversity). This chart shows, in dark grey, the kilos of carbon embedded in different foodstuffs (in kilos of CO₂-eq per kilos of product). The light grey is the 'opportunity cost of carbon' from producing the food. That is the carbon that, if we stopped farming on the land, could be sequestered in plants, trees and soil instead.

wildlife. In Britain, there happens to be a serendipitous overlap between large areas of land that would be best suited for each of these purposes. This covers much of the uplands; some land adjacent to the Solent and the New Forest; the greensand and chalk formations around the Weald and in the Chilterns; and the Fens. Of these, only the Fens are very significant for food production. If the farmers of unproductive land were properly incentivised, making environmental projects more lucrative than conventional agriculture, it would be possible to kill – or rather revive – two birds with one stone: meeting government targets for restoring nature while simultaneously sequestering carbon.

This is not a call for large-scale rewilding. On the contrary, it's amazing how little land it would take to achieve a huge amount. For the National Food Strategy, we calculated that around 5–8 percent of the least productive farmland in England should be taken out of agriculture altogether, largely to plant broadleaf woodlands and restore peat bogs.

Even so, the idea that farmers should be diverted from their ancient vocation – growing food – to militate against climate change raises eyebrows in some quarters. They already do a difficult job (and, in most cases, a pretty low-paid one). Do they really need a whole new raft of environmental duties imposed upon them?

Just cutting down their own carbon emissions will be challenging enough. The National Farmers' Union has committed its members to reaching net zero emissions by 2040 – a necessary but daunting task. Agriculture in the UK currently emits 54.6 million tonnes of carbon per year. Emissions caused by land use change (for example from converted peat bogs or forests) add a further 12.8 million tonnes. This tots up to over 67 million tonnes per year, a figure that has remained virtually unchanged since 2008.

(Over the same period of time, emissions from the whole of our economy have decreased by 32 percent.)

We are expecting farmers to perform quite a juggling act: produce enough food to feed the nation affordably, while simultaneously restoring wildlife, cutting their own carbon emissions, planting trees, managing flood plains and returning some land to the wild so that it can mop up the pollution produced by other sectors. If this seems a bit unfair – well, it is. Farmers are being asked to clean up everyone else's mess, on top of their own. But the unfortunate fact is, they are the only people who can do it. They manage 75 percent of our uninhabited land.

There are currently two main schools of thought about how to get all these balls into the air. One is the 'land-sparing' school. In this model, you make some farmland as productive as possible, thereby freeing up other land for environmental projects such as planting trees. By producing more food from a smaller area, you create the necessary elbow room for all the other purposes required of our land.

This idea rings alarm bells for some environmentalists, who point out that pushing up productivity almost always comes at a heavy cost to nature. Since the Green Revolution, farming has become what environmentalists call a 'mining' operation: productivity has increased hugely, but we have achieved this in an entirely unsustainable way, by digging up fossil fuels to create man-made fertilisers and pesticides while simultaneously wreaking havoc on watercourses and wildlife habitats.

Proponents of the land-sparing school, however, say that emerging technologies are breaking the link between productivity and environmental damage. The future, they say, lies in 'sustainable intensification'. Thousands of new techniques are being trialled which promise to wean farming from its reliance on industrial fertiliser and 'red diesel'. (Diesel for agricultural machinery is not taxed in the UK; it is dyed red to prevent it being sold on the black market for other uses.)

In my travels, I saw some wonderful new technologies at work. I met engineers developing robots that zap weeds with powerful electric currents; botanists dipping maize seeds into a solution of nitrogen-fixing bacteria to reduce the need for fertiliser; and farmers using drones and AI to treat outbreaks of disease in their crops before the effects are even noticeable to the human eye.

I met one entrepreneur whose AI can already identify every one of millions of plants in a field, and alert the farmer to any change in their condition. Sam Watson-Jones, co-founder of the Small Robot Company, foresees a future of 'per-plant' farming, where multiple different crops are grown in one field. For example, arable crops could be planted alongside legumes (to fix nitrogen in the soil) and flowers (to attract pollinators). This kind of symbiotic farming dates right back to the Mesopotamians, and there are farmers in the UK experimenting with similar models today. Agricultural robots would make it easier to harvest such fields, by separating the plants as they go.

There is no doubt that science and technology will be used to make high-yield farming much less destructive. But we can't know yet which of the techniques currently in development will turn out to be most transformational and cost-effective, or when they will be ready for large-scale use.

In the meantime, there is a model of farming that we already know to have tremendous benefits for nature. Some call this 'land sharing', because it performs two functions simultaneously – producing food and supporting wildlife – while others call it 'high nature value farming' or 'agroecological farming'. It is an approach that overlaps with organic principles but covers a larger range of farms. The terminology is unsettled and categories are blurry, but the basic principle of land sharing is that farmers consciously and deliberately share their land with nature.

Although many insects, birds and animals require an uncultivated environment to thrive, others actually do better in a certain kind of traditional, lower-yield farmland. For most of Britain's history, we farmed in roughly the same way: on smaller plots of land, divided by trees and hedgerows, cultivating many different kinds of produce and using rotations of crops and livestock to ensure the health of the soil. We farmed like this for so long that some species have adapted to thrive alongside us.

Skylarks, for example, flourish on farms that practise crop rotations, foraging in high cereal stubbles in the winter, but preferring lower and less dense crops for the spring and summer breeding season. Legume fallows – planted to restore the soil – offer ideal habitats for butterflies and brown hares. The yellowhammer requires scrub for nesting (hedges are perfect), insect-rich open habitats in summer (such as flower-filled field margins) and seed-rich open habitats in winter (provided by overwinter stubbles). These resources are generally most abundant on traditional, low-yield farmland.

But the Green Revolution created a new kind of farming landscape, which wiped out the habitats of many species. Even the most carefully managed high-yield farms are currently, by necessity, inhospitable to much wildlife. They produce large monocultural crops or livestock herds, often in giant fields, without the weeds, trees, ponds and hedgerows that give rise to abundant biodiversity.

Land-sharing farmers – in all their many guises – farm in a gentler way. They use pesticides and fertilisers in smaller quantities, if at all; maintain hedgerows, meadows and wild margins; and often deploy ruminant animals in rotations to help fertilise the soil. The end result is lower yields (typically 20–40 percent less), but a farmland that is much more hospitable to wildlife.

However, this model does require more land to produce less food. On its own, it would not be productive enough to maintain our national food security. And even in terms of biodiversity, it has its drawbacks. Although it is great for those species that thrive on traditional farmland, it does not offer much hope for those that require wilder landscapes. Because it occupies a lot of land, it leaves less room for the kind of truly natural spaces – forests, grasslands, marshes and peat bogs – that we urgently need, both to sequester carbon and to rescue our wildlife.

The debate about land-sharing versus land-sparing has, with dreadful inevitability, become quite polarised. Agroecological farming is often lined up against sustainable intensification as if the two were mutually incompatible. Yet both these models share a common goal: to end the agricultural system's reliance on fossil fuels and its environmental destruction. Both schools are striving to create regenerative forms of land management, albeit by different routes. And the greatest benefits will come from using both together.

Studies of England's native birds suggest that the best way to meet the needs of both humans and wildlife is to create a patchwork landscape. Sometimes known as the 'three-compartment model', this requires a mix of land uses: some high-yield farms, to secure the human food supply, but also lower-yield agroecological farms and some land returned to nature. Although it might not be the optimal situation for every species – some of which would prefer all the land to be either wild or gently farmed, depending on their evolved needs – it offers an improved landscape for most. Those animals that cannot thrive in one type of land can at least find sanctuary in another.

In the National Food Strategy we proposed that 5 to 8 percent of the least productive farmland should be restored entirely to nature, largely to plant broadleaf woodland and to rewet peat bogs. This would be the first of the three land-use 'compartments'. A further 12–15 percent of our land should be converted to the kind of low-intensity, nature-friendly farming that benefits so many of our native species. That's the second compartment. The third compartment would in reality be more of a continuum, taking in many different forms of high-yield (but, as new technology improves, increasingly sustainable) farming. A bit of land-sparing, a bit of land-sharing.

The current existence of unproductive farmland is what makes the three-compartment model possible. Because this land isn't much use for growing food – except meat, which provides very little of our nutrition at a high environmental cost – we wouldn't lose much by repurposing it. If the least productive 20 percent of farmland were ringfenced for a combination of agroecological farming and rewilding projects, this would 'only' reduce the number of calories we produce in this country by 3 percent.

'Only' goes in inverted commas because any reduction in domestic food production has political and practical implications. Food occupies an elemental spot in a nation's psyche. We need it to survive, after all. Even a modest dip in self-sufficiency, or a rise in food prices, could provoke serious unease – or even unrest.

CHAPTER SIXTEEN

You can't eat butterflies

Protecting nature doesn't have to compromise food security

Securing the nation's food supply has been a central role of states since history began. If you can't keep your population fed, you are unlikely to hold on to power. Food security was a standing item at every meeting of the assembly in ancient Athens. In Genesis, we learn how Joseph (he of the 'Technicolour Dreamcoat') saved the people of Egypt from famine. It's not as jolly as the musical. Joseph, working on behalf of the Pharoah, makes the starving Egyptians hand over all their money in exchange for the grain he has hoarded for seven years. When they run out of money, he takes their livestock, and finally their land and freedom. 'The land became Pharoah's, and Joseph reduced the people to servitude, from one end of Egypt to another.'

These days, in the developed world, food security is one of those political issues that usually lurks below the water-line of public consciousness. Like an iceberg, you hardly know it's there until – WHAM! – you're right up against it.

For decades, we have relied on a global system of food production and processing enabled by so-called 'just-in-time' logistics. Some things are cheaper to grow or process elsewhere and then import. But you don't want these things hanging around in storage, where they might perish or get spoiled. Plus, storage is expensive. So you carefully line up each link in the supply chain from farm to fork. The food moves as swiftly as possible between the different stages of production, manufacturing and transport, arriving at each point 'just in time'. Thanks to this global trading system, people in wealthier nations have grown accustomed to being able to buy food from all over the world, in any season, at prices that until recently were historically low. In that sense, the just-in-time system has been a tremendous success.

It does depend, however, on relatively stable conditions. We have been lucky to live through a prolonged period of peace, of the kind that enables, and is enabled by, global trade. One advantage of capitalism is its nimbleness: when stocks from one supplier run low, demand simply switches to another supplier. However, not keeping large stores of food means there isn't much of a safety buffer when things go wrong. And the long supply chains created by the just-in-time system can become vulnerable at unexpected points.

During the first Covid lockdown, for example, flour factories that were used to churning out huge sacks of flour for wholesale suddenly found themselves with no cafes or restaurants to sell to. They had to work out how to sell to individual consumers instead: a seemingly simple switch that actually meant reconfiguring factory lines, finding packaging suppliers capable of producing thousands of smaller bags at speed, and getting the new product into the shops. The fact that this logistical logjam coincided with a boom in lockdown home-baking explains why flour became one of the more conspicuous missing items on supermarket shelves.

A bigger worry, for those trying to keep food on the supermarket shelves, was the number of workers falling sick – not just in the UK, but across the world. Staff shortages meant that slaughterhouses, meat processing plants and food manufacturers struggled to keep up with demand, and in some cases had to shut altogether. A shortage of lorry drivers slowed the supply lines, and for a while there were fears that the short straits between Calais and Dover – across which a quarter of the UK's imported food is transported by ferry and tunnel – might be closed by the French government.

At one point, there was a sudden spike in the price of lemons coming into this country. A rumour went round that lorry drivers were being held at the border between Spain and France and told to go into quarantine. If true, this could have caused big problems: in March, when our own harvests are still a long way off, 60 percent of the UK's fruit and vegetables come from continental Europe. But GPS trackers on the vehicles of the major hauliers showed that trucks were in fact moving pretty smoothly across the Spanish border. So what had happened to the lemons? It turned out that manufacturers of hand sanitisers had bought them all up to scent their products.

Meanwhile, consumers were starting to panic. Temporary shortages of a handful of products (tinned tomatoes, pasta, flour) led to alarming pictures of empty shelves, which in turn led to stockpiling. Some commentators began to argue that the UK must start growing more of its own food to protect us from the vagaries of our global supply chains. Others called for the immediate rationing of fruit and vegetables, and the clamour grew loud enough for the government to deny that it had any such plans.

In retrospect, however, the disruptions caused by Covid were relatively easy to manage. They were mostly related to the lockdowns that were implemented across the world. Because governments had imposed these lockdowns, they were also well placed to mitigate them – for example, by exempting farm workers and lorry drivers from restrictions.

Russia's invasion of Ukraine has created a much more serious threat to food security. Long known as the 'breadbasket of Europe', Ukraine is coveted by Russia in part because of its agricultural value. It has vast, flat plains, plenty of rain and sun, and a rich, black soil that makes its fields some of the most fertile on Earth. Before the Russian invasion, Ukraine also benefited from a large, relatively cheap workforce and easy access to international trade through its Black Sea ports. This enabled it to grow and export half the world's sunflower oil, 18 percent of its barley, 16 percent of its maize corn and 12 percent of its wheat.

War makes farming extremely difficult. Fields become battlegrounds. Workers flee, or fight, and get killed and injured. In 2021, Ukrainian farmers sowed almost 17 million hectares of spring crops. In 2022, that fell by 22 percent – an area almost the size of Belgium.

The effects of food shortages are always felt more keenly in some places than others. Countries with large populations and limited farming capacity are especially vulnerable. Egypt, for example, has a population twice as large as can currently be fed from its own land. This situation is itself a side effect of the modern food system: the Green Revolution, combined with advances in food transportation, has enabled Egypt to grow a population much bigger than it could otherwise sustain. But being so dependent on imports makes a country vulnerable. Before the war, Egypt imported 85 percent of its wheat from either Russia or Ukraine, and 73 percent of its sunflower oil.

The war in Ukraine has not (at the time of writing) led to outright famine elsewhere, largely thanks to a deal brokered by the UN and Turkey which persuaded Russia to end its blockade of the Black Sea ports. But the price of basic commodities rocketed, and so did the price of fuel. This had knock-on effects all around the world, for anyone in the business of producing, processing, moving or selling food.

The UK is a comparatively wealthy country (even if that wealth is unevenly distributed), and we are not existentially dependent on food imports. Nevertheless, the combined effects of global commodity shortages and energy price rises can be felt right across our food system. Fertiliser – which requires a huge amount of energy to make – became much more expensive when war broke out in Ukraine. This meant that farmers, facing higher costs, had to put up their own prices. The rising price of animal feed pushed up the price of meat and eggs.

Further along the food chain, hospitality businesses find themselves having to cover the spiralling costs of ingredients and energy. Fish and chip shops – purveyors of Britain's national dish – face a perfect storm of price rises. They must buy litres of vegetable oil for their deep-fat fryers, and then pay to heat it to boiling point. On top of that, Russia, which is now subject to Western sanctions, controls 45 percent of the world's white fish supply. The price of cod rose by over 50 percent between October 2021 and 2022.

Overall, food price inflation in the UK hit a record high of 13.3 percent in December 2022. For the first time in my lifetime, the issue of food security has become a subject of ongoing public debate. Some commentators are now arguing – as they did during the pandemic – that we must start growing more of our own food. It is often assumed that this is the best way to improve food security. And the Egyptian example shows that over-dependence on imports is indeed perilous. But the opposite can also be true. If you rely exclusively on your own harvest, what happens when that harvest fails? Without sufficient alternative supply lines in place, you may not be able to feed your people. Indeed, the fragility of an entirely local food supply is one of the reasons why, since the mid-nineteenth century, this country has relied on imports for a significant part of our diet.

The historian Boyd Hilton argues that food security was one reason for the abolition of the Corn Laws. Introduced after the Napoleonic Wars, the Corn Laws had effectively banned foreign imports of wheat. This was justified at the time as a way of boosting British farming, but was widely recognised (and loathed) as a form of protectionism. It meant that landowners could command a high price for their crops, thereby enriching the gentry at everyone else's expense.

Widespread harvest failures in England, combined with the Irish potato famine, helped to make the Corn Laws politically unsustainable. The dangers of relying exclusively on local agriculture were revealed with painful clarity, and in 1846 the Corn Laws were repealed – an event so politically tumultuous that the Tories did not form a majority government for the next thirty years.

How secure is our food supply today? This is not an easy calculation to make. For one thing, the very meaning of the phrase 'food security' is disputed. One survey of academic literature has identified over 200 definitions of the term. Food security is often conflated with 'self-sufficiency', that is, the proportion of our food intake that is grown in this country, but they are not the same thing. Self-sufficiency does not guarantee security.

Currently, the UK's agricultural output is equivalent to 64 percent of our domestic food spend. This doesn't mean we grow 64 percent of the food we eat, because some of our produce gets exported. We actually grow around 50 percent of the food we eat. The remaining 50 percent we import, but not for reasons of necessity. Buying from abroad gives us more choice. We buy cheaper alternatives to our own produce, such as (lower-welfare) bacon from Denmark. And we import a lot of fruit and veg from Europe and further afield, in order to enjoy more variety across all seasons. I can buy Peruvian avocados from my local Costcutter on Christmas Day, if that's what I fancy.

We have the luxury of choice, but do we have the luxury of security? For the National Food Strategy, we defined food security as the ability to feed the population at a reasonable cost even in the face of future shocks such as a global pandemic, war, massive harvest failure or a general crisis of agricultural productivity caused by climate change.

This requires a careful balance of self-sufficiency and trade. It may be affected by many different factors, including the defence of supply lines (being confident they are not vulnerable to attack), the resilience of all parts of the food system, separately and combined (how quickly they can adapt in the face of sudden shocks), capacity (the skills and capabilities in the system) and control (how concentrated ownership of the system is, and what risks might arise from high levels of concentration).*

The UK government conducts occasional reviews to assess whether we have what you might call 'U-boat food security'. That's to say, if we were cut off completely from

* The food policy expert Tim Lang examines each of these factors in more detail in his book, *Feeding Britain*.

imports and obliged to adopt rationing and other forms of drastic government intervention, would we be able to restore ourselves to full self-sufficiency before we starved? The most recent attempt to answer this question was Defra's 2010 UK Food Security Assessment. It concluded that we already grow more of our own food than we did before the Second World War, so we would be starting from a better position. The UK is highly self-sufficient in those foods that can easily be grown in this country, such as wheat, barley, oats, sugar beet and seasonal fruit and veg. In this category, we grow around 75 percent of what we consume.

But becoming entirely self-sufficient would require a significant reduction in food waste, and a more efficient

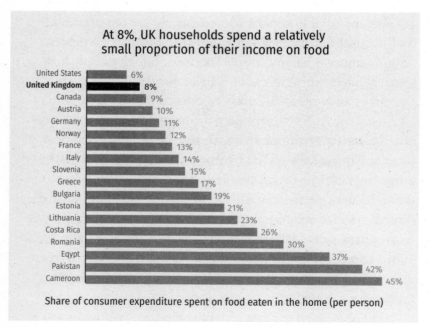

At 8%, UK households spend a relatively small proportion of their income on food

United States	6%
United Kingdom	8%
Canada	9%
Austria	10%
Germany	11%
Norway	12%
France	13%
Italy	14%
Slovenia	15%
Greece	17%
Bulgaria	19%
Estonia	21%
Lithuania	23%
Costa Rica	26%
Romania	30%
Egypt	37%
Pakistan	42%
Cameroon	45%

Share of consumer expenditure spent on food eaten in the home (per person)

The UK spends less on food – as a household average – than almost any other country in the world. However, the average disguises big differences in individual budget pressures. The least affluent households spend more than 25 percent of their household income on food.

use of the land. Above all, farmers would have to shift from meat to plants. As the review concluded: 'Maximising calorie production would require a dramatic reduction in livestock production, with all crop production used for human food where possible instead of animal feed.' In such a scenario we could produce more than enough calories per person per day.

So, as a nation we would not starve. But we would have to adjust to a much more limited and expensive range of foods. This would be harder for some people than others. The UK has the second-greatest level of income inequality in the G7, after the US. While on average we spend 11 percent of our household income on food (8 percent if you only include food eaten at home), the least affluent 10 percent of the population spend almost a quarter of their household income on food (and another 40 percent on housing and energy bills). These people have very little spare capacity for coping with price rises.

Should we be trying to increase our self-sufficiency now, to proof ourselves against future shocks? Critics of the government's Environmental Land Management schemes (ELMs), which are gradually replacing the old system of subsidies to farmers, argue that it is madness to pay farmers to grow trees or restore wetlands, instead of growing food. With so much geopolitical instability afoot, surely the government should encourage maximum food production. 'You can't eat butterflies', goes the grumbling refrain.

But quite apart from the environmental arguments, it doesn't make economic sense to subsidise conventional agriculture.* Crops are commodities. Their price is set by the global market. Paying our farmers to grow, say,

---

* Although this hasn't stopped governments in the past.

sunflower oil, would effectively be a subsidy to the entire global sunflower oil market. It would be expensive for the UK taxpayer, and the overall effect on price would be minuscule. Besides, the market contains its own incentives. If sunflower oil is in short supply, prices rise – making it more worthwhile for farmers to grow it.

In terms of food security, there is actually more to be gained from paying for environmental projects. The biggest threats to the food system now – even bigger than Putin's war – are ecosystem collapse and widespread harvest failure caused by climate change. If the forecasts outlined on p.126 are correct, unchecked climate change will cause crop yields to shrink dramatically throughout much of the southern hemisphere. This will compromise the food supplies of every country, including our own.

Nor can we be confident of maintaining our own yields. Although the UN predicts that the countries of the northern hemisphere will become more productive overall, climate change is intrinsically destabilising. Droughts and floods will become more common, leading to harvest failures. If melting icecaps cause the Gulf Stream to slow to a standstill, UK temperatures would abruptly fall – as would rainfall. This could dramatically reduce our yields. Warmer temperatures, on the other hand, could lead to the spread of crop pests and livestock diseases. On top of all this, soil degradation and the loss of pollinating insects will make farming increasingly difficult.

Modern agriculture is stuck in a vicious cycle of its own: the way we produce food is causing climate change and biodiversity collapse, which in turn threatens our food supply. Changing the way we use our land – giving some of it back to nature, and using it to mop up carbon – is bound to create new uncertainties. But it is also, in itself, a vital food security measure.

UK SELF-SUFFICIENCY OVER TIME

UK self-sufficiency has fluctuated hugely over the last 250 years. We grew almost all our own food until the Corn Laws were repealed in 1846. This, combined with the Industrial Revolution, began a century-long slump in food production. Workers moved away from the countryside and into the rapidly expanding factory towns – a demographic shift, enabled by foreign food imports, that made Britain an economic superpower.

By the beginning of the twentieth century, the population was mostly fed on imports from the Empire and beyond, brought in by the Merchant Navy and guarded by Britain's vast fleet. As Rudyard Kipling explained:

the bread that you eat and the biscuits you nibble,
The sweets that you suck and the joints that you carve,
They are brought to you daily by All Us Big Steamers
And if any one hinders our coming you'll starve!

During the two world wars, their coming was indeed hindered, and Kipling's warning was very nearly realised.

UK self-sufficiency over time

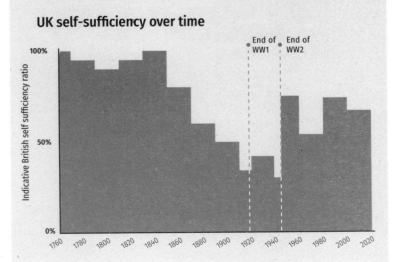

The nation was urged to 'dig for victory', and Britain's self-sufficiency rose again. After the last war, agricultural subsidies were introduced in an effort to ensure the nation's long-term food security.

In 1973, Britain joined the Common Agricultural Policy (CAP), with its system of subsidies largely designed to encourage food production within the European Union. By the mid-1980s, when CAP subsidies and tariffs were at their height, Britain's self-sufficiency reached a peak of almost 80 percent.

But this feat was achieved through distorted economics. Farmers within the Common Market were receiving twice as much for their produce as they would have done without such protectionist measures – with most of that bonus paid by the State. Unsurprisingly, these incentives resulted in surpluses of food, including the famous butter mountains. The subsidies were tweaked, and UK self-sufficiency began to decline again.

CHAPTER SEVENTEEN

Can we have it all?

Only if we stop being so wasteful

Can we have it all? The short answer is: yes. We can maintain a secure food supply while cutting emissions and restoring some land to nature – but only if we tackle the shocking amount of waste in the system.

I don't just mean the kind of consumer waste that first springs to mind: the lettuce that rots in the back of the fridge before being guiltily slipped into the bin, or the vegetables rejected by truculent children. I mean systemic waste, which comes in three principal forms: food that's never eaten, agricultural inefficiency and unproductive land.

Over a quarter of all the food grown in the UK never makes it into our bellies. This accounts for 6–7 percent of total UK greenhouse gas emissions. Globally, the figures are even more eye-popping: 28 percent of the world's agricultural land is used to grow food that is never eaten. This squandered harvest generates 8–10 percent of global greenhouse gas emissions – meaning that, if uneaten food were a country, it would be the largest global emitter of greenhouse gases after the US and China.

In the UK, just under a third of uneaten food never even makes it out of the farm gate. This is partly because farmers habitually produce more crops than we need. They have to do this – even though it costs them – because of the stranglehold that supermarkets have over food retail in this country. Our four biggest supermarkets control 66 percent of the UK groceries market. Their business model is to offer consumers plenty of food, of a consistent type and quality, at affordable prices, all year round. In order to secure their own profit margins, supermarkets drive a hard bargain with suppliers. And because they have a near-monopoly, suppliers have little choice but to comply.

Supermarkets use sophisticated forecasting tools to anticipate which foods will sell best at various points in the year, enabling them to keep their shelves fully stocked. They use these forecasts when they place advance orders with farmers. But if something unexpected happens, and the forecast proves wrong, it's generally up to the farmer – not the supermarket – to deal with the resulting glut or shortage. Tomatoes, for example, are highly vulnerable to the vagaries of British weather. A spell of hot weather will produce a glut of delicious ripe tomatoes – and, if the good weather holds, consumers will be in the right mood to eat them. But if the skies suddenly cloud over, those tomatoes won't sell. People eat much less salad when it is cold.

When farmers are planting their crops, they have to allow for more than enough to satisfy our expected appetites. Otherwise, if disease or bad weather ends up reducing their yield, they might be unable to fulfil their supermarket orders. Overproduction is therefore built into the system. Supermarkets also write all sorts of specifications into their contracts: not just the quantity, but the shape, size and colour of produce. Fruit and veg that is wonky, bruised, too big or too small is usually discarded before it can leave the farm.

In strict statistical terms, supermarkets themselves hardly generate any waste. Beyond the farm gate, the biggest contributors to food waste are households (70 percent), followed by manufacturers (18 percent), the hospitality and food industry (10 percent), and then food retailers, with an impressively paltry 2 percent.

How is it that supermarkets produce so little waste? Partly, this is just good capitalism. Waste is – well, wasteful. It costs money to dispose of, and eats into profits. Supermarkets are therefore scrupulously careful about minimising waste within their own operations. But they do this partly by pushing it outwards, to those on either side of their business model. Farmers on one side, consumers on the other. Persuading consumers to buy more than we need – which inevitably leads to waste – is an integral part of supermarket economics. UK households throw away around £14.9 billion of food a year – the majority of it bought from supermarkets.

Of course, consumers can't evade responsibility for our own choices. As our shopping habits show, we like the supermarket model. We enjoy having so much choice, such abundance, such neat and regular products, all (in historical and international terms) at very low prices. On the other hand, we don't like wasting food. In a 2020 survey commissioned by the anti-waste charity WRAP, 93 percent of us agreed that 'everyone, including me, has a responsibility to minimise the food they throw away'.

So why is it that UK households continue to bin 6.6 million tonnes of food per year? Despite our current economic troubles, the UK is much richer now, in terms of average income per head, than in our grandparents' day. And food has become much cheaper, as a proportion of average household income. We (again, I am talking in averages) have stopped thinking of food as a precious commodity, and grown accustomed to buying and discarding it without too much anxiety.

This behaviour has been exacerbated by the decline in cooking skills across the population. Previous generations (mostly, it should be said, women) were adept at planning thrifty menus across multiple days, and choosing ingredients that could be used, and reused, in lots of different dishes. This ability to visualise meals and plan ahead makes it much easier to shop efficiently, buying only what you know you need.

Being a confident cook also makes it easier to use up any stray food. Instead of having to follow someone else's recipe, buying every ingredient required, you can open the fridge, survey its scattered remains – a bowl of rice, a lump of cheese, a lonesome carrot – and begin instinctively to devise a meal in your head. Someone who feels comfortable with all kinds of different foods is also less likely to throw out products when they reach their 'best-before' date, as opposed to their later 'use-by' date – one of the most common causes of household food waste. If you know what a particular food should look, smell and taste like, and you trust the evidence of your own senses, you can judge for yourself when it is no longer safe to eat.

There is a feedback loop in action here, between the loss of kitchen confidence and the supermarket culture of over-purchasing. The less capable we are of planning meals, cooking and using up leftovers, the more easily we are lured into scattergun shopping. We buy products because of discounts or clever marketing, or because we have an unrealistic idea about how we intend to eat. (Salad is one of the most wasted foods in the UK, with around 40 percent of bagged leaves ending up in the bin.)

This is one reason why improving food education in schools is so important. Making sure that children are familiar with a wide range of ingredients, and that they leave school knowing how to shop and cook cleverly, would benefit the environment as well as public health.

In 2007, the government set a target of reducing food waste by 50 percent by 2030. WRAP estimates that we are about halfway to meeting this target, although progress has slowed after an energetic start. One of the most effective policies for bringing down household waste has been the introduction of food waste caddies. Bagging up your discarded food, so that you can see it and weigh it in your hand, is a visceral way of confronting your own waste.

But the most powerful incentive not to waste food is budgetary. This applies both at a global level – rich countries produce much more domestic food waste than developing nations – and at an individual level. The smaller the household budget, the more careful the weekly shop. The state of the economy can be measured by the contents of our bins. Between 2007 and 2012, household food waste fell by 15 percent, due to the financial crisis and the recession that followed it. Although there is no clear data available at the time of writing, it is likely that the Covid pandemic, followed by the cost of living crisis, will have also pushed down levels of food waste.

Poverty is clearly not a sustainable or just mechanism for reducing waste. Most waste is produced by richer households anyway, in part because they buy more perishable goods such as fruit and vegetables. (The speed with which fresh ingredients go off is another reason why people on tight budgets buy less fruit and veg.)

So the onus, really, is on wealthier consumers to shop and eat more carefully, and on retailers to encourage this. Several supermarkets are in the process of ditching 'best-before dates', which will help reduce the amount of perfectly good food that gets jettisoned by anxious eaters. But the commercial imperative of supermarkets – to sell us as much as possible – remains fundamentally at odds with the goal of waste reduction.

Inefficient farming is our second form of waste. Livestock farming is the most obvious example (more on that below), but even arable farming could be more productive.

After livestock pasture and feed, cereals grown for human consumption occupy the biggest proportion of UK farmland: more than 3 million hectares, or 13 percent of our total land. Compared to most European countries, we get a high yield out of this land. We are fortunate to have long summer days, good soil and world-class rainfall. Wheat harvests in this country average around 9 tonnes per hectare. The UK's record wheat yield – set in 2015 by Rod Smith, a farmer from Northumberland – is 16.5 tonnes per hectare.*

But there is a lot of variation in how much each farmer manages to produce from each hectare of land. A recent academic study concluded that the UK could improve its yields by 13–15 percent simply by sharing information about best practice between farmers. This might include methods for improving soil quality, such as planting cover

---

* This was also the world record until 2017, when it was beaten by a New Zealander Eric Watson, who managed to squeeze out an extra 0.9 tonnes per hectare.

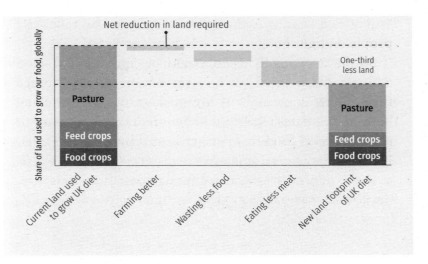

On a global basis, if we improved crop yields by 15 percent, halved food waste and ate 30 percent less meat, we could produce the same amount of nutritious food from a third less land. The greatest impact would come from meat reduction.

crops to 'lock in' nutrients over winter, or using traditional rotations to encourage favourable soil microbes.

There are further gains to be made through crop genetics. The UK government's Climate Change Committee, having studied detailed assessments of crop yields, concluded they could be increased by 25 percent through a combination of judicious crop breeding and improved farming practices. The Committee also believes that new precision technologies – such as AI, which can monitor the health of every plant within a field – will increase yields further still.

The third kind of waste is land use. Growing plants produces around 12 times more calories per hectare than rearing meat. Yet 85 percent of UK farmland is used for feeding and rearing livestock. In other words, reducing meat consumption is the single most effective lever we have for improving the productivity of our land.

This is not a summons for everyone to go vegan. Just cutting back is enough. If everyone in the UK reduced their intake of meat and dairy by one third, that would free up around 20 percent of our farmland. This might be a lifestyle change for many, but it can hardly be described as a privation. If you usually eat meat and dairy at every meal, why not try going without on Mondays and Tuesdays? Job done.

Cutting down on all three kinds of systemic waste would make it easy for us to have it all. To take a plausible scenario, if we were to reduce our food waste by 50 percent, increase our farm yields by 15 percent and reduce meat consumption by 30 percent, we could produce the same number of calories from 30 percent less land (see the chart on the previous page). If we were to set our sights higher still – increasing productivity by 30 percent and reducing meat-eating by 35 percent – we could produce the same amount of food from 40 percent less land.

Both these scenarios would free up enough land for us to make space for nature again – restoring areas of wilderness, but also enabling the gentler forms of farming that some of our native species prefer. It would give us plenty of room to feed ourselves, while also creating that patchwork landscape our wildlife needs, full of beauty and diversity.

PART THREE

Our Future

CHAPTER EIGHTEEN

Goujons of hope

Can alternative proteins save us?

What kind of food system do we actually want? In February 2019, shortly before Covid reached the UK, the National Food Strategy team gathered in a small tearoom in Bristol to discuss food policy with thirty-six citizens. This was the first of five 'deliberative dialogues' that we staged around the country, to get a better understanding of how 'ordinary people' feel about our food system, and how far they would go to improve it.

Each panel was selected to be demographically representative of their region. They came from all walks of life and every political affiliation (or none). They spent a total of twelve and a half hours with us over four days, switching to Zoom once the pandemic took hold. They were able to question experts from different parts of the food system, as well as discuss their own experiences of its strengths and weaknesses. They debated which political or commercial interventions they would be prepared to tolerate for the sake of improving the environment and public health.

Although there were differences of opinion within each panel and between the regions, some subjects elicited a remarkable degree of agreement. There was overwhelming support for much stronger restrictions on the advertising and promotion of junk food. Many participants wanted a ban on fast food joints opening near schools, and tougher regulations for retailers selling junk food.

Across the board, there was a higher tolerance for state intervention than we had anticipated – except in one respect. The idea of introducing a 'meat tax' was a non-starter. Every time we raised it, the atmosphere would crackle with hostility. Although a minority of our panellists liked the idea, many more were vehemently opposed – and the arguments between these instantaneous tribes were fierce. It is easy to understand why. Britain has always had an omnivorous food culture, and we produce some of the best meat, milk and cheese in the world. Meat is culturally important to us, a symbol of plenty as well as a culinary centrepiece. Any government intervention designed to force a reduction in meat-eating would be seen as unacceptably overbearing.

A meat tax might be the quickest way to reduce consumption, but it would also be expensive and regressive. If it were devised as a straightforward Pigouvian tax, and the cost of carbon emissions simply added to the price tag, the cost of beef and lamb would rocket overnight. This alone would cause public fury. To make matters worse, the biggest price increases would be on cheaper cuts of meat, because carbon emissions are measured by the weight of the product, not the cut. The cost of rump steak – which is already expensive – would rise by 31 percent. But the cost of mince – one of the most popular and economical ingredients for feeding a family – would increase by 145 percent. A kilo of beef mince that had cost £4.80 would increase to a daunting £11.76.

After our deliberative dialogues, we ran a public poll on the idea of a meat tax, and got a similar response. Although 62 percent of people believe the government should set a target for meat reduction, only 25 percent like the idea of a tax on fresh meat. Almost three-quarters are either 'opposed' or 'strongly opposed' to the idea.

The government is alert to this public mood. When asked in 2021 about the potential for a meat tax, a Number 10 official was quoted as saying: 'This is categorically not going to happen. We will not be imposing a meat tax on the great British banger or anything else.'

Attitudes do change, and as the impact of climate change is increasingly felt, people's views about what interventions are acceptable might soften. But we cannot afford to wait for that day. As we saw in *Chapter Thirteen*, reducing meat consumption – thereby reducing methane emissions and freeing up land to sequester carbon and restore biodiversity – is one of the very few tools we have left for protecting our ailing planet. And we must act now.

There is one direct and immediate method by which the government can reduce our national meat consumption, and that is through state procurement. Currently, 5.5 percent of all food served outside of our homes is procured by state-funded institutions. This includes all the meals served in prisons, hospitals, government buildings, the armed forces and of course schools. When food is produced in such bulk, small changes can have a big impact. Including minced mushrooms in a lasagne, for example, or putting more beans and less beef in a chilli, can significantly reduce the environmental impact of a dish.

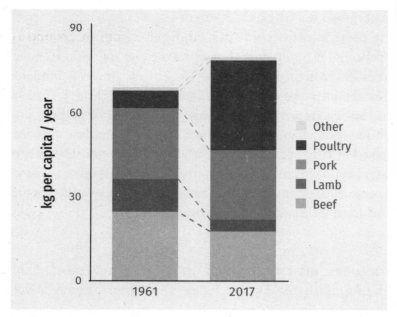

We have changed our meat preferences significantly since 1961. As the price of chicken has come down, we have bought far more of it.

The government can also use grants and subsidies to encourage change in the commercial sector. For example, it could provide funding for research into breeding programmes and feed additives that reduce methane emissions from livestock.* This would speed up innovation, and have the added benefit of boosting the 'green economy'. But we must be realistic. There are drawbacks associated with methane reduction technologies, and limits to how they can be used. Food additives need to be given regularly, which means they aren't suitable for cows that spend most of their days in fields. For the National Food Strategy, we

---

*   Various types of seaweed – and in particular a crimson marine grass called *Asparagopsis taxiformis* – has been shown to reduce methane emissions from cows when added in relatively small quantities to their diet.

estimated that the methane reduction techniques currently in development could cut farming emissions by around 10 percent. A good start, but not nearly enough on its own. Besides which, it would do nothing to free up land for environmental projects.

So we return to the problem of consumer habits, and how to change them. This is something that the free market tends to do better and faster than politicians can. The retail industry, with its highly developed powers of persuasion, can nudge us towards certain products using all manner of subtle suggestions, ranging from the layout of a supermarket aisle to the way in which dishes are ordered on a menu.

But the most obvious way to change consumer behaviour is through price. Chicken, for example, used to be a relatively expensive meat, eaten on special occasions. Then intensive chicken farming brought the price down, and consumers responded accordingly. In the 1960s, as the chart opposite shows, we ate four times more beef than chicken in the UK. Today, we eat almost twice as much chicken as beef.

We may be on the brink of a much more dramatic shift – this time away from farmed meat altogether, and towards a completely new, hi-tech form of industrial food production. The rapidly developing field of 'alternative proteins' looks set to transform the landscape of our current food system, both literally and metaphorically, just as the Green Revolution did before it.

The headline-grabber is lab-grown meat. This involves harvesting stem cells from a small stock of animals. These cells are then fed with a nutrient-rich solution until they multiply and grow into a sort of meaty pulp. No one has yet worked out how to produce lab-grown meat at scale, or

(Photo credit © Dr Emma Lewis)

Is this the future of meat-eating? The author with a tasty but pricey meatball, grown from stem cells in a bioreactor.

how to create whole cuts of meat – such as steak or chops – which require complex structures including fat and sinews.

I recently sampled a pork meatball that had been grown in a pressurised stainless steel bioreactor at the headquarters of Ivy Farm Technologies, in North Oxford. The cultured cells had been mixed with plant proteins for bulk, so only about 60 percent of it was technically meat. It was more finely ground than the ideal meatball (the texture of real meat being one of the hardest qualities to mimic), but the taste was delicious, and genuinely porky. However, it cost £50 to produce that solitary meatball. Right now, lab-grown meat is too expensive to present a challenge to the livestock market, and there is still a degree of public squeamishness about it. But that may change if the price comes down enough.

For the time being, the cheaper and more appealing option is to create products that taste like meat but contain no animal protein. So far, most companies have been using wheat, soy or pea protein as their base, although other plants may follow. The British start-up Brilliant Planet has been developing a sustainable, protein-rich food source from algae held in pools in the Moroccan desert, filled with water pumped from the Atlantic.

Most new alternative protein products are not just – or even chiefly – aimed at vegetarians. They are also designed to appeal to meat-eaters, in order to reach the biggest possible market. The US company Impossible Foods adds soy leghaemoglobin to its products to give them a meaty flavour. This is a red protein, originally produced by nodules on the roots of soy plants but now fermented in tanks, which contains the same heme iron that gives meat its distinctive bloody taste. Leghaemoglobin has not yet been approved for human consumption in the UK, but in America it has helped move plant-based products into the mainstream.

The so-called Impossible Burger – a vegetarian patty that 'bleeds' when cooked, just like a real burger – already accounts for 10 percent of all the Whoppers sold by Burger King in the US. This is not because 10 percent of Burger King customers are vegetarian: in fact, retail data shows that most of the people who buy Impossible Burgers will also eat the beef variety. A wholesale conversion to vegetarianism is not necessary if the plant-based option is tasty enough.

The most futuristic – and potentially disruptive – form of alternative protein has emerged from the science of 'precision fermentation'. This involves genetically modifying yeast cells so that they produce a particular kind of protein as a by-product of their fermentation. The yeast cells are then put in a tank and fed either a sugar solution or a mixture of carbon dioxide and hydrogen, so that they ferment and produce large amounts of protein.

This technique has long been used to replace certain animal-derived products, such as rennet for setting cheeses and the insulin with which diabetics inject themselves. It is also similar to the process that makes the meat alternative Quorn,* which has been around since the 1980s. But in recent years scientists have learned how to engineer yeast to produce all kinds of different protein molecules – including the leghaemoglobin that goes into Impossible Burgers.

This scientific breakthrough has been accompanied, and enabled, by advances in machine learning and information technology. As scientists sample and tweak their food products, to make them more palatable or nutritious, they feed information back into their database, enabling rapid improvements in production methods and ingredients. Eventually, proponents of this technology argue, scientists will be able to use these databases to design proteins for every foodstuff imaginable. The formula for, say, a perfect burger patty may one day be contained within a data file, allowing any franchise restaurant – or garage forecourt, or even corner shop – to download the file and use its own (next generation) machinery to produce that burger patty on demand. Perfectly consistent every time.

Although that particular future is a long way off, the precision fermentation industry is moving at speed. An

---

* Quorn is fermented from a naturally occurring microfungus.

Israeli start-up, Imagindairy, is developing a 'milk' protein mix from yeast which it says is already indistinguishable from the real thing. If this is true – and if the public is willing to accept the substitution – the commercial opportunities (and environmental benefits) could be massive. Almost 30 percent of Chinese milk imports, for example, are not drunk as a liquid or eaten as yoghurt or cheese, but converted into milk powder before being used in processed foods. If milk powder produced by precision fermentation became cheaper than that from cows (a tipping point that some commentators believe is not far off) this would significantly disrupt the global dairy market.

A 2019 report by RethinkX, a US-based future-forecasting think tank, argued that the products created by precision fermentation will soon be so good – authentic-tasting, nutritious and cheap – that they will sweep the entire livestock industry before them. Cattle farming, it predicted, will be the first victim, with demand for beef and dairy products falling by 70 percent by 2030. Other livestock markets, including pork, chicken and fish, will soon follow suit. This will lead to mass bankruptcies, not just in livestock farming, but in every part of the economy that serves the livestock industry: crop farming for animal feed, abattoirs, fertiliser and pesticide manufacturing, farm machinery – even the banks that specialise in lending to farmers. And because making alternative proteins requires much less land than rearing meat, land prices will tumble.

In other words, there may be hard times ahead for anyone currently involved in the livestock industry. Policymakers, businesses and employees would do well to start preparing themselves for this possible future. But new opportunities would arise from a reconfigured food landscape: jobs in the factory or the lab, others managing the land in new ways. And the ramifications for the environment – and therefore humanity as a whole – could be miraculous. RethinkX predicts that, in America, the displacement of livestock farming by precision fermentation will free up 182 million hectares of land by 2035. That is an area six times the size of Germany. If that land were planted and tended in such a way as to maximise carbon sequestration, it could capture 5.5 billion tonnes of CO_2 every year – enough to offset all America's current greenhouse gas emissions.

Not everyone believes the coming food revolution will be this swift and comprehensive. Another 2019 report, this time by the Royal Society, predicted that 10 percent of the global meat industry could be replaced by alternative proteins within 10 years. Still – 10 percent of a $1.1 trillion industry is a big deal. And once this new industry finds its way into the mass market, public acceptance is likely to increase rapidly, economies of scale will push down prices, and exponential growth may become inevitable.

I was uncertain about the commercial viability of alternative proteins until I got sent a bag of fake chicken goujons to test at home. I didn't have high hopes. Both my sons are devout carnivores, and even their vegetarian sister refuses to eat most 'meat alternatives', on the sensible grounds that they are gross. But these goujons! These goujons will change the world.

I served them fried, with mash and peas. The children took tiny, cautious nibbles at first, but then their faces relaxed into the kind of blissed-out junk food smiles that would normally set my parental alarm bells ringing. 'These are amazing!' they shouted. 'They taste exactly like chicken!' (They do.) 'More please!'

Chicken goujons are easier to fake than, say, a rump steak. The 'meat' centre (in this case fashioned from vegetable proteins rather than precision fermentation) is relatively small, and the breadcrumb coating provides structure and a moreish crunch. Even so, these goujons are proof of concept. It is now possible to create plant-based products that precisely match – and even somewhat exceed – the tastiness of processed meat.

What is good for the planet, however, may not be so good for our bodies. As the smiles on my children's faces attest, plant food can also be junk food: fatty, salty, ultra-processed nuggets of strange-sounding ingredients, scientifically configured for optimal addictiveness.

An Impossible Burger uses 96 percent less land, 87 percent less water, and generates 89 percent less greenhouse gases than a conventional beef burger. But it also contains a quarter of your daily allowance of salt, and just as much saturated fat as a regular burger.

This isn't really surprising: most alternative protein companies are deliberately targeting the fast food and ready meal markets, because this is where it will be easiest and most profitable to replace meat. Ultra-processed food is particularly well-suited to switching to alternative proteins. A typical ready meal or snack will contain ingredients – anything from mince to dairy powder – that could easily be replaced with more environmentally friendly alternatives. There is, however, no imminent likelihood of novel proteins being able to imitate a good-quality steak or Sunday roast.

Within these ultra-processed markets, many (although not all) alternative protein products will turn out to be just as unhealthy as their meaty predecessors. In fact, it's possible that vegetarians – who until now were largely obliged to cook from scratch, because the processed options

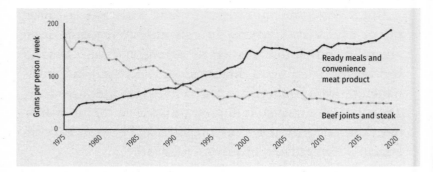

Over the last fifty years we have increased our consumption of ready meals and convenience food, and decreased our consumption of fresh cuts of meat.

were so unappealing – will get sucked into the Junk Food Cycle too, once these temptations are laid before them.

In theory, precision fermentation enables scientists to tinker with and improve the nutritional content of new foods at a molecular level. Personally, I find it hard to believe that food made in giant vats, literally from thin air, could ever match the nutritional richness and complexity of, say, a lentil. In a recent letter to the *Guardian*, Dr David Hanke, from the Department of Plant Sciences at the University of Cambridge, argued that 'no industrially-generated food could provide the right mix of dietary constituents essential for health, such as balanced vitamins, minerals and bulk fibre'. Dr Hanke surely has a point. For optimal health we should all be eating more vegetables and pulses, not fake meat.

But we have to recognise how people actually behave, rather than just wishing they would behave differently. The UK is now a nation that eats vast quantities of burgers, processed meat and ready meals, as we can see from the chart above. The trend towards convenience food has been at least five decades in the making, and will not be quickly reversed.

Right now, we are trying to fight two fires at once: diet-related disease and environmental destruction. It is always tempting to hope that there might be one solution for both. A simple, commonsense, ideologically pure method for dousing all the flames within the food system. The reality is disappointingly complicated. Solutions to one kind of problem don't necessarily have beneficial effects elsewhere in the system.

Alternative proteins probably won't do much for our dietary health. But the environmental benefits of making this switch are so important that, in my view, the trade-off is worthwhile. The UK should be positioning itself at the forefront of this new industry. We have the right market for it, with our devotion to ready meals and our growing tendency towards 'flexitarianism' (part-time vegetarianism). Already, the UK buys a third of all the plant-based meat or dairy alternatives sold in Europe. Developing and manufacturing alternative proteins in the UK, rather than importing them, would create an estimated 10,000 new factory jobs, and secure a further 6,500 jobs in farming (to produce inputs for manufacturing processes). It would also make it much easier to regulate this new industry – ensuring that the science behind it is distributed judiciously, so that it doesn't get captured at birth by a handful of corporations – and to monitor its impact on health and the environment.

Developing alternative proteins does not require a lot of land or input. It can happen just about anywhere – and it will. If one country proves reluctant to embrace this new industry, it will blossom elsewhere. So far, the UK government has been slow to offer support and investment to companies developing novel proteins. As a result, most of this work is currently happening elsewhere (chiefly Singapore, Israel, the Netherlands and Canada), fostered by initiatives such as Canada's Protein Industries Supercluster. We are in danger of missing a prime opportunity for green growth.

With or without UK companies on board, the protein transition is coming. This will almost certainly create painful economic upheavals in the agricultural sector, which will have to be ameliorated by wise policymaking.

CHAPTER NINETEEN

Stewards of the land

*The government must ask more of farmers,
but protect them better*

Shortly after I joined Defra, I was told a story about a veteran politician who had served in the department back in the 1990s. Then a junior minister, he paid a visit to a hill farm in his constituency, where he sat at the kitchen table with a group of local farmers and listened to their troubles. When he asked what he could do to help, one of the farmers replied: 'Your job is very straightforward. It is to make sure my grandson has a future on this farm.' The minister nodded sympathetically. 'I do understand,' he said. 'My own grandfather was a miner.'

The point of this anecdote was not to suggest that farming was, or is, doomed, but to highlight the unusual position it occupies in our economy. Unlike most commercial industries, farming across the UK is still propped up by the State – to the tune of £3.4 billion every year. There are good reasons for this: farmers are essential to our food security, to the fabric of our rural communities and to the look of our countryside. The British public has, historically, been content to pay for the expertise of the stewards of our land.

However, the services we require from farmers are changing fast as the environmental crisis gathers pace. And within a few decades, the agricultural sector itself may have changed almost beyond recognition. If the alternative protein industry does indeed supplant much livestock farming (creating a knock-on effect for arable farmers, whose crops would no longer be needed for animal feed), large areas of our land may fall out of cultivation. What will that mean for farmers, rural communities and the landscapes we love? Will we still need people to care for that now-fallow land – and, if we do, how should we reward them?

Since Britain left the European Union, politicians and civil servants have been gradually, painfully, hammering out a new system of payments to farmers. The difficulty is not that anyone feels particularly wedded to the old system. On the contrary: one of the few post-Brexit sentiments most officials can agree on is that the Common Agricultural Policy (CAP) will not be missed.

Although the worst excesses of European protectionism – the tariffs and subsidies that created the 'butter mountains' and 'milk lakes' of the 1970s – are long gone, the CAP was always a rotten deal for the British taxpayer. It rewarded landownership above good husbandry, encouraged the kind of intensive farming that has done such terrible damage to our wildlife, and did little to improve the quality or price of our food supply.

Under the CAP system, payments to farmers were mostly based on the size of their land: the bigger the farm, the bigger the payment. Before Brexit, more than two-thirds of these 'basic payments' went to just one fifth of the UK's farmers. Rewarding wealthy landowners merely for owning a field, regardless of what they do with it, is clearly not a good use of public money. It provides no incentive for commercial or environmental innovation, and it also pushes up the value of farmland, making it harder for young farmers to get a foot on the ladder.

After the Brexit vote, some free-marketeers fantasised about doing away with farming subsidies altogether. This is what happened in New Zealand in 1984. Until then, around 40 percent of the gross income of livestock farmers in New Zealand had come from state subsidies. But the government, facing a budget crisis, decided it could no longer afford such largesse – and got rid of all agricultural payments at a stroke.

It was brutal at first, this sudden exposure to the pitiless forces of the global market. Land prices tumbled, many farms went bankrupt and rural unemployment rose. There were national protests, and more than fifty suicides. But most farms survived the upheaval and became more efficient. Productivity growth in the agricultural sector rose from an annual average of 1.8 percent in the era of subsidies to around 4 percent in the two decades after their banishment.

There were some environmental benefits, too. State subsidies had provided an incentive to farm on even the least productive land. When the subsidies ended, much of that land simply went out of production, and was reclaimed by the wild. Farmers began to diversify into new markets, such as wine. The number of sheep grazing on New Zealand's uplands fell from 70 million in 1984 to 29 million today.

On the other hand, there has been a massive shift towards intensive dairy farming. The number of dairy cattle in New Zealand has almost trebled in thirty years, from 2.3 million to 6.5 million. Dairy cows now account for a quarter of all New Zealand's greenhouse gas emissions – more than cars. New Zealand dairy farms are typically densely stocked, with cows kept within a short walk of a milking shed and fed on crops that require a lot of fertiliser and water. The use of nitrogen fertiliser rose by over 600 percent between 1991 and 2019, and 60 percent of all water used in New Zealand now goes on irrigating crops. Run-off from intensive farming is polluting the country's beautiful rivers, a third of which are regularly deemed unfit to swim in.

After decades of deliberately leaving farmers to their own devices, the New Zealand government is now having to step in to curtail the environmental damage. In October 2022, it announced plans to introduce a levy on agricultural emissions, taxing farmers according to how much methane or carbon dioxide they produce.

The New Zealand 'miracle' is not one the British public would want repeated here. We have a complicated, almost romantic, relationship with our 'green and pleasant land'. We don't just want it to produce food. We want to walk around it, holiday in it, admire its beauty, and draw consolation and inspiration from it. Some of the least productive farmland in this country is especially dear to the nation's heart: the rolling uplands that run like a broken spine down the length of England.

I must admit that these days, when I walk around the uplands, I mostly see an environmental disaster zone: blasted, treeless fields where rainforests should be; dry, nitrogen-fed pasture underfoot, instead of squelchy peat bogs. Once you have seen all the damage done by conventional ruminant grazing, you can't unsee it. On the other hand, there are places – mostly on the lower reaches of the uplands, such as in the Yorkshire Dales – where the landscape created by livestock farming is undeniably precious. These green fields, speckled with grazing sheep and dissected by ancient dry-stone walls, constitute what we think of, with pride, as the English countryside. Like stately homes, they are repositories of history and culture and skills passed down through generations.

Farmers in upland areas are some of the poorest in this country. The land they work is so unproductive that they cannot survive on what they sell. In fact, half of all farms in this country make a significant loss on their produce. If basic payments were removed overnight, nearly 40 percent of farmers would go bankrupt. Agriculture can be a lucrative business – the top 25 percent of farmers make a good profit – but only where the land is suited to it.

Under the basic payment system, taxpayers have effectively been employing upland farmers (on very low wages) to maintain heritage landscapes. Now, basic payments are being phased out. The new system of payments – the Environmental Land Management schemes (ELMs) – aim to reward farmers for providing 'public goods', rather than merely occupying land. The goods we most urgently require are carbon sequestration and nature restoration. But preserving our rural heritage is a public good too, and there should be a place for traditional sheep farming in our uplands. Just not all over them.

The three-compartment model of farming that we recommended in the National Food Strategy allowed for a pretty conservative, gentle transition in land use – nothing like the sweeping transformation that might accompany an alternative protein revolution. It would still allow for up to 53 percent of England's total land area to be used to farm beef, dairy and lamb, depending on the needs of the market. The aim would not be to bring about a wholesale swap of one kind of land management for another, but to broaden the range of good practice for which farmers can be paid. Rewarding better, more sustainable farming, as well as carbon sequestration, would allow a continuation of the warp and weft of field and hedge that characterises the English countryside.

Even if alternative proteins do sweep the world, people will still buy some real meat. It will become more of a luxury, artisanal item. Something to have on special occasions. This shift into a more high-end niche may actually increase demand for, and therefore the viability of, the kind of gentle, nature-friendly farming that suits so many of our native species – and which creates exceptionally beautiful countryside to boot.

Devising a flexible, forward-looking system of land-management payments now will help smooth whatever transitions lie ahead. But ELMs are bound to be a more complicated system to administer than basic payments, because they will reward several different, sometimes competing, forms of land use (including ensuring a secure food supply). How are officials to decide which public good any given area of land would best serve?

One of the proposals in the National Food Strategy was that the government should create an in-depth, easy-to-use, digitised map of the UK. This would contain layers of data about each area of the land: everything from flood risks to soil composition, health outcomes to housing density, to endangered species, to tourism numbers and more. A dedicated team of civil servants would be put in charge of collecting and verifying the data, to keep it 'clean' and up-to-date.

This digital map, we suggested, should be used to inform a proper 'Rural Land Use Framework' for England. Planners and policymakers would be able to click on any part of the map to get the information they need about how that land would best be used. I realise this may not be the sexiest policy idea you've ever heard, but many a good intention has been derailed by bad data. Changing the outcomes of any complex system requires detailed, consistent and accurate information, arranged in such a way that it is easy to visualise and analyse. This is self-evident to those who spend their lives trying to influence complex systems, but it is rarely done.

In a 2018 article, the former UN secretary general Kofi Annan described how detailed data maps developed by the University of Washington had transformed efforts to tackle malnutrition across Africa. These interactive maps made it possible – indeed, easy – to find statistics on nutritional indicators such as childhood stunting, 'almost down to the village level', and to use these metrics to track progress. Not only did 'such fine-grained insight bring tremendous responsibility to act', said Annan, but it also showed governments, NGOs and others precisely where to act and which measures were likely to be most effective.

The way we use our land is changing. It has to. Farmers know this better than anyone. They live and work on the land. They see how depleted the soil is, and how diminished the wildlife. Nevertheless, many have deep – and understandable – anxieties about the future. Livestock farmers, especially those on tenant farms, often complain that meat is being unfairly vilified. They feel that their jobs and way of life are at risk, and the ongoing lack of certainty about exactly how ELMs will work makes it hard for them to envisage a new way of working on the land.

Farms are businesses, not philanthropic hobbies. They need to make a profit. Many farmers are keen to develop or adopt more sustainable practises – including some that will deliberately lower their commercial yields in order to benefit nature. But they can't do this if it makes them go bust.

We are asking farmers to start managing their land for the public good. The public (the taxpayer) must pay them properly for this work. At the time of writing, it is unclear how much, say, an upland farmer will get paid to plant an area of land with broadleaf trees. But it must be a decent living. Otherwise, why bother? They might as well give up and become delivery drivers instead.

For their part, farmers need to recognise that ELMs may be their best hope of survival. If the protein transition does come to pass, large areas of farmland will no longer be required for food production. In some areas, this land will become valued chiefly for its environmental assets – flood plains, forests, peat bogs and wetlands that can help restore our depleted natural capital. Careful management of such land improves its capacity for sequestering carbon and fostering wildlife. It's not farming, but it would utilise the talents and expertise of farmers. Being paid to deliver such public goods would allow the stewards of the land to remain on the land.

Many upland farmers are already changing the way they manage their land, in order to restore it. Some are reducing the number of animals they graze, or introducing hardy native cattle that have not been bred to thrive on fertilised grass, or allowing areas of land to flood, building ponds and hedges, planting trees, or letting scrub grow back. In his book *English Pastoral*, the Cumbrian shepherd James

Rebanks describes how the landscape he grew up in is changing as a result of these endeavours:

> As we travel into the valley bottom, I see around me on all sides an ancient working landscape that still lives and breathes, but also with twenty years of changes written across its surface. I see ancient oak woodland above us trying to regenerate. Little mountain ash trees are sprouting up all over the wilding fell, trying to beat the deer. The vegetation is growing denser and deeper, with alder and thorny scrub creeping up the ghylls. The floodplain is half-abandoned and half-wild. The valley has become much shaggier and wilder than it ever was in my childhood, with far fewer sheep dotted around. Some of my neighbours are confused or angry about that, while others are adapting, keeping more cattle or finding other ways to earn a living from the land.
>
> I see farmers starting to work together to make this place even better, finding ways to farm around wilder rivers. Miles of hedges are being laid once more, drystone walls rebuilt, and old stone barns and field houses restored. I see river corridors fenced off and ponds dug; the blanket peat bog on our commonland has been restored. Wild flower meadows liberated from artificial fertilisers and pesticides are now shimmering with clouds of insects, butterflies, moths and birds.
>
> And I see other people in our community who aren't farmers also planting trees and hedges, or creating wetlands, or helping to coordinate our efforts. These things bring separate worlds together, and the old 'us' and 'them' divide is fading. There is a love of this place that unites us all.

In the meantime, of course, most farmers are still chiefly in the business of producing food. And they are understandably concerned about the impact of new trade deals on that business. British farmers have some of the highest animal welfare standards in the world. Many practices that are illegal here, such as fur farming and the force-feeding of geese for foie gras, are still practised in continental Europe, never mind the rest of the world. We also have relatively strict rules on antibiotic use and environmental protection. These rules impose costs on farmers.

Now, we also want farmers to reduce their carbon emissions to net zero, nurse our ailing wildlife back to health, and clean up the greenhouse gases emitted by other industries. This will only be possible if our trading arrangements reflect the same priorities.

Trade is a vital part of our food system. It underpins our security, and has improved the variety, price and quality of our food. Perhaps more surprisingly, trade can also reduce the environmental impact of some foods. Importing tomatoes from Spain generates less carbon than growing them in hothouses in the UK, because Spain has such a natural abundance of sun.

On the other hand, the carbon footprint of Brazilian beef is almost twice as large as UK beef, because of the rainforests that are being cleared to create pasture and to produce soy and other feed crops. Australian beef, too, has a higher carbon footprint than our own, because of continuing deforestation.

Our consumption of environmentally destructive imported food is already negating our attempts at reforestation at home. Between 2010 and 2013, the UK planted enough new trees to cover 17,000 hectares. But the imported food we ate during that same period was produced at a cost of 31,000 hectares of forest.

Almost all the trade we do now with the world is conducted under the same terms as before we left the EU. (After the Brexit vote, the British government hurried around the globe signing deals with individual countries to continue trading as before.) Contrary to popular opinion, these terms do not include particularly strong environmental or welfare standards. We already allow the import and sale of food produced in ways that would be illegal in this country. Danish bacon, from pigs whose mothers are kept in sow stalls, for example; or Ukrainian rapeseed oil, grown using pesticides that have been banned in the UK. This means UK farmers are already at some disadvantage. Their products can be (and are) undercut by cheaper imports made to lower standards.

In signing new trade deals, the government must be scrupulously careful not to undermine our own agriculture sector. What is the point of imposing high standards on UK farmers if we then sign trade deals with countries that have lower ones? Not only does this subject our farmers to unfair competition; it also means that all the harms we wish to prevent – carbon emissions, biodiversity loss and animal cruelty – are simply moved overseas. It renders pointless, even fraudulent, the entire project of creating a sustainable agricultural system in this country.

Poll after poll has shown that the British public do not want any compromise of our existing food standards. People are particularly concerned about imports of meat that has been reared or prepared in ways we would not allow here (chlorinated chicken, hormone-treated beef), and about animal welfare. In the focus groups organised by the National Food Strategy, participants repeatedly told us they want high standards, but don't have time to research the provenance of every shrink-wrapped chicken or the animal welfare laws in whichever country it came from. They want to feel confident that what they eat has been produced sustainably, and they believe, quite reasonably, that this is a job for government.

In its 2019 manifesto, the Conservative Party pledged: 'In all of our trade negotiations, we will not compromise on our high environmental, animal welfare, and food standards.' Two years later, the then Trade Secretary, Liz Truss, negotiated a new trade deal with Australia. Actually, 'negotiated' is too strong a word. Australian commentators were baffled by our generosity. 'It is hard to overstate this achievement by the Australian negotiating team,' wrote one. 'Tariff elimination on this scale through a free trade agreement is almost unprecedented ... Remarkably, it is not clear what UK negotiators managed to extract in reciprocal concessions. Sure, Australia has agreed to eliminate its own tariffs, but that is somewhat like landlocked Switzerland offering to eliminate its navy.'

There's no question that animal welfare standards are lower in Australia than in the UK. For example, battery cages for laying hens are still legal in Australia, as (in many states) are sow pens. And then there's the horrific tradition of 'mulesing'. Intended to prevent flystrike infestations in breeding ewes, this is common practice in Australia. The farmer trusses up a young lamb, with its legs chained up by its head, and suspends it from a metal clamp. He then slices the skin off its buttocks in strips, creating a butterfly-shaped expanse of raw and bleeding flesh across its backside. This is often done with no anaesthetic. When it eventually heals, the flayed area doesn't grow back its wool, which makes it less hospitable to flies.

Amazingly, there is still some debate in Australia about whether mulesing constitutes cruelty. But we don't need to have that debate here. It would never be allowed under British law, and the British public would be appalled if anyone suggested it should be. Yet the Australian trade deal means it is now legal to import into this country lamb born to mothers who have endured this barbaric practice. When I pointed this out to Liz Truss in private (I was a non-executive director at Defra at the time), she got so annoyed that she banned me from future government meetings on trade. In public, she continued to insist there was nothing in the Australia deal that would compromise our food standards. George Eustice – who was the minister in charge of Defra when the deal was struck – has since gone public to deplore the deal. The UK, he says, went into the negotiations with the strongest hand. But Truss was in such a hurry to agree a deal, so that she could unveil it at the imminent G7 summit, that she failed to press this advantage.

Australia is very far away, and its food exports are relatively expensive, so it may be that this deal does not have a significant impact on our domestic food market. (Although if China and Australia entered a trade war, the UK would inevitably become a dumping ground for surpluses of Australian exports.) The deal is dangerous nonetheless, because it sets a precedent. The way we do one trade deal inevitably feeds into how we do the next. Brazil – which has significantly worse environmental and welfare standards than our own (or indeed Australia's) – is also being lined up for a trade deal. Having been seen to lower our standards for Australia will make it harder to hold the line with Brazil – or the next potential trading partner, or the next.

Opening up our markets to lower-standard imports from around the world would make it much harder for the UK government to meet the environmental goals it has set itself. It would push up the true carbon footprint of our food – the food we consume, not just the food we grow ourselves – while subsidising environmental destruction abroad. And it would also imperil our own farming sector, by undercutting it with cheap imports made to lower standards than our own.

George Eustice is surely right to warn that 'unless we recognise the failures that the Department for International Trade made during the Australia negotiations, we won't be able to learn the lessons for future negotiations'.

At a time when the government is asking our own farmers to raise their environmental standards higher than ever, the Australian trade deal was an extraordinary failure of joined-up thinking. It must not be repeated.

CHAPTER TWENTY

The power of love

Good food cultures don't just happen:
they are made by us

In 2019, while visiting Tokyo, I was knocked over in a crowded street. I landed on a short piece of scaffolding pole that had been cemented upright into the ground to prevent cars mounting the pavement. It punched into my torso, just above my left hip, with stunning pain – something, I imagine, like taking a body shot from George Foreman. But once I got my breath back the pain lifted, and a cursory inspection revealed nothing but a nasty graze. Reassured, I headed out for a sushi dinner.

At about 2am, I woke up feeling weirdly rigid. Not a muscular stiffness, but a strange sense of having been inflated like a rubber dinghy. I tried to sit up, but I couldn't bend at the waist. I swivelled round horizontally, tipped my legs onto the floor and staggered over to my phone.

In hospital, scans revealed that I had significant internal bleeding. I was kept in for three days under observation, as the left side of my body, from navel to knee, cycled through a daily symphony of colours: oranges, purples, yellows and greens.

I had once lived in Japan, and friends told me that the hospital food was so good it was worth getting ill for. It turned out they weren't joking. Breakfast was pickles, rice porridge and grilled fish. Lunch and dinner would always include a miso soup and steamed vegetables. Then a simple but beautifully presented piece of grilled meat or fish, or an omelette. A little salad and a side of rice, or buckwheat noodles topped with shredded nori. Everything was set out in dainty bowls, bento style.

Japan is often, and rightly, held up as the archetype of a healthy nation. Its people are the world's longest-lived, with an average life expectancy, across both sexes, of 84.6 years. (That compares to 77.3 for the USA, and 80.9 for the UK.) Even more impressive is how fit and well this ageing population is. The nation's 'healthy life expectancy' – how long the average person lives without experiencing significant illness or disability – stands at 74.1, compared to 66 for America and 70 for the UK. The Japanese have remarkably low rates of heart disease and cancers of the reproductive system (both common afflictions of age in most Western countries). Not coincidentally, they also have one of the lowest obesity rates in the world: 4.4 percent.

Normally, rates of obesity correlate closely with a nation's wealth. The thinnest populations (such as Afghanistan or Chad) are almost all poor. But Japan is a rich country that has somehow managed not to get fat. How has it pulled off this trick?

The answer one often hears is that Japan has 'a great food culture' – as if this were an inbuilt national trait. It's certainly true that the Japanese are justly proud of their cuisine, and they eat very well. Their diet contains a lot of fresh fish, vegetables and non-meat proteins such as soy. Compared to Western nations they don't eat much ultra-processed food, and they tend to drink unsweetened beverages such as green tea with their meals. But this elegant diet, which we have come to think of as quintessentially Japanese, is in fact a relatively recent invention.

The food writer Bee Wilson, in her book *First Bite*, traced the evolution of Japanese cuisine through several distinct phases.

Until the twentieth century, Japan was an isolationist country, with a correspondingly limited diet. Meals were eaten in silence, and usually consisted only of rice and pickles. During the Meiji period (1868–1912), Japan opened up to outsiders for the first time. Government advisors, struck by the height and strength of Western visitors, argued that the Japanese must drink more milk and eat more meat to build themselves into a 'true imperial race'. Eating foreign styles of food became a patriotic act. In 1872, the emperor declared he was a meat-eater himself, breaking a 1,200-year taboo against red meat.

Then in 1921, the Japanese army, concerned at ongoing levels of malnutrition among its recruits, set up the Military Diet Research Committee. This recommended that soldiers should be fed on Chinese- and Western-style dishes that contained more protein and fat. Canteen menus included breaded chicken, curry sauces, beef stews and various croquettes. (Katsu curry – now a staple of Japanese cuisine – was inspired by the Anglo-Indian curries served on British naval ships of the time.) In an effort to improve the dietary health of the whole nation, the government had military chefs do radio broadcasts and give public cookery demonstrations.

The final large-scale state intervention came after the Second World War, when Japan was a defeated – and starving – nation. Of the 1.7 million military deaths the country had suffered during the war, as many as 1 million were due to starvation. The occupying Americans introduced a school lunch programme to build up the next generation. All children were given milk and bread, made from US wheat, and a hot meal made from stockpiles of canned food.

During the 1950s, the average annual income of the Japanese people doubled. Ordinary citizens finally had real choices about how they ate. As the food historian Noamichi Ishige has observed, it soon became clear that they were not returning to the dietary traditions of the past. Instead, they were creating new eating habits. Once, serving more than three dishes had been seen as wild extravagance. Now it became commonplace. Foreign dishes were copied, but not wholesale. The Japanese adopted the European omelette, for example, but didn't serve it with chips. They even started talking at dinner. 'At last,' Wilson writes, 'Japan had started eating the way we expect them to: choosily, pleasurably, and healthily.'

The Japanese are not impervious to the temptations of Western-style junk food. So the State works hard – much harder, and more bossily, than our own – to keep obesity in check. Protectionist laws introduced in the 1990s prevent supermarkets and food manufacturers from dominating the food system, and have helped create a more diverse consumer landscape. The State is clear with its citizens – and, to Western ears, incredibly blunt – about the importance of maintaining a healthy weight. Under the 'Metabo Law' (named after 'metabolic syndrome'), everyone between the ages of 40 and 74 is required to have their waistbands measured annually. If your belly is found to be expanding, you may be referred for medical treatment.

The State also oversees a mandatory lunch programme, for all schoolchildren up to age 16. No one is allowed to bring a packed lunch, and school food is heavily subsidised to ensure that all children, whatever their family background, eat the same high-quality meal. The Japanese government compiles detailed information on the food served in schools, to ensure that standards remain high. Menus have to be approved by nutritionists, and all meals are cooked with fresh ingredients – never frozen or processed. Lunch is usually served in the classroom and, while they eat, pupils are taught about the food on their plate and its nutritional qualities.

In other words, Japan's food culture is the result of deliberate state intervention, as well as historical accident. It is not a flawless creation: Japan relies heavily on imported crops, making it one of the least food-secure of the developed nations. But it is a food culture to be proud of, and a useful demonstration of how countries can shape their own eating habits.

It is sometimes said that Britain 'lacks a proper food culture'. Again, the implication is that this is somehow innate to our national character. But even a bad food culture is a culture of sorts. And ours, like Japan's, has changed enormously over the centuries – if not by design, then by accident.

The British were once envied by the hungry French peasantry for our comparatively abundant food, our farmhouse tables laden with suet puddings, savoury pies and joints of beef. But the Industrial Revolution – which happened much earlier in Britain than in the rest of the world – created a mass movement of the population away from the countryside. The resulting shortage of agricultural workers meant that food had to be imported from the colonies and beyond. The rural poor, who had

eaten frugally but from the land, were replaced by the new
urban poor, who often survived on little more than bread
and tea. As a nation, we became severed from the rural
cuisine that had been our forte. It could be argued that we
have never fully recovered from this wrench.

More recently, a different kind of revolution has further
eroded our culinary skills. The march of women into
the workplace has also been a (partial) exodus from the
kitchen. It's important to remember this, when we wax
nostalgic about a time when 'everyone' knew how to
cook. It wasn't everyone. Except in fancy restaurants, it
was nearly always women. Shopping for, cooking and
then clearing up two or three meals a day is extremely
hard work. Although some women took great pride and
pleasure in feeding their families, for many (perhaps most)
this unpaid drudgery was only tolerable because it was the
expected social order.

Convenience foods must have felt like a space age
miracle to the busy superwomen of the 1970s: just add
water to feed your whole family! Feminism had 'liberated'
women, but it had not yet removed the social expectation
that a good wife, or mother, should do the housework –
including the cooking. (Even now, 42 percent of women in
the UK say they cook from scratch at least once a week,
compared with 32 percent of men.)

The steady expansion of the convenience food market
– from Smash and Angel Delight, to 'microwave meals'
and TV dinners, to today's enormous range of ready
meals, delivery apps and 'ready-to-cook' meal kits –
has arisen from necessity, not laziness. In most modern
households, both adults have to work, just to pay the rent
or mortgage. Over the past sixty years, the amount of time
spent preparing an evening meal in the UK has gone from
an average of one and a half hours to just over 30 minutes.

But we now find ourselves stuck in another reinforcing feedback loop: the less we need to cook, the less likely we are to learn to cook, which makes us more and more dependent on convenience food.

While our kitchen skills have dwindled – along with the time available for cooking – other aspects of our food culture have actually improved. With a few honourable exceptions, British restaurants used to be dismal places: stuffy, overpriced institutions serving starters of orange juice and congealed knock-offs of French food. Since the end of the Second World War, the UK has experienced the longest sustained period of immigration since the Vikings. Many of these immigrants, spotting a gaping hole in the market, and wanting to serve their own communities, became restaurateurs. It was Indian, Chinese, Turkish and Thai entrepreneurs who taught the British that eating out could be informal, cheap and delicious.*

One of the four stated objectives of the National Food Strategy was to 'Create a long-term shift in our food culture'. This is less woolly than perhaps it sounds. It means putting an end to the drift. It means taking a more Japanese (or, for that matter, Finnish, or South Korean, or Singaporean) approach: deciding what kind of food culture we want, and taking positive action to bring it into being. We cannot break free of the Junk Food Cycle without government intervention. Neither can we develop or implement a new framework for using, and nurturing, our land. As citizens, we must demand that our government takes these responsibilities seriously.

* This improvement has not yet been fully recognised by other nations. There was a map doing the rounds on Twitter recently, showing how the Japanese see other countries. On France was written 'No Fat People'; on Denmark, 'Everyone is Happy'; and on Britain, simply 'Bad Food'. This – along with our stiff upper lip, concealing terrible teeth – remains probably our most famous national stereotype.

However, state intervention is rarely, if ever, sufficient in itself. You can't send in the army to improve the cooking in schools, or imprison people for serving bad hospital meals. Every delicious and nourishing plate of food that has ever been set before a hungry person tasted good because of the skill and effort of the individual who made it. Every school that serves its pupils appetising, nutritious lunches – instead of fodder that is bland, boring, beige and bad for you – does so because of a headteacher, school cook or business manager who cared enough to do better. This care – you might even call it love – is a powerful catalysing force.

Change has to come from both directions: top-down, in the form of government legislation, taxes and regulations, but also bottom-up, with talented and dedicated people determined to improve the food in their own families, schools or communities.

I said at the beginning of this book that each of us is an unwitting cog in the vast, complex, strangely invisible food system. Every choice we make, everything we buy and eat, is informed by the movements of this giant machine. But the cogs also move the machine. Precisely because we are so deeply embedded in the food system, we do have some power to reverse its direction.

I urge you to take a moment to think about the food around you – in your workplace, your neighbourhood, or just at home. What is working? What isn't? Think of one positive change you could make.

Parents often ask me what they can do to improve the food at their child's school. The first thing I suggest is that they ask to have lunch at the school. It's always fun to eat with the children (and the children love these state visits from parents – at primary school anyway). By showing an interest, you are signalling to the headteacher and kitchen staff that you care. You'd be surprised how effective this simple gesture can be: the food eaten by thousands of schoolchildren in this country has been transformed because a handful of parents decided to take a look, triggering a chain reaction of concern.

The same applies to staff canteens, youth clubs, care homes, hospitals and all other forms of institutional catering. If you think it isn't good enough, say so. Get involved. If you're the one in charge of catering, aim higher. Go in search of other people who are doing it better, and learn from them. Share your own stories of success and failure with others in your industry.*

If you are in any kind of position of power, use it wisely. Politicians are lobbied continually by the businesses that benefit from the current food system, arguing in favour of the status quo. Often – as with the ITV executives mentioned in *Chapter Eight* – this lobbying is overt. But it also takes subtler, more pernicious forms, such as funding or deliberately misinterpreting research in order to downplay the environmental or health costs of the modern diet (the half-a-Smartie argument). Food company bosses have mastered the art of polite intransigence: making sympathetic noises about doing the right thing, while refusing to do the right thing. Any politician who attempts to force through change using legislation will be visited by a stream of hand-wringing CEOs, all assuring them – in a Sir-Humphrey-ish tone of regretful pragmatism – that such a law would wipe out their profits and put an irreparable hole in the economy.

---

* The School Food Plan, which I wrote with John Vincent in 2013, provides a comprehensive blueprint for how schools can transform the meals they serve and the way they educate children about cooking and diet. It can be downloaded at www.schoolfoodplan.com

These bosses know that change is needed. But they will never call for it in public, or stop lobbying against it. Tim Rycroft, a spokesman for the Food and Drink Federation, hinted at this conundrum in the BBC documentary *What are we Feeding our Kids?* Asked whether the priority of food companies should be profit or public health, he answered without hesitation: 'Profit.' But he added: 'The industry has to be guided by the government. If the government says there is a reason why these [foods] are no longer acceptable, of course we will change.'

If you work in the food sector, be brave. Speak out. Don't let the professional naysayers be the loudest voices in the corridors of Whitehall. Whatever your profession, lobby for change. Write to your MP. Use your own expertise to jump-start improvements in your sector. I made this challenge recently in a speech to bosses from across the private and public sector. One of them works in prisons, and has now set himself the task of reviving prison farms. (If you are currently Prime Minister and happen to be reading this, please refer to the Appendix for your to-do list.)

If you have time, get involved with community or charity projects. You could help out at a local food bank, or deliver hot meals to the vulnerable. Make changes in your home, too. It could be as simple as cutting down your own meat consumption – not theoretically, some day in the future, but now. If you normally eat meat every day of the week, make tomorrow a veggie day. And the next day. There you go: a cut of almost 30 percent straight off the bat.

Going flexitarian would benefit you as well as the planet. Tim Spector, the microbiome expert, recommends eating as many varieties of fruit and vegetables as possible – ideally, more than thirty different foods a week. But if your budget can't stretch to that, start by making a few meals, such as dhal or pasta with chickpeas, that use cheap pulses rather than meat as their base.

If you want to be healthier, practise eating. Not snacks or 'treats' that make you feel miserable, but actual food. Stop worrying about calories – which tell you next to nothing about the contents of your food – and tune into your hunger. Which foods do you find yourself craving, and when? Which leave you feeling content, and which just make you hungrier? The better you understand your own appetite, and how it responds to the promptings of the Junk Food Cycle, the less fraught your relationship with food will become.

If you cook more of your meals from scratch, including lots of fibrous vegetables, you may end up losing weight – and you will definitely end up healthier. Try out some new recipes to improve your kitchen confidence. If you have children (or grandchildren, godchildren, nephews or nieces), get them cooking with you. The earlier they become familiar with different ingredients, flavours, tools and techniques, the more likely they are to be able to feed themselves well in adulthood. Equip the next generation with the skills they need to build a better food system.

You will be amazed at what the power of love can achieve.

CHAPTER TWENTY-ONE

Utopia or dystopia?

The future is coming for us.
We must get ready to meet it

Change, to misquote Ernest Hemingway, happens in two ways: gradually, then suddenly. Look at the two pictures opposite, both of Fifth Avenue in New York. The first was taken in 1900. There is only one car in the picture, circled in case you should miss it. The second was taken just thirteen years later. There is only one horse in the picture, circled in case you should miss it.

In retrospect, history looks obvious. Of course the car was going to overtake the horse, as soon as it became cheap enough. But it didn't seem obvious at the time. As late as 1903, Henry Ford's lawyer was advised by his banker not to invest in the car-making business: 'You might make money for a year or two, but in the end you would lose everything you put in. The horse is here to stay, but the automobile is only a novelty – a fad.' And yet within thirteen years, a 10,000-year-old method of transport – along with all the industries that had evolved to support it – had almost completely vanished. A large part of the economy simply didn't exist any more. Wheelwrights, whip makers, horse breeders, street car drivers, stable masters, grooms, ostlers, feed merchants, vets, even street cleaners (the horses of New York are estimated to have produced 1,000–2,000 tonnes of manure a day at the turn of the century), suddenly found themselves out of a job.

These car images are taken from a talk by Tony Seba, co-founder with James Arbib of the not-for-profit thinktank RethinkX, whose report into alternative proteins I mentioned in *Chapter Eighteen*. Arbib and Seba specialise in identifying the innovations that are likely to change the world. They believe we are on the cusp of the 'fastest, deepest, most consequential transformation of human civilisation in history', driven by the plummeting cost of renewable technologies. In their 2020 report *Rethinking Humanity*, they argue that the technology behind green energy is improving so fast that energy will soon be cheaper than at any time in history. This, they say, could 'lead to a third age of humankind – the Age of Freedom'.*

Super-abundant energy would reduce manufacturing and transport costs, which would make most products, including food, vastly cheaper. The development of new food manufacturing technologies such as precision fermentation would be enabled and accelerated by cheap solar power. Those hot, dry parts of the world that have historically struggled to feed their own populations would suddenly find themselves uniquely well placed to produce this new kind of food. Blessed with plenty of sunlight with which to power fermentation plants, they could become the new breadbaskets of the world.

Hunger and poverty could become horror stories from history. Our basic needs – food, energy, transportation, information and shelter – could be so easily met that there

---

* They identify three ages. The first, 'The Age of Survival', lasted until the Holocene in 10,000 BCE. The second, 'The Age of Extraction', encompassed both the agrarian and the industrial period.

would no longer be any need for armed conflict over scarce resources. Clean energy and improved manufacturing techniques would lift the heavy burden of human activity from the natural world, putting an end to pollution and climate change. 'We may, ultimately,' Seba and Arbib write, 'be able to escape toil and drudgery entirely and, for the first time in history, achieve real freedom – the freedom to spend our time creatively, unburdened by financial precariousness and the need to provide for ourselves and our families.'

But just because this miracle could happen doesn't mean it will. As Seba and Arbib admit, the way that new technologies change the world is largely dependent on the world they come into. Peace, international cooperation, financial stability, well-functioning government, high levels of education, social cohesion and trust in civic institutions: these are the ideal conditions for successfully adapting to rapid technological change. Any transition creates turbulence. Money moves from one region or industry to another, whole professions get wiped out, and the people on the losing end must be looked after. If the wrong conditions prevail – financial instability, political unrest, fraying social bonds – the disruption caused by new technologies may only hasten societal collapse.

I am writing this in December 2022. A cold snap has just set in. Avian flu is wiping out poultry in the thousands; there is talk of a shortage of turkeys at Christmas. The NHS is struggling with the backlog created by Covid, and rampant inflation has triggered a cost of living crisis, resulting in the most widespread public service strikes since the 1970s. Meanwhile, the shattering war in Ukraine shows no sign of ending, and the process of exporting

Ukrainian harvests to the rest of the world is proving difficult and stuttering.

Poverty in the UK is increasing, in both the short and long term. Growth in household income has been stagnant since 2010 and, with high levels of inflation, is now falling for most people. At the same time, successive rounds of quantitative easing have made the richest significantly richer, as the value of their assets has been inflated by cheap debt. It isn't just social media that has set populism on the march; it is basic economics. Right now, the Age of Freedom seems a long way off.

The food system sits right at the centre of many of our current problems. It is making us ill, which makes us less productive, which is dragging down the economy. A 2022 report by the Institute for Public Policy Research found that 2.5 million people in this country were off sick from work: more than at any time since records began in the 1990s. Although this statistic reflects the fallout from the pandemic – a sharp rise in mental health problems, as well as long Covid – it also illustrates the underlying ill health of the nation. Almost every form of long-term illness, from back pain to cancer and even depression, is either caused or exacerbated by bad diet.

Unless the government takes meaningful action to rebalance the commercial incentives within the food system, we face a future of escalating ill health. It isn't hard to imagine that future: we only need look across the Atlantic. In America, almost 70 percent of the population is now overweight or obese. Around 40 percent have 'metabolic syndrome', which means they are suffering from at least three of the following conditions: obesity or excessive visceral fat; elevated blood triglycerides (fat in blood) and low levels of HDL (good) cholesterol; high blood pressure; elevated blood sugar; or insulin resistance. Metabolic syndrome massively increases the risk of heart disease, stroke and type 2 diabetes. An estimated one third of the US population is pre-diabetic, although 80 percent of them don't even realise it.*

The 'fat acceptance' movement that has taken off in America is an attempt to destigmatise a condition that has, in fact, become the norm. I share Gen Z's dislike of 'fat-shaming', but perhaps for slightly different reasons. Berating or despising individuals for being overweight is unkind, counter-productive (it exacerbates the depression and self-reproach that so often characterise disordered eating) and, above all, misplaced. It's the Junk Food Cycle that is shameful, not the people caught up in it.

Junk food doesn't even have to make you fat to make you ill. People with a 'healthy' BMI can still carry excessive visceral fat around their organs, and suffer from high blood pressure, high cholesterol and poor circulation. One in four Americans of normal weight – the so-called 'skinny fat' – have pre-diabetes. Perhaps because they often don't realise they are ill, slender diabetics actually have a higher mortality rate than obese ones.

---

* This is no longer just a Western problem. Many developing nations now face the twin problems of borderline starvation in some of the population and 'metabolic syndrome' in others. In 2017, I visited the Bourj el Barajneh Palestinian refugee camp in Beirut, Lebanon, to meet a nutritionist who had set up a centre to improve residents' diets. Born and raised in the camp herself, she told me she was seeing an increasing number of obese children in her practice, thanks to the Western-style fast food chains that have sprung up around the perimeter of the camp. The two of us found that, in completely different contexts, we were wrestling with many similar questions – for example, how to improve school food so that the children prefer it to burgers.

'Healthy at any size!' goes the fat-positive slogan. But a truer motto for America (as the US doctor and entrepreneur Casey Means put it) would be: 'Unhealthy at any size.' In 2021, life expectancy across the US population fell for the second year in a row. One in five deaths every year is directly linked to diet, and many more are diet-related. Perhaps even more depressingly, the years that Americans do spend on Earth are increasingly marred by serious ill health. Every year, for example, the population of the US loses 73,000 lower limbs to amputation, caused by type 2 diabetes. Americans currently spend two and a half times more per capita than us on health care – but that money cannot protect them from the commercial incentives that are built into the Junk Food Cycle.

Britain is always quick to follow American trends, including the obviously destructive ones. We have embraced American-style junk food with gusto, and now we are seeing the results. The poorest people in the UK (who eat the most junk food) are already starting to die earlier (see p.88), and spend more of their lives either ill or disabled because of bad diet.

Even if the modern food system didn't make us sick, it would still be life-threatening. Climate change is not a distant threat; it is already happening, around the world and in the UK. Since the Industrial Revolution, greenhouse gas emissions have led to a rise in the mean global temperature of almost 1.1 °C, according to a 2022 report by the UN Intergovernmental Panel on Climate Change (IPCC). The effects of this relatively small increase (relative, that is, to the likely eventual figure) have so far been worse than anticipated, with permafrost melting, peat drying out, wildfires ripping through precious forests and 50 percent of the world's coral wiped out.

Depleted soil and unpredictable weather patterns are already reducing agricultural productivity in parts of the world, including Europe and the US. If global warming goes above 2 °C, the combined effect of sea-level rises, droughts, heatwaves, floods and insect infestations will make it impossible to feed the world using our current technologies.

For some years now I have been agitating for the government to intervene in our malfunctioning food system. People often ask me, in a pitying tone, whether I really think politicians will act. The answer to this is yes. They will have to, eventually. The only question is how bad things will get before they do.

One of the problems with tackling this threat is that most people (including most politicians) either don't know or can't accept that it is real. The existence of an actual food system, per se, is seldom even discussed, although the problems it creates – particularly obesity – are often debated in isolation. People don't consciously experience food in a systemic way. Rather, they worry about their own personal choices and circumstances: what they want to eat, what they ought to eat, what they can afford.

When people do think about the system that feeds them, it tends to be with a kind of vague, nervous adherence to the status quo. The shelves are somehow full, and the food is clean, appetising and relatively cheap. Isn't this about as good as it's likely to get? The idea that the system that feeds us might also be killing us sounds almost fantastical.

Those politicians who do understand the extent of the danger (and there are some in all the main parties) face a chorus of incomprehension, scepticism or fury, not least from their own colleagues. Trying to actually change the system, through legislation, taxes or subsidies, always means inviting media controversy – which can prove fatal to political careers.

The recommendations in the National Food Strategy were carefully calibrated to be politically feasible. We even asked political polling specialists to test our proposals in focus groups and surveys, to ensure that they did not represent electoral suicide. Yet still it proved extraordinarily difficult to get the government to take them seriously. In the end, we had to enlist the help of a footballer.

Marcus Rashford's collaboration with the National Food Strategy is a good example of how haphazard, media-led and opportunistic the process of government policymaking can be. The Manchester United striker, who relied on free school meals as a child, had spent the early part of the first Covid lockdown delivering food to families in poverty. When the government announced that free school meals would not be provided over the summer holidays, he wrote an open letter to MPs imploring them to reverse this decision. 'This is about humanity,' he wrote. 'Looking at ourselves in the mirror and feeling like we did everything we could to protect those who can't, for whatever reason or circumstance, protect themselves.' The government gave in to the public pressure marshalled by Rashford, and announced a £130 million food fund to cover that summer holiday.

While this was going on, we were about to publish Part One of the National Food Strategy, which included our own set of recommendations for tackling food poverty. On a whim, I sent the document to a friend who worked at Manchester United, asking if he might pass it on to their star striker. I then promptly forgot about the whole thing, assuming I was unlikely to get a response. Three weeks later my friend wrote back: 'Marcus will be reaching out to you soon.' That autumn, Rashford launched a campaign to back our recommendations. He set up a petition which secured over 1 million signatures, and enlisted most of the major supermarkets to support him. The government found itself once again facing growing public anger. Finally, in October, it backed down and agreed to adopt two of our recommendations: increasing the value of Healthy Start vouchers, to pay for fresh fruit and vegetables for families and pregnant women on low incomes; and rolling out the HAF (Holiday Activities and Food) programme across all schools in England, to provide hot lunches, sports, cooking lessons and fun activities for children during school holidays.

Thrilling though it is to have such a formidable campaigner in your corner, and grateful though we were, this is not how food policy would ideally be decided. Governments should not have to be strong-armed by footballers into doing the right thing. Ensuring that all citizens can eat – cheaply, healthily and sustainably, both now and in the future – ought to be a strategic priority. But the frenzied pace of the news cycle, and the short-termism that is built into electoral politics, act against wise, long-sighted decision-making.

One thing the UK government is not short of is targets. Right now, these include: getting the UK to net zero by 2050; setting aside 30 percent of the land 'for nature' by 2030; and halving childhood obesity by 2030. All these targets were self-imposed, by various prime ministers from 2018 onwards.

Having seen progress from the inside, I predict a lot of missed deadlines. The policies that are currently being pursued are not enough, either singly or together, to effect such big changes; and, even if they were, they may be dithered out of existence. It's as if a huge asteroid is careering towards the Earth, and our politicians are working on plans to divert it with a pea shooter.

In some areas of food policy, progress has actually gone into reverse. Having promised to bring in restrictions on junk food advertising and in-store promotions, the government has now 'delayed' this until after the next election. The more chaotic the overall political picture becomes, with recession at home and war abroad, the harder it gets to push through meaningful change.

So we continue to drift towards a future shaped for us by the market. That market has been distorted by two classic system traps. The reinforcing feedback loops within the Junk Food Cycle have led us into *escalation*: our appetite steers us towards junk food, so companies invest more in it, we eat more, they invest more, we get sicker. The 'invisibility of nature' – created by our failure to record and value the natural capital of the planet – means we end up *seeking the wrong goal*: we destroy nature to generate short-term profits, regardless of long-term viability.

Perhaps a technological miracle will save us. But if so it will bring inevitable turmoil in its wake. If advances in renewable energy and food production are about to revolutionise human existence, shouldn't we at least be talking about it? We will need to prepare our farming and manufacturing sectors for the changes to come; work out whether, and how, we want to facilitate the development of high-tech food; ensure that new food products are as healthy as possible; find jobs for those made redundant by shifting agricultural markets; and decide how to reward farmers for restoring our natural world.

Almost everyone I have spoken to who works in the food system – in farming, manufacturing, retail, science or hospitality – agrees that the system has to change. And many are already working hard to change it. The problem is, they often disagree vehemently about how this should be done. There are endless quarrels over the correlation between meat-eating and carbon emissions, local versus global supply, the dangers (or otherwise) of genetic modification or editing, and the potential of high-tech sustainable agriculture versus the more traditional, nature-friendly kind. Too often, the tone of these debates is dogmatic and moralistic.

The science writer Charles C. Mann analysed this ideological tussle in his book *The Wizard and the Prophet*. In discussions about the environment and sustainability, he says, people tend to fall into one of two tribes. There are the Wizards, who believe that science will come to the rescue, allowing economic growth to continue unimpeded; and there are the Prophets, who believe we are living so far beyond the planet's means that we must drastically reduce consumption in order to survive.

'Wizards view the Prophets' emphasis on cutting back as intellectually dishonest, indifferent to the poor, even racist (because most of the world's hungry are non-Caucasian),' writes Mann. Following this route, they believe, 'is a path toward regression, narrowness, and global poverty'. In return, Prophets sneer at the optimism of the Wizards. Such faith in human resourcefulness, they argue, is wishful thinking, and often driven by greed. Wizards don't want to cut back on consumption, because that would cut into corporate profits and put a brake on global capitalism. The Wizards' false sense of security will, say the Prophets, ultimately lead us into 'ecocide'. 'As the name-calling has escalated,' says Mann, 'conversations about the environment have increasingly become dialogues of the deaf. Which might be all right, if we weren't discussing the fate of our children.'

This problem has been amplified by social media, which forces us to entrench. Rather than examining our own positions, we expend all our energy defending ourselves from enemy attack, dismissing our opponents as Luddites, libtards, industry shills or 'watermelons' (green on the outside but Commie red on the inside). We seize on evidence that supports our arguments and ignore what doesn't. All this self-righteousness serves only to blind us to complexity and nuance. In the words of Adam Smith: 'Virtue is more to be feared than vice, because its excesses are not subject to the regulation of conscience.'

The would-be reformers within the food system have wasted too much time and energy fighting each other. These squabbles have been confusing and offputting for politicians, who don't want to appear to support one side's agenda if it means being attacked by the other. It is impossible to lobby effectively for reform when the reformers can't even agree on what they want.

But the good news is that – in the food system, at least – the Wizards and the Prophets are now finding ways to edge closer together. This is partly thanks to the fast-developing science of complex systems, which is changing perspectives on both sides. The Wizards are using science to better understand some of the old wisdom of the Prophets. Improving the complexity of soil is a good example of this process. Both sides now regard a healthy soil biome as vital to sustainable – and profitable – agriculture: the Wizards, because of their faith in network science; and the Prophets, because of their instinctive sense that we must work with nature and not against it. I expect a similar convergence to happen as scientists increase our understanding of the workings of the gut microbiome and the health impacts of ultra-processed food.

To create a better food system, we will need the insights of both Wizards and Prophets. And applying these insights will require both state intervention and capitalist self-interest. If more sustainable methods of food production become cheaper, and therefore more economically competitive, farmers and food manufacturers will have a natural incentive to change their methods.

This is what has been happening across the world in the energy industry. Even in Texas – where anything that smacks of liberal do-gooding prompts knee-jerk dislike – green energy is rapidly supplanting gas and oil. This is simply because it has become cheaper, and therefore more profitable, to produce. In 2022, Texas had three times more green energy infrastructure under construction (wind and solar plants, and battery storage) than the supposedly progressive state of California.

This shift hasn't happened spontaneously, out of a clear blue sky. US government subsidies have helped to shift the market towards renewable energy. The most effective way to bring about change is ideologically double-pronged: state intervention combined with the profit motive.

The future resilience of the food system will depend on its diversity – both practical and ideological. A diverse system, in which there are lots of different ways to produce food, is more flexible: if one part of the system gets struck by disaster, the others can pick up the slack. By letting many flowers bloom, we can develop methods of farming and food production that better suit our rapidly changing world.

In this ideal version of the future, organic farms will live alongside solar-powered high-rise greenhouses growing fruit and vegetables in cities. There will be more space for wild landscapes, as well as nature-rich upland farms. This will be made possible by a completely new kind of food production – precision fermentation – which will take some of the pressure off the land.

Governments will invest in biodiversity restoration and carbon sequestration, but also in agricultural innovation, so that farmers can use new technology to increase their yields without slathering the land in chemicals. Weed-zapping robots and blight-spotting drones will become as much a part of the landscape as cattle from local native breeds restored to their natural environment. To reduce the need for pesticides and herbicides, biologists will use photons of light of a specific frequency to switch on immune defences in genetically modified crops. None of this is science fiction: these are all real innovations currently being developed in universities across this country.

Putting more public money into improving dietary health – particularly for those on the lowest incomes – will mean the NHS no longer has to squander its resources on treating the diseases caused by the Junk Food Cycle. Using a wide portfolio of public health policies – including taxes on junk food, better cookery lessons, universal free school meals and measures such as 'social prescribing' to get more fruit and veg into the hands of those struggling to eat well – we could begin to turn around the juggernaut of sickness created by the modern diet.

This is not profligate – nor ideological – but sound financial planning, as it is always far cheaper to prevent illness than to cure it. On top of which, a healthier population would become a wealthier population, one that could remain productive for longer.

We are at a fork in the road. The path to health, wealth and happiness – well into old age – is open to us. But to take it we must set aside tribalism and dogma, and make use of the political and scientific levers available. We must bring true variety – agricultural, commercial, ideological and nutritional – into food and farming. Only then can we make a real difference. Only then can we get ourselves and our planet into shape for the future.

APPENDIX

How to change the food system

How to change the food system: *actions for government*

The National Food Strategy recommended a series of government actions designed to shift the UK food system towards a sustainable mode of operation. Success, we argued, would be achieved when the system:

* Makes us well instead of sick.

* Is resilient enough to withstand global shocks.

* Helps to restore nature and halt climate change so that we hand on a healthier planet to our children.

* Meets the standards the public expect on health, environment and animal welfare.

Meeting these four goals will require significant, although not necessarily painful, changes to our national diet, and to the way we grow our food. The chart overleaf shows how our diets will need to change across the next ten years if we are to meet the government's existing commitments on health, climate and nature.

Most of the **fifteen recommendations** on the following pages come straight from the National Food Strategy, although I have had to add or adapt some in response to political events. They are designed to be implemented over three years, as essential first steps in a longer-term transition. Much more detail and evidence can be found in the appendices to *National Food Strategy: The Plan*, which can be downloaded online at www.nationalfoodstrategy.org

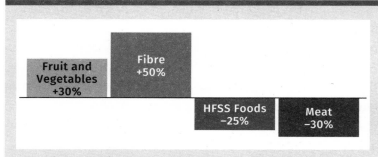

Changes needed in the national diet by 2032 (compared to 2019) to meet health, climate and nature commitments:

* A 30 percent increase in consumption of fruit and vegetables would bring us in line with the Eatwell recommendation of five pieces of fruit and vegetables per day.

* A 50 percent increase in fibre would bring us in line with the Scientific Advisory Committee on Nutrition recommended 30g/day.

* A 25 percent reduction in consumption of HFSS (high in fat, sugar or salt) foods will take us towards the required 60 percent reduction in salt, 20 percent reduction in saturated fat and 50 percent reduction in free sugars.

* A 30 percent reduction in meat is needed to achieve our statutory carbon reduction targets and 30x30 nature commitment – the creation and maintenance of at least 410,000 hectares of woodland, maintaining and restoring 325,000 hectares of peatlands, and managing 200,000 hectares mainly for nature.

☛ ESCAPE THE JUNK FOOD CYCLE

Exercise and willpower are not enough. We cannot escape this vicious cycle without rebalancing financial incentives within the food system.

#1 Introduce a sugar and salt reformulation tax. This tax is designed to lead to large-scale reformulation by manufacturers, rather than food price increases. If scientific research finds that artificial sweeteners are a risk to health, it might need to be extended to cover these. We estimated this tax would raise £2.9 to £3.4 billion for the Treasury. Some of that should be used to support the diets of low-income families.

Status: *No action taken.*

#2 Restrict the promotion and advertising of junk food, especially to children. This would mean ending in-store promotions for junk food, such as BOGOFs, and banning junk food adverts online and before the TV watershed. This wasn't in our original set of recommendations, because the government had already promised to bring in the necessary legislation.

Status: *Government has reneged on its promise.*

#3 Introduce mandatory reporting for food companies. What gets measured gets done. All food companies with more than 250 employees should publish an annual report based on the following set of sales metrics: junk food; types of protein; fibre, saturated fat, sugar and salt; fruit and vegetables; and food waste. Publishing these numbers will allow investors, government, and others, to track whether businesses are heading in the right direction. It will enable better scrutiny, and maintain public pressure on companies to do the right thing.

Status: *Partial commitment to some reporting. No commitment to making data public, or detail of how enforcement will work.*

☞ REDUCE DIET-RELATED INEQUALITY

The same households that cannot afford to eat healthily may sometimes find themselves unable to eat at all. We cannot wait around for the food system to be fixed: those in poverty need help now. The priority should be children, to protect their long-term health.

#4 Extend eligibility for Free School Meals (FSM). Children with empty stomachs struggle at school: they find it hard to concentrate, their behaviour deteriorates, and they are more likely to be disruptive in class. Currently, only children from households with a pre-benefit income of less than £7,400 a year qualify for FSM. The government should expand eligibility now to everyone on Universal Credit. The ultimate goal should be universal free school meals.

Status: *Not done. However, FSM has been expanded to those with 'no recourse to public funds' (NRPF) – usually children awaiting immigration judgements.*

#5 Make the Holiday Activities and Food (HAF) programme permanent, and free to all children from households on Universal Credit. HAF provides activities for children in the school holidays: four days a week for four weeks in summer, and a week over each of the Easter and Christmas holidays. Children on HAF programmes also receive at least one hot meal a day, which meets the school food standards. The majority of local authorities have also been offering the programmes to non-free-school-meal children, for a small fee. The programme is currently due to end in 2023.

Status: *Government has rolled out the programme to all schools across England, but has not yet confirmed whether it will be permanent. Eligibility still limited to children already on FSM, rather than being extended to all on Universal Credit.*

#6 Expand the Healthy Start scheme. Healthy Start is a means-tested scheme for low-income pregnant women, and families with children under the age of 4. It is also a universal entitlement for mothers under 18 years of age. The scheme provides coupons for vouchers which can be used to buy fruit and vegetables, as well as milk and vitamins. It should be expanded to everyone on Universal Credit, in line with FSM.

Status: *Government increased the level of payments, but has not yet expanded them to all on Universal Credit.*

#7 Introduce a 'Community Eatwell' programme, helping those on low incomes to improve their diets. Before the pandemic, the government spent £130 billion on the NHS every year. Of this, 95 percent was spent on treating illness, with just 5 percent going towards prevention. It would be far more cost-effective to increase spending on preventative measures. This recommendation is modelled on successful programmes from around the world. The Produce Prescription programme in Washington, DC, for example, allows doctors to prescribe vouchers for fresh fruit and vegetables, along with cooking lessons, nutritional education and guided tours of shops and supermarkets to teach people how to shop cleverly. The scheme has been shown to increase consumption of fruit and vegetables and improve nutritional understanding. Of the 120 patients who received vouchers between 2012 and 2017, 50 percent lost weight over the course of a prescription.

Status: *In its Levelling Up White Paper, the government committed to running a pilot. Progress unclear.*

☞ MAKE THE BEST USE OF OUR LAND

The government is asking farmers to change the way they work for the public good. We must ensure they are properly recompensed and protect them from unfair competition. The government needs a trade policy that supports both our farmers and our environmental ambitions.

#8 Use public money that was previously allocated to the Common Agricultural Policy to pay landowners to deliver public goods. The government has pledged to do this but is moving too slowly. Roughly a third of the money for agricultural payments – £500–700 million per year – should go on paying farmers for carbon sequestration and biodiversity projects. Our calculations suggest this would provide a fair return for managing the land required for these projects: roughly 400,000 hectares of broadleaf woodland, 325,000 hectares of restored upland peat and around 200,000 hectares of heath and species-rich grassland. The rest of the money should be used to promote increased productivity, flood prevention, soil improvement, animal welfare and nature-friendly farming.

Status: *The Agriculture Act has set out a basic framework for the new Environmental Land Management schemes. If implemented well, it would be world-leading. However, the details are still being thrashed out behind the scenes. Implementation is well behind schedule.*

#9 Create a 'Rural Land Use Framework' based on the Three Compartment Model. The only way to meet the UK's targets on net zero and nature restoration is to change the way we use our land (see *Chapter Fifteen*). To ensure each area of land serves the purpose it is best suited to, we need a framework which explicitly lays out what the government is trying to achieve, which incentives, payments and regulations it will use to achieve nature recovery, climate and food goals, and the metrics it will use to monitor progress. To help with planning decisions, the government should create a digital National Rural Land Map, containing layers of detailed data on each area of land.

Status: *Commitment to create a land use strategy. But little visible progress.*

#10 Define minimum standards for trade and a mechanism for protecting them. Polls show that 93 percent of the UK population want our high food standards to be maintained in all post-Brexit trade deals, and 81 percent are specifically worried about livestock farming standards being compromised in order to secure trade deals. The government should draw up a list of core minimum standards which it will defend in any future trade deals. These should cover animal welfare, environment and health protection, carbon emissions, antimicrobial resistance and zoonotic disease risk. It must then set out which mechanisms it intends to use to protect these standards. The easiest way to do this is to allow reduced tariffs in trade deals only when food imports meet these production standards.

Status: *Not done.*

☞ CREATE A LONG-TERM SHIFT IN OUR FOOD CULTURE

We cannot make lasting changes to the food system without innovation in the widest sense – in agriculture, manufacturing, retail, science, medicine, schools and local and national politics. Some of this is beyond the immediate remit of government. The State can never replace, or enforce, individual passion and entrepreneurialism. But it can invest, to encourage creativity and help bring new products to the market. It can set targets and institutional goals, bring in legislation and collect and disseminate accurate data.

#11 Launch a new 'Eat and Learn' initiative for schools. Since the publication of the School Food Plan in 2013, schools have had a legal requirement to teach cookery and nutrition to all children up to the age of 14. The curriculum states that schools should attempt to 'instil a love of cooking in pupils', while teaching them the kitchen skills necessary 'to feed themselves and others affordably and well, now and in later life'. In too many schools, this is still not happening. 'Food Tech' remains a second-class subject – a fun but frivolous distraction from the real business of learning. It is time to take food education seriously. This initiative includes a suite of actions – including mandatory certification of food served, curriculum changes, Ofsted inspection of lessons and increased funding.

Status: *Partial commitment in the Levelling Up White Paper. However, funding looks insufficient.*

#12 Invest £1 billion in innovation to create a better food system. This money should be split between support for agricultural innovation, research into alternative proteins, and a 'challenge fund' for projects that make the food system better in practice, rather than in the lab. At present, most of the government money that goes into food-related innovation is directed towards scientists and academics. In many of the other areas where innovation happens – on farms, for example, or in start-up businesses or community projects – there has long been a funding drought.

Status: *£500 million committed.*

#13 Create a National Food System Data programme. This is essential in order to collect and share data so that government departments and businesses involved in the food system can track progress, make efficiencies and plan ahead. The programme should span two main areas of evidence. The first is data about the land, as collected for the 'Rural Land Use Framework'. The second is data from beyond the farm gate: on food production, distribution and retail, and the environmental and health impacts of that food.

Status: *Food Data Transparency Partnership launched. Does not have the political backing required to make meaningful change.*

#14 Strengthen government procurement rules to ensure taxpayer money is spent on healthy and sustainable food. The government spends £2.4 billion every year buying food for schools, hospitals, the armed forces, prisons and government offices. This represents 5.5 percent of all meals eaten outside the home. During term time, children consume as much as 50 percent of their food at school, and for some a free school lunch is their only substantial meal of the day. The government should redesign its Buying Standards for Food and Catering Services to ensure that taxpayer money is spent on food that is both healthy and sustainable. It should also work to break up the quasi-monopoly in public food procurement, which is currently dominated by a small number of large corporations, creating little incentive for innovation and improvement. The government is already developing a trial scheme in south-west England in which local food suppliers can sell their produce via an online procurement page. Early evidence is that it works extremely well, with users reporting more choice, better quality and no increases in costs. Localism is the best way to foster genuine care and commitment within a system. The government should accelerate the rollout of this scheme, and use its new procurement standards to encourage caterers to try a broader range of suppliers.

Status: *Consultation launched on making buying standards mandatory. No commitment to change standards or to roll out scheme in the south-west.*

#15 Set clear targets and bring in legislation for long-term change. For real change we need clear, long-term targets, ongoing political attention, and a joined-up approach not only within government but across the food industry and communities. A strong framework of legal targets is essential. The government has already set itself a statutory target for carbon emissions. The 2022 Environment Act did the same for nature – imposing a legally binding target to halt biodiversity loss in England by 2030. We recommend adding a statutory target to improve diet-related health through a Good Food Bill, as proposed in the chart opposite. To maintain political focus, we recommend that the role of the Food Standards Agency (FSA) should be expanded to cover healthy and sustainable food as well as food safety. The FSA is governed independently, and well placed to take a whole-system perspective.

Status: *No progress.*

A possible legislative framework to create a healthier and more sustainable food system.

BILL	PROVISION	FOR	DUTIES (EXCEPT WHERE STATED)
Good Food Bill	Health targets	Government	Define long-term health targets and put into secondary legislation
	Action plans and independent reports	Government	Prepare and publish a Good Food Action Plan every five years, which sets out interim food system targets and measures to meet them
		Government	Consult the FSA while developing its Good Food Action Plans
		FSA	Provide a regular independent progress report to Parliament on the government's progress against the Good Food Action Plan
		FSA	Consult with the OEP, the CCC and the OHP in drawing up its advice and reports
		OEP, CCC and OHP	Advise the FSA on emerging issues within the remit of each body that are relevant to the scope of the FSA
	Other duties	FSA, working closely with the OHP and Defra	Establish and periodically update a healthy and sustainable Reference Diet, to be used by all public bodies in food-related policy making and procurement
		Government	Establish and periodically update a healthy and sustainable Reference Diet, to be used by all public bodies in food-related policy making and procurement
		Local authorities in England	Develop local food strategies, with reference to national targets and in partnership with the communities they serve
		Large food businesses	Expand obligation to promote consumer interest to include our collective interest in tackling climate change, nature recovery and health
Finance Bill	Levy	Government	Powers to apply a tax to sugar and salt

Acknowledgements

Our thanks first of all to the fantastic team at Profile Books. In particular, our editor, Mark Ellingham, for his enthusiasm and hard work; Henry Iles for the design; Georgina Difford for getting the book over the line; head honcho Andrew Franklin; and Ruth Killick, Niamh Murray and Flora Willis for getting it out to the world. Also to Jon Petre, Bill Johncocks, Jonathan Harley and Nikky Twyman, who took great care over the finer details. And to Gordon Wise, of Curtis Brown, for finding it such a good home.

Thank you to: Janine Gibson for the title, and Natania Jansz for the subtitle; the team at Bolinda for their diligent work on the audiobook; Mike Berners-Lee, Tim Spector, Charles Godfrey, Chris Goodall, Myles Allen, Kevin Hall, Hattie and Tom Deards, David Dimbleby, Dolly Theis, Duncan Clarke and Chris and Xand van Tulleken for their input on various drafts; Ian Boyd and Paul Clarke for helping to develop some of the thinking on systems dynamics; and Peter Dominiczak for providing strategic nous. Thank you Tracey Bade and Georgina Ware for keeping our logistics on track.

This book was born out of the National Food Strategy, and contains much of its DNA. We are therefore profoundly indebted to the team of civil servants who helped collate, sort, triple-check, analyse and stress-test the mountains of data that have gone into both works. Led by the indefatigable Tamsin Cooper – sometimes literally, across muddy fields and blustery moors – this team consisted of Daisy Lainoff, Joseph James, Jacques Launay, Eleanor Dowding, Jessica Heinemann, Simon Davies, Oliver Dye, Sarah Haley, Emma Quarterman, Grace Brocklehurst, Joanna Nixon, Tamas Borbely and Isabella Watney. Specialist help was provided by Dustin Benton, Tom MacMillan, James Kane and Will Brett, while Anna Taylor, executive director of the Food Foundation, brought her characteristic energy to the role of chief independent adviser. Bain & Company, SYSTEMIQ, Technopolis Group, Energy Systems Catapult, Policy Lab and Fleetwood Strategy all provided additional analysis. Most of the charts were originally designed by 10 Associates. We also drew heavily on the work of Hannah Ritchie and Max Rosser at Our World in Data, who provide an extraordinary wealth of free, reliable and beautifully visualised data online.

The National Food Strategy's Advisory Panel, made up of experts from right across the food system, provided invaluable behind-the-scenes insights and robust opinions. Thank you to: Minette Batters, President of the National Farmers' Union; Denise Bentley, Co-Founder and CEO, First Love Association; Baroness Boycott, Member of the Food, Poverty, Health and the Environment Committee of the House of Lords; Helen Browning, Chief Executive, Soil Association; Paul Clarke, former Chief Technology Officer of Ocado; Dr Meredith Crowley, Reader in International Economics, University of Cambridge; Dr David Halpern, Chief Executive, Behavioural Insights Team; Professor Susan Jebb, Professor of Diet and Population Health, University of Oxford; Tony Juniper, Chair of Natural England; Justin King, Former Chief Executive of Sainsbury's, Non-Executive Director Marks & Spencer; Rebecca Laughton, Campaign Coordinator, Landworkers' Alliance; Dr Tim Leunig, former economic adviser to the Treasury and Associate Professor of Economic History, London School of Economics; Craig Livingstone, farm and estate manager at Lockerley Estate; Professor Theresa Marteau, Director of Behaviour and Health Research Unit, University of Cambridge; Professor Steve McCorriston, Professor of Agricultural Economics, University of Exeter; Sarah Mukherjee, Chief Executive, Institute of Environmental Management and Assessment; Sebastian Munden, Executive Vice President & General Manager, Unilever UK & Ireland; Jeremy Oppenheim, Founder & Senior Partner, SYSTEMIQ; Andrew Selley, Chief Executive, Bidfood; John Shropshire, CEO, G's Group; Daisy Stemple, our citizen member of the Advisory Panel; Alastair Storey, Founder and Chief Executive, Westbury Street Holdings (WSH); Professor Jonathan Valabhji, National Clinical Director for Diabetes and Obesity, NHS England; Gerard van der Hut, Managing Director, Rijk Zwaan UK Ltd; Roger Whiteside, former Chief Executive of Greggs.

Many other experts have been generous with their time, knowledge and wisdom. They include: Dave Lewis, former Tesco CEO and now WWF Chair of Board of Trustees; Professor Dame Rachel Griffith, Research Director, Institute for Fiscal Studies and Professor of Economics, University of Manchester; Sir Ian Boyd, Professor of Biology, University of St Andrews, former Chief Scientific Adviser, Defra; Professor Martin White, Professor of Population Health Research, Centre for Diet and Activity Research, MRC Epidemiology Unit, University of Cambridge; Professor Sir Partha Dasgupta, Emeritus Professor, Frank Ramsey Professor Emeritus of Economics, Cambridge University; Dr Peter Scarborough, Nuffield Department of Population Health, University of Oxford; Dr Kevin Hall, Senior Investigator, Integrative Physiology Section, Laboratory of Biological Modelling,

Intramural Research Programme, National Institutes of Health; Lazlo Barabási, Giulia Menichetti and Peter Ruppert, from the Barabási Lab; Dr Richie Harrington, senior researcher Big Data Institute, Nuffield Department of Population Health, University of Oxford; Professor Lord Krebs, Emeritus Professor of Zoology, University of Oxford; Sir Dieter Helm, Professor of Economic Policy at the University of Oxford; Dr David Nabarro, Professor of Global Health at Imperial College London, and curator of the UN's Food Systems Dialogues; Sir Charles Burrell, conservationist and founder of the Knepp Wildland; Stefano Agostini, CEO of Nestlé UK & Ireland; Michael Dixon, Co-Chair, Social Prescribing Network; Sam Hall, Director of the Conservative Environment Network; Emily Miles, Chief Executive, Food Standards Agency; Professor Dame Ottoline Leyser, Regius Professor of Botany at the University of Cambridge and Chief Executive Officer of UK Research and Innovation; Professor Tim Spector, epidemiologist and science writer; Professor Tim Lang, Emeritus Professor of Food Policy at City University; Professor Guy Poppy, former Chief Scientific Adviser to the Food Standards Agency; Sue Pritchard, Chief Executive of the Food, Farming and Countryside Commission; Professor Corinna Hawkes, Professor of Food Policy, City University of London; Richard Benwell, Chief Executive of the Wildlife and Countryside Link; Mark Bridgman, President, Country Land and Business Association; Martin Lines, UK Chair, Nature Friendly Farming Network; Gavin Lane, Farmer; David Fursdon, Chair of Beeswax Dyson Farming Ltd; Peter Brotherton, Director of Science, Natural England; Louise Davies, founder, Food Teachers Centre; Fiona Gatley, Royal Academy of Culinary Arts; Jack Monroe; Judith Batchelar, outgoing Director of Corporate Responsibility and Sustainability at Sainsbury's; Sarah Bradbury, Group Quality Director; Marie Polley, Co-Chair, Social Prescribing Network; James Rebanks, sheep farmer and author; Professor Herman Pontzer, Associate Professor in Evolutionary Anthropology, Duke University; Professor Alan Dangour, Professor in Food and Nutrition, London School of Hygiene and Tropical Medicine; Dr Rosemary Green, Associate Professor in Sustainability, Nutrition and Health, London School of Hygiene and Tropical Medicine; Dr Pauline Scheelbeek, Assistant Professor in Nutritional and Environmental Epidemiology, London School of Hygiene and Tropical Medicine; Iain Porter, Joseph Rowntree Foundation; Professor Jonathan Bradshaw, Emeritus Professor of Social Policy, York University; Dr Ben Richardson, Reader in International Political Economy, University of Warwick; Dr Paige Stanley, Colorado State University; and Dr Fiona Smith, Professor of International Economic Law, University of Leeds.

The National Food Strategy was fortunate to receive funding

from several outside sources, which meant we could do things that independent reviews normally can't. The Sustainable Healthy Food Systems consortium, funded by the Wellcome Trust, Esmée Fairbairn Foundation and the Health Foundation, funded our youth engagement programme. The Food People, together with Fix Our Food, funded the Holiday Activities and Food film we made with Marcus Rashford. The Mark Leonard Trust, the Linbury Trust, the Ashden Trust, the European Climate Foundation and the Rothschild Foundation all provided funding for communication.

Some politicians, past and present, have understood the problems in the system and put a shoulder to the wheel of change. They include: Michael Gove (who commissioned both the School Food Plan and the National Food Strategy), Sharon Hodgson, Stephen Twigg, Ed Balls, David Laws, Danny Alexander, Nick Clegg, Jo Gideon, George Eustice, Ian Byrne, Zac Goldsmith, Barry Sheerman, George Freeman, Sue Hayman, Emma Lewell-Buck, Caroline Lucas, Kerry McCarthy, Victoria Prentis, Richard Benyon, Meg Hillier, Jo Churchill, Philip Glanville and Robert Halfon. Thank you to those people working in the devolved authorities who gave us their thoughts on the food system: from Northern Ireland, Joy Alexander, Fiona Ferguson, Louise Brady, and Colette McMaster; from Scotland, George Burgess, David Gally, Ian McWatt, Gillian Provan, Garry Mournian, David Johnston; and, from Wales, David Lloyd-Thomas and Nicholas Shilton.

Many thanks to Tamara Finkelstein, Defra's marvellously resilient and conscientious permanent secretary, and to Lizzie Noel, Elizabeth Buchanan, Colin Day, Ben Goldsmith, Maureen Kavanagh and Linda Thomas.

Thank you to John Vincent, co-author of the School Food Plan. Also to Nicole Pisani, Naomi Duncan and all of the trustees, trainers and chefs at Chefs in Schools, who are doing the vital work of nourishing and educating the next generation.

Finally, we would like to thank our respective mothers, Petra Lewis and Josceline Dimbleby, who taught us to cook; and our exacting in-house food tasters, George, Johnny and Dory.

Sources and endnotes

This section lists the main research sources for each chapter, as well as papers or books that we found particularly illuminating.

Much of the data analysis was done for the National Food Strategy, by a dedicated team of civil servants assisted by Bain & Company and SYSTEMIQ. It was checked by Defra's statistical department. Detailed references for this work can be found in the two parts of the National Food Strategy – Part One and The Plan – at www.nationalfoodstrategy.org. The website also contains some documents containing more granular detail than we could fit into the strategy. These include: The Impact of a Tax on Added Sugar and Salt: An Institute for Fiscal Studies Working Paper in Collaboration with the National Food Strategy; Impact of Production Changes on Food Prices; and two documents of supplementary evidence which might be useful to researchers.

Introduction

p.11   Chart derived from: Bar-On, Y. M. et al. (2018) The Biomass Distribution on Earth. Proceedings of the National Academy of Sciences, 115(25), 6506–6511.

p.12   Food system greenhouse gas emissions: Allen, M. (2015) Short-Lived Promise? The Science and Policy of Cumulative and Short-Lived Climate Pollutants. Oxford Martin Policy Paper.

Shocks on food system from climate change: Wageningen Economic Research (2018) Climate Change and Global Market Integration: Implications for Global Economic Activities, Agricultural Commodities and Food Security. SOCO 2018 Background Paper, Rome, FAO.

Hannah Ritchie's blog Did Humans Cause the Quaternary Megafauna Extinction? – posted at the ourworldindata. org – is a good primer on the role of prehistoric humans in destroying wildlife.

p.13   Health profiles of processed food: Access to Nutrition Initiative (2019) UK Product Profile 2019. Access to Nutrition Initiative.

Relative price of processed food: Food Foundation (2020) The Broken Plate 2020. Food Foundation.

Cost of type 2 diabetes treatment: 2019 data: Global Health Data Exchange (GHDx) (2021) Global Burden of Disease, accessed March 2021.

Obesity over time: Bain analysis for the NFS. 1955 mean BMI interpolated from US historic BMI trends and UK BMI from 1977 onwards. Distribution before 1980 is directional using normal distributions around mean value and, therefore, is not an exact representation. Source: NHS Digital (2018) Health Survey for England 2017 [NS]. NHS Digital; Euromonitor (2019); NHS Digital (2019) National Child Measurement Programme. Gov.uk (2018); Population Pyramid (2019); Davey, R. (2003) The Obesity Epidemic: Too Much Food for Thought?; National Bureau of Economic Research (2010) The Trend of BMI Values of US Adults by Centiles, Birth Cohorts 1882–1986.

p.15 One fifth (20%) of food is bought out of home if you include only food categories where it can be reasonably assumed that consumption is from the out-of-home (OOH) sector; 25%, if you include food categories that are likely to include items purchased out of home (from the OOH or retail sectors) and items brought from home. Source: Public Health England (2019) National Diet and Nutrient Survey Years 1–9, 2008/09–2016/17.

Proportion of calories coming from school food: breakfast, lunch and snacks at school = 0.67 of weekday food, therefore 0.47 over seven days; Royston, S. et al. (2012) Fair and Square: A Policy Report on the Future of Free School Meals. The Children's Society.

p.17 The government responded to the National Food Strategy in three forms: through the actions it took after Marcus Rashford's campaigning in 2020 and in two white papers – Levelling Up the United Kingdom (2022) and Government Food Strategy (2022) The main responses on health were due to appear in the Health Disparities white paper in 2022, but this was dropped after Boris Johnson's resignation.

Trapped in the system

p.20 Chart: Foresight Obesity System Map, GOV.UK. Available at www.gov.uk/government/publications/reducing-obesity-obesity-system-map.

p.21 We read a lot on the science of system dynamics and the work of Jay Wright Forrester and his team at MIT. Donella Meadows' *Thinking in Systems* (written in 1993 but published posthumously in 2008) remains the best introduction to the topic.

p.22 Chart: Kelly Parsons (2020) Who Makes Food Policy in England? A Map of Government Actors and Activities. Rethinking Food Governance Report 1. London: Food Research Collaboration.

PART ONE: Our Bodies
Chapter 1: A miracle and a disaster

p.32 UK self-sufficiency over time: Food Chain Analysis Group, Department for Environment Food & Rural Affairs (2006) *Food Security and the UK: An Evidence and Analysis Paper*. National Archives; Barnett, M. (1985) *British Food Policy During the First World War*. Australia: Allen & Unwin; Department for Environment, Food & Rural Affairs (2013) *Agriculture in the United Kingdom*. HMG.

The U-boat peril: Dimbleby, J. (2016) *The Battle of the Atlantic: How the Allies Won the War*. Penguin Books.

p.33 Chart: Bain Analysis for the National Food Strategy (2019), based on Population data for 1800–1950: University of Groningen (2018) *Maddison Project Database 2018*; population data for 1950: un.org (2015) *Population 2030 Demographic Challenges and Opportunities for Sustainable Development Planning*; Global agricultural production data for 1960–2010: FAO (2020) *Net Agricultural Production Index*; Global agricultural data 2010 onward: FAO (2018) *The Future of Food and Agriculture: Alternative Pathways to 2050*.

Charles C. Mann's *Wizard and the Prophet: Two Remarkable Scientists and their Battle to Shape Tomorrow's World* (London: Pan Macmillan, 2018) is a beautifully crafted introduction to the work of Norman Borlaug and the controversy that followed it.

p.34 Picture: Norman Borlaug. © Keystone-France / Gamma-Rapho via Getty Images.

p.35 Mexican wheat production: Mann, C. (2018) *Wizard and the Prophet: Two Remarkable Scientists and their Battle to Shape Tomorrow's World*. London: Pan Macmillan, p.130.

Global life expectancy: Roser, M. et al. (2013) Life Expectancy. *Our World in Data.*

Global calorie production: Ritchie, H. and Roser, M. (2021) Crop Yields. *Our World in Data.*

p.36   Famines: Hasell, J. (2018) Famine Mortality over the Long Run. *Our World in Data.*

UK wheat yields: Department for Environment, Food & Rural Affairs et al. (2020) *Agriculture in the UK 2019.* HMG.

p.37   Russian land use calculated using data from *Agriculture of the USSR: Statistical Compendium* (1960) and *Regions of Russia: Social and Economic Indicators* (2022). Moscow: Rosstat, in Russian.

UK greenhouse gases from the food system: Allen, M. (2015) *Short-Lived Promise? The Science and Policy of Cumulative and Short-Lived Climate Pollutants.* Oxford Martin Policy Paper.

Farmland use UK: Department for Food & Rural Affairs et al. (2018) *Agriculture in the United Kingdom 2018.* HMG

p.38   Chart: Hayhow, D. B. et al. (2019) *The State of Nature 2019.* The State of Nature partnership; crop yields from Bain analysis for National Food Strategy. Based on: Department for Food & Rural Affairs (2018) *Agriculture in the UK.* HMG; Ritchie, H. and Roser, M. (2019) Crop Yields. *Our World in Data.*

Environmental collapse: wildflower meadows: Hayhow, D. B. et al. (2019) *The State of Nature 2019.* The State of Nature partnership; ancient woodland (decline since 1900): Woodland Trust (2000) *Why the UK's Ancient Woodland Is Still Under Threat,* pp.3–5; heathland (extrapolated from data on Dorset): Fagúndez, J. and Bot, A. (2013) Heathlands Confronting Global Change: Drivers of Biodiversity Loss from Past to Future Scenarios. *Annals of Botany,* 111(2), 151–172; Lowland Ponds: Hayhow, D. B. et al. (2019) *The State of Nature 2019.*

Obesity profile: short statistical commentary (July 2022), Office for Health Improvement & Disparities. HMG.

p.39   Proliferation of KitKats: KitKat.co.uk (counted in 2021).

Chapter 2: Boiling the frog

p.41   Link between genes and obesity: Loos, R. and Yeo, G. (2022)

The Genetics of Obesity: From Discovery to Biology. *Nature Reviews: Genetics*, 23, 120–133.

pp.42 –44 The charts showing the bell curve of UK weight over time were inspired by Anthony Warner's *The Truth About Fat: Why Obesity is Not that Simple*. Bain analysis for the NFS. 1955 mean BMI interpolated from US historic BMI trends and UK BMI from 1977 onwards. Distribution before 1980 is directional using normal distributions around mean value and, therefore, is not an exact representation. Source: NHS Digital (2018) *Health Survey for England 2017* [NS]. NHS Digital; Euromonitor (2019); NHS Digital (2019) *National Child Measurement Programme*; *GOV.UK* (2018); Population Pyramid. (2019); Davey, R. (2003) *The Obesity Epidemic: Too Much Food for Thought?*; National Bureau of Economic Research (2010) The Trend of BMI Values of US Adults by Centiles, Birth Cohorts 1882–1986.

p.44 Fat and sugar ratios: DiFeliceantonio, A. et al. (2018) Supra-Additive Effects of Combining Fat and Carbohydrate on Food Reward. *Cell Metabolism*, 28(1), 33–44.

p.45 Impact of BOGOFs: Smithson, M. et al. (2015) *An Analysis of the Role of Price Promotions on the Household Purchases of Food and Drinks High in Sugar*. Public Health England.

Expandability of chocolate: Kantar Worldpanel Division (2016) *Expandability Study Based on FMCG Panel*. Kantar Worldpanel.

p.46 Chart: Department for Environment, Food & Rural Affairs (2020) Family Food Surveys. *GOV.UK*.

Calories from food cooked from scratch: Griffith, R. et al. (2021) *The Decline of Home Cooked Food*. IFS.

p.47 Confectionery vs fruit and vegetable sales: fruit and vegetables: Department for Environment Food & Rural Affairs (2020) *Horticulture Statistics 2019*. HMG; confectionery: Office for National Statistics (2020) *UK Manufacturers' Sales by Product*. ONS.

Relative health profiles of processed food: Access to Nutrition Initiative (2019) *UK Product Profile 2019*. Access to Nutrition Initiative.

p.48 The chart of circles showing the relative loss of healthy life because of avoidable factors is from 2019 data, accessed July

2021. Global Burden of Disease: Global Health Data Exchange. (2021) GBD Results Tool. Institute for Health Metrics and Evaluation.

Obese people tend not to be happy about it: Godoy-Izquierdo, D. et al. (2020) Body Satisfaction, Weight Stigma, Positivity, and Happiness among Spanish Adults with Overweight and Obesity. *International Journal of Environmental Research and Public Health*, 17(12), 4186.

p.49   Economic cost of obesity: Organisation for Economic Co-operation and Development (2019) *The Heavy Burden of Obesity: The Economics of Prevention,* United Kingdom country note.

Chapter 3: You can't outrun a bad diet

p.52   Level of knowledge about a healthy diet: Prior, G. et al. (2011) *Exploring Food Attitudes and Behaviours in the UK: Findings from the Food and You Survey 2010.* FSA.

Manual labour: Lindsay, C. (2003) *A Century of Labour Market Change: 1900 to 2000.* Labour Market Trends.

p.53   Coal mining vs jogging: Griffith, R. et al. (2016) Gluttony and Sloth? Calories, Labour Market Activity and the Rise of Obesity. *Journal of the European Economic Association,* 14(6), 1253–1286.

Distance walked over time: Townsend, N. et al. (2012) *Physical Activity Statistics 2012.* British Heart Foundation.

pp.53 Herman Pontzer's book *Burn: The Misunderstood Science of*
–62   *Metabolism* is a good read on the science in the rest of this chapter. References are from there. All have been checked back to primary sources.

p.55   Chart: Herman Pontzer (2021) *Burn: The Misunderstood Science of Metabolism.* London: Allen Lane.

p.62   *ibid.*

Chapter 4: Appetite

p.63   Story of the Chilean rugby players: Read, P. P. (2002) *Alive: The True Story of the Andes Survivors.* London: Arrow.

p.64   The role of the hypothalamus and hormones in appetite control: Austin, J. and Marks, D. (2008) Hormonal Regulators of Appetite. *International Journal of Pediatric Endocrinology*, art. 141753.

p.68 The Minnesota Experiment: Keys, A. et al. (1950) ⌈*The Biology of Human Starvation*. University of Minnesota Press.

p.70 Picture: 'Three "Guinea Pigs" of Starvation Experiments'. *Minneapolis Morning Tribune*, 1 June 1950. © Hennepin County Library.

p.71 *Hongerwinter*: Lumey, L. H. et al. (2007) Cohort Profile: The Dutch Hunger Winter Families Study. *International Journal of Epidemiology*, 36(6), 1196–1204.

Chapter 5: Anatomy of an egg sandwich

p.74 Manufacturing rapeseed oil: Kovalevskaya, S. (2020) *Industrial Production of Rapeseed Oil and Its Application*. Tampere University of Applied Sciences.

p.76 Definition of ultra-processed food: Monteiro, C. et al. (2019) *Ultra-Processed Foods: What They Are and How to Identify Them*. Public Health Nutrition.

p.77 European consumption of ultra-processed food by country: Monteiro, C. et al. (2018) *Household Availability of Ultra-Processed Foods and Obesity in Nineteen European Countries*. Public Health Nutrition.

p.78 Kevin Hall's study: Hall, K. et al. (2019) Ultra-Processed Diets Cause Excess Calorie Intake and Weight Gain: An Inpatient Randomized Controlled Trial of Ad Libitum Food Intake. *Cell Metabolism*, **30(1), 67–77.**

p.80 Barabási on the dark matter of nutrition: Barabási, A., Menichetti, G. and Loscalzo, J. (2020) The Unmapped Chemical Complexity of Our Diet. *Nature Food*, 1, 33–37.

p.82 Expert disagreements on nutrition: Spector, T. (2022) *Food for Life: The New Science of Eating Well*. Jonathan Cape.

p.84 Hours of nutritional training for doctors: Macaninch, E. et al. (2020) Time for Nutrition in Medical Education. *British Medical Journal Nutrition, Prevention & Health*, 3(1), 40–48.

Dr Casey Means quote: *Eating Ourselves to Death: Honestly*

with Bari Weiss [podcast] (2022), available at https://open.
spotify.com/episode/1ffU1eqXZtoRsfeWIqVani.

Chapter 6: Inequality

p.86   Chart: NCD Risk Factor Collaboration (NCD-RisC) (2020)
         Height and Body-Mass Index Trajectories of School-Aged
         Children and Adolescents from 1985 to 2019 in 200 Countries
         and Territories: A Pooled Analysis of 2181 Population-Based
         Studies with 65 Million Participants. *Lancet*, 396(10261),
         1511–1524.

p.87   Rise of 'Victorian' diseases: Secondary Care Analysis, NHS
         Digital (2021) *Number of Admissions for Scurvy, Rickets
         and Malnutrition, Broken Down by Age Group, for the Years
         2007–08 to 2020–21.*

         Chart: National Food Strategy analysis of NDNS: Public Health
         England & Food Standards Agency (2020) *National Diet and
         Nutrition Survey: Rolling Programme Years 9 to 11 (2016 to
         2017 and 2018 to 2019)* HMG.

p.88   Life expectancy going backwards: Marmot, M. et al. (2020)
         Health Equity in England: The Marmot Review 10 Years On.
         Institute of Health Equity.

         Chart: NFS Analysis of PHE Public Health Outcomes
         Framework: Public Health England (2013) *Public Health
         Outcomes Framework.* HMG.

p.89   Household food security: Department for Work and Pensions
         (2021) *Family Resources Survey: Financial Year 2019 to 2020.*
         HMG.

p.91   Chart: Prevalence of fast food outlets: Public Health England
         (2018) *Obesity and the Environment – Density of Fast Food
         Outlets at 31/12/2017.* HMG.

         Car ownership: Lucas, K. et al. (2019) *Inequalities in Mobility
         and Access in the UK Transport System.* Government Office for
         Science.

p.92   Ownership of cookers, freezers and fridges: Turn2Us (2020)
         Living Without: The Scale and Impact of Appliance Poverty.
         Turn2Us.

Chapter 7: Should Nanny tell us what to eat?

p.96   The North Karelian project: author interviews with Pekka
        Puska; Puska, P. et al. (2016) Background, Principles,
        Implementation, and General Experiences of the North
        Karelia Project. *Global Heart Journal*, 11(2), 173–8.

p.100   Nanny State Index: Snowdon, C. (2021) *Nanny State Index*.
        Institute of Economic Affairs.

p.101   Government intervention on obesity: Theis, D. R. Z. and White,
        M. (2021) *Is Obesity Policy in England Fit for Purpose? Analysis
        of Government Strategies and Policies, 1992–2020. The
        Milbank Quarterly*, 98 (March).

p.102   Andy Haldane quote: Haldane, A. and Rebolledo, I. (2022):
        Health is Wealth? Strengthening the UK's Immune System.
        REAL Challenge annual lecture. The Health Foundation.

        Economic cost of food-related disease: Organisation for
        Economic Co-operation and Development (2019) United
        Kingdom country note, *The Heavy Burden of Obesity: The
        Economics of Prevention*. OECD Publishing.

p.104   Impact of sugary drink levy: soft drinks: Scarborough, P. et
        al. (2020) Impact of the Announcement and Implementation
        of the UK Soft Drinks Industry Levy on Sugar Content, Price,
        Product Size and Number of Available Soft Drinks in the UK,
        2015–19: A Controlled Interrupted Time Series Analysis. *PLoS
        Medicine*, 17(2).

Chapter 8: Hacking the system

p.107   Average sugar consumption: Public Health England (2019)
        *National Diet and Nutrition Survey Years 1–9, 2008/09–
        2016/17*.

p.108   Percent of sugar and salt eaten in processed foods: Sugar: AB
        Sugar (2021) *The UK Sugar Sector*. AB Sugar; salt: Murray, C. et
        al. (2002) *Cardiovascular Death and Disability Can be Reduced
        by More Than 50 Percent* [news release]. World Health
        Organization.

        Modelling of sugar and salt reformulation tax: Griffith, R. et al.
        (forthcoming) *The Impact of a Tax on Added Sugar and Salt*.
        Institute of Fiscal Studies/University of Manchester. Available
        on nationalfoodstrategy.org.

Calorie reduction required to stop the nation putting on weight: Department of Health and Social Care (2011) *Statement of the Calorie Reduction Expert Group.* HMG.

p.111 Junk food advertising: Public Health England (2015) *Sugar Reduction: The Evidence for Action.* PHE; Department of Culture, Media & Sport (DMCS)/Department of Health and Social Care (DHSC) (2019) *Introducing a 2100–0530 Watershed on TV Advertising of HFSS (Food and Drink That Are High in Fat, Salt and Sugar) Products and Similar Protection for Children Viewing Adverts Online: Impact Assessment (IA).* HMG.

The Smartie study: Russell, S. J., Croker, H. and Viner, R. M. (2018) The Effect of Screen Advertising on Children's Dietary Intake: A Systematic Review and Meta-analysis. *Obesity Reviews*, 20(4), 554–568.

Chapter 9: Hacking the body

p.114 For more on bariatric surgery, the surgeon Andrew Jenkinson's *Why We Eat (Too Much): The New Science of Appetite* (Penguin Life, 2020) is excellent.

p.115 Chart: Gastric sleeve vs gastric bypass. Bariatric surgery weight loss procedures comparison. © Shutterstock.

PART TWO: Our Land

Chapter 10: How humanity ate the world

p.124 The disappearance of snow crabs: Wetzel, C. (2022) Why Have Billions of Snow Crabs Disappeared from Alaskan Waters? *New Scientist*, 17 October; NF Staff (2022) Bering Sea Crabbers Welcome Disaster Relief, Seek Temporary Area Closure. *National Fisherman*, 27 December.

p.125 Heatwave impact on European harvest: Das, D. (2022) EU Maize Import Surge Seen Cushioning Impact of Drought-Hit Crop, *European Supermarket Magazine*, 10 October; ANSA (2022) Drought: Crop Yields Down by up to 45% – Coldiretti. *ANSA*, 25 July.

p.126 UK emissions: Garnett, T. et al. (2016) *Food Systems and Greenhouse Gas Emissions.* University of Oxford: Food Climate Research Network.

Chart: Food and Agriculture Organization of the United Nations (2018) *The State of Agricultural Commodity Markets 2018*. FAO.

p.127   Mekong rice: The Anh, D., Van Tinh, T. and Ngoc Vang, N. (2020) The Domestic Rice Value Chain in the Mekong Delta. In Cramb, R. (ed.), *White Gold: The Commercialisation of Rice Farming in the Lower Mekong Basin*. Singapore: Palgrave Macmillan, pp.375–396.

Volume of fresh water and use in farming: World Wildlife Fund (2021) *Freshwater Systems*. World Wildlife Fund; FAO (2017) *Water for Sustainable Food and Agriculture*. FAO.

p.128   Number of people who rely on fertiliser for food: Ritchie, H. (2017) How Many People Does Synthetic Fertilizer Feed? *Our World in Data*.

Emissions caused by the Haber–Bosch process: 1% of global emissions come from ammonia production: Gilbert, P. and Thornley, P. (2010) *Energy and Carbon Balance of Ammonia Production from Biomass Gasification*. Tyndall Centre, Department of Mechanical, Aerospace and Civil Engineering, University of Manchester.

p.129   Decline in fish stocks: European Environment Agency (2018) *European Waters: Assessment of Status and Pressures 2018*. EEA; Marine Scotland Directorate (2022) *Salmon Fishing: Proposed River Gradings for 2023 Season*. Scottish Government; Enevoldsen, H. et al. (2022) *State of the Ocean Report*. Intergovernmental Oceanographic Commission.

Decline in wild birds: Burns, F. et al. (2020) *The State of the UK's Birds 2020*. Sandy, Bedfordshire: RSPB, BTO, WWT, DAERA, JNCC, NatureScot, NE and NRW.

p.130   For 'blue carbon', see National Food Strategy (2021) *The National Food Strategy: The Evidence*, July, p.66.

Decline in fish stocks: Thurstan, R. H. et al. (2010) The Effects of 118 Years of Industrial Fishing on UK Bottom Trawl Fisheries. *Nature Communications*, 1, art. 15; Harrabin, R. (2021) Bottom Trawling Ban for Key UK Fishing Sites. *BBC News*, 1 February. Available at www.bbc.co.uk/news/science-environment-55894608.

Chapter 11: The invisibility of nature

p.135   Distribution of CAP payments: Scown, M. et al. (2020) Billions in Misspent EU Agricultural Subsidies Could Support the Sustainable Development Goals. *One Earth*, 3(2), 237–250.

p.137   Chart: Global Farm Metric Framework, Global Farm Metric. Available at www.globalfarmmetric.org/about-the-global-farm-metric.

p.139   Chart: SYSTEMIQ analysis for the National Food Strategy, based on Food and Land Use Commission: *Growing Better: Ten Critical Transitions to Transform Food and Land Use* (2019); Sustainable Food Trust: *The Hidden Cost of UK Food* (2017); Ellen MacArthur Foundation: *Cities and Circular Economy for Food* (2019); World Business Council for Sustainable Development: *The True Value of Food – a Powerful Aid to Business Decision-Making* (2021).

Pigouvian taxes: Pigou, A. (1924) *The Economics of Welfare*. London :Macmillan.

Chapter 12: Warming meals

p.145   The balloon analogy is adapted from Charles C. Mann's *Wizard and the Prophet: Two Remarkable Scientists and their Battle to Shape Tomorrow's World*. London: Pan Macmillan.

p.146   Greenhouse gas emissions from the food system: Allen, M. (2015) *Short-Lived Promise? The Science and Policy of Cumulative and Short-Lived Climate Pollutants*. Oxford Martin Policy Paper.

p.147   Tree burning in the Amazon: Qin, Y. et al. (2021) Carbon Loss from Forest Degradation Exceeds that from Deforestation in the Brazilian Amazon. *Nature Climate Change*, 11, 442–448; European Space Agency (2021) Forest Degradation Primary Driver of Carbon Loss in the Brazilian Amazon. *European Space Agency*. Available at www.esa.int/Applications/Observing_the_Earth/Space_for_our_climate/Forest_degradation_primary_driver_of_carbon_loss_in_the_Brazilian_Amazon.

The UK's wildwoods: Whitehouse, N. and Smith, D. (2010) How Fragmented Was the British Holocene Wildwood? Perspectives on the 'Vera' Grazing Debate from the Fossil Beetle Record. *Quaternary Science Reviews*, 29(3–4); Forest

Research (2021) *Provisional Woodland Statistics: 2021 Edition.* Forest Research; Forest Research (2021) *Tools and Resources: Area of Woodland: Changes Over Time.* Forest Research.

p.148   Peat: Anderson, R. (2020) *Peatlands, Forestry and Climate Change: What Role Can Forest-to-Bog Restoration Play?* Forest Research; Bernal, B. et al. (2018) Global Carbon Dioxide Removal Rates from Forest Landscape Restoration Activities. *Carbon Balance Management,* 13, art. 22.; UK Centre for Ecology & Hydrology (n.d.) *Peatlands Factsheet.* UK Centre for Ecology & Hydrology; Brown, P. et al. (2021) *UK Greenhouse Gas Inventory, 1990 to 2019: Annual Report for Submissions Under the Framework Convention on Climate Change.* Ricardo Energy & Environment. Annex 3.; IUCN (2018) *UK Peatland Strategy.* IUCN National Committee, United Kingdom.

p.149   Emissions from fertiliser production and use: 1% of global emissions come from ammonia production: Gilbert, P. and Thornley, P. (2010) *Energy and Carbon Balance of Ammonia Production from Biomass Gasification.* Tyndall Centre, Department of Mechanical, Aerospace and Civil Engineering, University of Manchester; 12% of total agricultural emissions (2.9% of total emissions) from synthetic ammonia use: Smith, P. M. et al. (2014) *Agriculture, Forestry and Other Land Use (AFOLU).* In Edenhofer, O. et al. (eds), *Climate Change 2014: Mitigation of Climate Change. Contribution of Working Group III to the Fifth Assessment Report of the Intergovernmental Panel on Climate Change.* Cambridge University Press; In total, then, synthetic fertiliser is about 4% of global GHGs and 12% of total agricultural emissions (2.9% of total emissions) from synthetic ammonia use.

Chart: National Food Strategy analysis based on: Garnett, T. (2008) *Cooking up a Storm: Food, Greenhouse Gas Emissions and our Changing Climate.* Food Climate Research Network, Centre for Environmental Strategy; Department for Business, Energy & Industrial Strategy (2019) *Final UK Greenhouse Gas Emissions National Statistics.* Data tables; WRAP (2020) *Courtauld Commitment 2025, Annual Report 2020.* WRAP.

p.150   Nestlé emissions reduction: private correspondence with Nestlé UK.

Chapter 13: Peak meat?

p.151   Enteric fermentation and wastes and manure management account for 68.4% of UK agricultural emissions. See Committee on Climate Change (2020) *The Sixth Carbon Budget – Dataset*. Committee on Climate Change. Available at www.theccc.org.uk/publication/sixth-carbon-budget/.

p.155   Chart: Allen, M. (2015) *Short-Lived Promise? The Science and Policy of Cumulative and Short-Lived Climate Pollutants*. Oxford Martin Policy Paper.

p.157   Chart: Ritchie, H. (2020) Less Meat is Nearly Always Better than Sustainable Meat, to Reduce Your Carbon Footprint. *Our World in Data*.

p.159   Chart: Kim, B. et al. (2020) Country-Specific Dietary Shifts to Mitigate Climate and Water Crises. *Global Environmental Change*, 62.

p.161   Carbon cowboys: Peter Byck has published a compendium of published AMP grazing research at carboncowboys.org/amp-grazing-research. His new films on AMP grazing – *Roots So Deep (You Can See the Devil Down There)* – will be out soon; *Science*'s recent paper provides a less optimistic take: Bai, Y. and Cotrufo, M. (2022) Grassland Soil Carbon Sequestration: Current Understanding, Challenges, and Solutions. *Science,* 377(6606), 603–608; Dr Paige Stanley's work is at paige-stanley.com.

Chapter 14: Sentient food

Much of this chapter is adapted from the RSPCA's inaugural Wilberforce Lecture 2022, given by the author. The text can be found at rspca.org.uk/whatwedo/latest/wilberforcelecture.

p.163   Number of animals on the planet: Ritchie, H. Rosado, P. and Roser, M. (2017) Meat and Dairy Production. *Our World in Data*.

p.164   Description of a pig house: Shu, A. (2022) Under Construction: A 26-Storey Pig House. *Pig Progress*, 11 October.

          Suffocated pigs: O'Neill, N. (2020) Pigs Roasted Alive in Coronavirus Mass-Extermination, Probe Uncovers. *New York Post*, 29 May; Baysinger, A. et al. (2021) A Case Study of Ventilation Shutdown with the Addition of High Temperature and Humidity for Depopulation of Pigs. *Journal of the American Veterinary Medical Association*, 259(4), 415–424.

p.165   Picture: Composite of 'Guangxi Yangxiang's high-rise pig farm buildings are seen at Yaji Mountain Forest Park in Guangxi'. © Reuters/Thomas Suen.

p.169   Picture: 'A Venerable Orang-outang', *The Hornet*, 22 March 1871. Photo: University College London Digital Collections.

p.172   Maternal cows and chickens: Mance, H. (2021) *How to Love Animals*. Viking.

p.176   Antimicrobials: global trends: Boeckel, T. et al. (2019) Global Trends in Antimicrobial Resistance in Animals in Low- and Middle-Income Countries. *Science*, 365(6459); Antimicrobial Resistance Review (2016) *Tackling Drug-Resistant Infections Globally: Final Report and Recommendations: The Review on Antimicrobial Resistance*; Boeckel, T. et al. (2015) Global Trends in Antimicrobial Use in Food Animals. *Proceedings of the National Academy of Sciences*, 112(18), 5649–5654.

Zoonotic disease: for a broad assessment of zoonotic disease risk, see Jones, B. A. et al. (2013) Zoonosis Emergence Linked to Agricultural Intensification and Environmental Change. *Proceedings of the National Academy of Sciences of the United States of America*, 110(21), 8399–8404. For low genetic diversity enabling rapid viral spread in factory farms: United Nations Environment Programme (2020) *Coronaviruses: Are They Here to Stay?* United Nations Environment Programme. For cross-species pandemic-capable infection: Ali, A. et al. (2012) Identification of Swine H1N2/Pandemic H1N1 Reassortant Influenza Virus in Pigs, United States. *Veterinary Microbiology*, 158(1–2), 60–68. For related poultry data: Rozins, C. and Day, T. (2016) The Industrialization of Farming May be Driving Virulence Evolution. *Evolutionary Applications*, 10(2), 189–198. For agricultural intensification's effect on pandemic risk: Willyard, C. (2019) Flu on the Farm. *Nature*, 573(7774), S62–S63; Johnson, C. et al. (2020) Global Shifts in Mammalian Population Trends Reveal Key Predictors of Virus Spillover Risk. *Proceedings of the Royal Society B: Biological Sciences*, 287(1924); Loh, E. H. et al. (2015) Targeting Transmission Pathways for Emerging Zoonotic Disease Surveillance and Control. *Vector-Borne and Zoonotic Diseases*, 15(7).

Chapter 15: Making the most of our land

p.179   Chart: National Food Strategy, based on: Poore, J. and
         Nemecek, T. (2018) Reducing Food's Environmental Impacts
         Through Producers and Consumers. *Science*, 360, 987–992;
         de Ruiter, H. et al. (2017) Total Global Agricultural Land
         Footprint Associated with UK Food Supply 1986–2011. *Global
         Environmental Change*, 43, 72–81; ONS (2019) *UK Natural
         Capital: Urban Accounts*. ONS; WWF (2020) *Bending the Curve:
         The Restorative Power of Planet-Based Diets*. WWF; Forestry
         Commission (2020) *Forestry Statistics 2020: A Compendium
         of Statistics About Woodland, Forestry and Primary Wood
         Processing in the United Kingdom*. National Statistics; Centre
         for Ecology & Hydrology: Environmental Information Data
         Centre (2000) UKCEH Land Cover Map 2000. UKCEH. Available
         at https://catalogue.ceh.ac.uk/documents/14a9ec05-071a-
         43a5-a142-e6894f3d6f9d; European Environment Agency
         (2016) Corine Land Cover 2012. EEA; Easton, M. (2017) Five
         Mind-Blowing Facts About What the UK Looks Like. *BBC News*,
         9 November.

p.181   Frequency of heatwaves: Abnett, K. (2022) Explainer: How
         Climate Change Drives Heatwaves and Wildfires. *Reuters*, 21
         July.

p.183   20% of land produces 3% of food: NFS Analysis, based on
         data from Department for Environment, Food & Rural Affairs
         (2021) June Survey of Agriculture and Horticulture. *GOV.UK*.

p.184   Chart: Searchinger, T. D. et al. (2018) Assessing the Efficiency
         of Changes in Land Use for Mitigating Climate Change. *Nature*,
         564, 249–253.

p.185   Land taken out of agriculture: National Food Strategy
         Analysis. Available at nationalfoodstrategy.org.

         Agricultural greenhouse gas emissions: Committee on
         Climate Change (2020) *The Sixth Carbon Budget – Dataset*.
         Committee on Climate Change. Available at www.theccc.
         org.uk/publication/sixth-carbon-budget/; Emissions are
         net LULUCF emissions for the UK. We followed UNFCCC
         conventions on separating agricultural emissions from land
         use emissions. For more information on the relationship
         between agriculture, LULUCF and AFOLU: Iversen, P. et al.
         (2014) *Understanding Land Use in the UNFCCC*; Department

of Business, Energy and International Strategy (2021) 2019 UK
Greenhouse Gas Emissions, Final Figures. *GOV.UK.*

p.186   Percent of land managed by farmers: for sources, see note for
p.179.

p.189   Land-sharing yields: Poux, X. and Schiavo, M. (2021) *Modelling
an Agroecological UK in 2050: Findings from TYFA.* IDDRI for
FFCC.

p.190   20% of land produces 3% of food: NFS Analysis, based
on data from Defra June Survey. See: Department for
Environment, Food & Rural Affairs (2021) June Survey of
Agriculture and Horticulture. *GOV.UK.*

Chapter 16: You can't eat butterflies

p.193   Fruit and vegetables from Europe: Office of National Statistics
(2020) Trade in Goods: Country-by-Commodity Imports. *GOV.
UK.*

p.194   Ukraine food production and the war: Morrison, O. (2022) Why
the Ukraine Crisis Could Spark 'Dangerous Times' for Food
Prices and Food Security. *FoodNavigator*, 25 February; Wilson,
M. (2023) Ukraine Agriculture: Numbers Paint a Picture of
Devastation. *Farm Progress*, 1 January.

Egyptian imports: MPOC (2022) The Russia–Ukraine War
Impact on Egypt's Food Supply; Emphasis on Oils and Fats,
MPOC, 11 April.

p.195   White fish: Duncan, G. (2022) Whitefish Prices Set to Rise as
Tariff on Product from Russia and Belarus is Introduced. *The
Grocer*, 20 July; Nilsen, S. (2022) Atlantic Cod Prices Are at
Record Highs; Russia Could Send Them Even Higher. *IntraFish*,
23 March.

UK food inflation: Mosolova, D. (2023) UK Food Inflation Hits
13.3%, Retail Sector Data Find. *Financial Times*, 4 January.

p.196   Definitions of food security: Gibson, M. (2012) Food Security
– A Commentary: What Is It and Why Is It So Complicated?
Foods, 1(1), 18–27.

p.197   Current UK self-sufficiency: Department for Environment,
Food & Rural Affairs et al. (2019) Agriculture in the UK. *GOV.UK.*

p.198   Full self-sufficiency: Department for Environment, Food &

Rural Affairs (2009) UK Food Security Assessment: Detailed Analysis. *GOV.UK.*

Chart: Our World in Data (2017) Share of Consumer Expenditure on Food. *Our World in Data.*

p.199   UK income inequality: OECD data. Income inequality. *GOV.UK.*

Proportion of income spent on food: Clark, D. (2022) Average Weekly Household Expenditure Breakdown in the United Kingdom in 2020/21, by Income Decile and Category. *Statista.* Available at www.statista.com/statistics/379934/household-expenditure-categories-uk-by-decile/.

p.201   Chart: Food Chain Analysis Group, Department for Environment Food & Rural Affairs (2006) *Food Security and the UK: An Evidence and Analysis Paper.* National Archives; Barnett, M. (1985) *British Food Policy During the First World War.* Australia: Allen & Unwin; Department for Environment, Food & Rural Affairs (2013) Agriculture in the United Kingdom. *GOV.UK.*

Chapter 17: Can we have it all?

p.203   Food waste: 22% of post-farm gate food is wasted: WRAP (2021) Food Surplus and Waste Arisings in the UK. *WRAP;* FAO (2013) Food Wastage Footprint: Impacts on Natural Resources. *FAO.*

p.204   Farmgate food waste: WRAP (2020) Food Surplus and Waste in the UK – Key Facts. *WRAP.*

Supermarket concentration: McKevitt, F. (13/09/2022) *Big Four Line-up Changes as UK Grocery Price Inflation Accelerates Again.* Kantar, 13 September.

p.205   Beyond-farm-gate food waste: WRAP. (2020) Food Surplus and Waste in the UK – Key Facts. *WRAP.*

Household food waste: WRAP (2019) Retail Survey 2019. *WRAP.*

p.207   Wasted salads: WRAP (2019) Retail Survey 2019. *WRAP.*

Government food waste target: Dray, S. (2021) Food Waste in the UK. UK Parliament: House of Lords Library. Available at https://lordslibrary.parliament.uk/food-waste-in-the-uk/#:~:text=6.6%20million%20tonnes%20(70%25),%25)%20from%20the%20retail%20industry; WRAP (2020) Food Surplus and Waste in the UK – Key Facts. *WRAP.*

Household food waste 2007–2012: ONS (2021) A Review of Household Behaviour in Relation to Food Waste, Recycling, Energy Use and Air Travel. *Office for National Statistics.*

Waste from richer households: van den Bos Verma, M., de Vreede, L., Achterbosch, T. and Rutten, M. M. (2020) Consumers Discard a Lot More Food than Widely Believed: Estimates of Global Food Waste Using an Energy Gap Approach and Affluence Elasticity of Food Waste. *PLoS ONE* 15(2).

p.208   Area of land used for cereals: Department for Environment, Food & Rural Affairs (2020) Farming Statistics – Provisional Arable Crop Areas, Yields and Livestock Populations at 1 June 2020 – United Kingdom. *GOV.UK.*

Average wheat yields UK and world record: Department for Environment, Food & Rural Affairs et al. (2020) Agriculture in the UK 2019. *GOV.UK*; Crop Science/Bayer (2018) How do You Grow a Record-Breaking Wheat Crop? We Spoke to the Current and Former Record-Holders to Find Out. *Crop Science/Bayer.*

Yield improvement potential: Schils, R. et al. (2018) Cereal Yield Gaps Across Europe. *European Journal of Agronomy*, 101, 109–120.

p.209   Chart: NFS analysis based on: Poore, J. and Nemecek, T. (2018) Reducing Food's Environmental Impacts Through Producers and Consumers. *Science*, 360, 987–992; and de Ruiter, H. et al. (2017) Total Global Agricultural Land Footprint Associated with UK Food Supply 1986–2011. *Global Environmental Change*, 43, 72–81. See National Food Strategy (2021) *The National Food Strategy: The Evidence*, July, pp.42, 56, for details. Available at nationalfoodstrategy.org. Scenario assumes land released is split equally across the overseas and domestic land footprint of UK diets.

CCC yield assessments: Committee on Climate Change (2020) *The Sixth Carbon Budget – Dataset.* Committee on Climate Change. Available at www.theccc.org.uk/publication/sixth-carbon-budget/Sixth Carbon Budget.

Plants vs meat: NFS analysis based on Poore, J. and Nemecek, T. (2018) Reducing Food's Environmental Impacts Through Producers and Consumers. *Science*, 360, 987–992; and de Ruiter, H. et al. (2017) Total Global Agricultural Land Footprint Associated with UK Food Supply 1986–2011. *Global Environmental Change*, 43, 72–81. See National Food Strategy

(2021) *The National Food Strategy: The Evidence*, July, pp.42, 56, for details.

p.210   Plausible scenario as per the chart on p.209.

PART THREE: Our Future
Chapter 18: Goujons of hope

p.215   Attitudes to government intervention: NFS-commissioned polling – Fleetwood (2021) *National Food Strategy Polling*. Fleetwood.

Proportion of food served outside the home by public sector: Department for Environment, Food & Rural Affairs (2014) A Plan for Public Procurement: Food and Catering. *GOV.UK*.

p.216   Chart: FAOSTAT (2021) *Meat Food Supply Quantity*, Food and Agriculture Organization of the United Nations [online].

p.218   Picture: Henry Dimbleby. © Dr Emma Lewis.

p.219   Whoppers: based on data from Carrols Restaurant Group, the largest Burger King franchisor in the US, in 2019; Schultz, C. (2020) Impossible Whopper Momentum Slows Down. *Seeking Alpha*; NPD Group (2019) Checkout Data for Year Ending May 2019.

p.221   China dairy imports: USDA (2022) *China: Dairy and Products Annual*. Attaché Report (GAIN).

RethinkX (2021) Food and Agriculture. *RethinkX*. Available at www.rethinkx.com/food-and-agriculture.

p.222   Royal Society (2019) *Future Food: Health and Sustainability, Conference Report*. 12 December. Available at https://royalsociety.org.

p.223   Impossible Burger: United Nations Climate Change (n.d.) *Impossible Foods: Creating Plant-Based Alternatives to Meat – Singapore, Hong Kong, USA, Macau*. Bonn: UNFCCC.

p.224   Chart: National Food Strategy analysis based on Department for Environment, Food & Rural Affairs (2020) Family Food 2018/19. *GOV.UK*.

p.225   UK consumption of alternative proteins: ING Research (2020) *Growth of Meat and Dairy Alternatives is Stirring up the European Food Industry. INGWB*, 22 October.

Job creation potential of alternative proteins: NFS analysis based on feed conversion ratios in Good Food Institute (2021) *Anticipatory Life Cycle Assessment and Techno-economic Assessment of Commercial Cultivated Meat Production.* GFI; tonnes per hectare of input in Department for Environment, Food & Rural Affairs (2019) *Farming Statistics – Final Crop Areas, Yields, Livestock Populations and Agricultural Workforce at 1 June 2019 – UK. GOV.UK*; and agricultural workers per hectare in Nation Master (n.d.) Agricultural Workers per Hectare. Available at www.nationmaster.com/.

Chapter 19: Stewards of the land

p.228 UK CAP payments: Marshall, J. (2021) *Agriculture Subsidies after Brexit: Replacing the CAP*. Institute for Government.

p.229 Removal of New Zealand Subsidies: New Zealand Ministry for Primary Industries (2017) *New Zealand Agriculture: A Policy Perspective, November 2017*; The Economist (2020) British Farming After the Common Agricultural Policy. *The Economist*, 26 November.

p.231 Profitability of UK farmers: Department for Environment, Food & Rural Affairs. (2019) The Future Farming and Environment Evidence Compendium. *GOV.UK*.

p.233 Data on African malnutrition: Annan, K. (2018) Data Can Help to End Malnutrition Across Africa. *Nature*, 555(7), 28 February.

p.236 Carbon footprint of traded food: Kim, B. et al. (2020) Country-Specific Dietary Shifts to Mitigate Climate and Water Crises. *Global Environmental Change*, 62.

UK tree planting vs trade: Pendrill, F. et al. (2019) Deforestation Displaced: Trade in Forest-Risk Commodities and the Prospects for a Global Forest Transition. *Environmental Research Lett*ers, 14(5).

Chapter 20: The power of love

p.242 Life expectancy data by country: World Health Organization (n.d.) *Life Expectancy and Healthy Life Expectancy – Data by Country*. Available at https://apps.who.int/gho/data/node. main.688

Obesity data by country: Ritchie, H. and Roser, M. (2017) Obesity. *Our World in Data*.

p.243 Wilson, B. (2015) *First Bite: How We Learn to Eat.* London: 4th Estate.

p.246 Cooking from scratch: Wunsch, N. (2021) UK: Frequency of Cooking from Scratch 2019/2020, by Gender. *Statista.*

Time spent cooking: Temple, N. (2021) How Humanity Has Changed the Food it Eats. *BBC Future.*

p.249 Dimbleby, H. and Vincent, J. (2013) The School Food Plan. *GOV. UK.*

Chapter 21: Utopia or dystopia?

p.252 Picture: Composite of 5th Avenue, New York, in 1900 and 1913. © Photo 12/Alamy Stock Photo, and George Granthan Bain Collection/Library of Congress, Prints & Photographs Division, [LC-DIG-ggbain-11656].

p.254 Seba, T. and Arbib, J. (2020) *Rethinking Humanity: Five Foundational Sector Disruptions, the Lifecycle of Civilizations, and the Coming Age of Freedom.* RethinkX.

p.256 UK stagnation: Harford, T. (2023) Is Life in the UK Really as Bad as the Numbers Suggest? Yes, it is. *Financial Times,* 20 January.

People off sick: Thomas, C. (2022) *Getting Better? Health and the Labour Market.* Institute for Public Policy Research.

American obesity, metabolic syndrome, diabetes and pre-diabetes: CDC (2022), *National Health and Nutrition Survey 1999–2022,* Centers for Disease Control and Prevention; O'Hearn M. *et al.* (2022) *Trends and Disparities in Cardiometabolic Health Among U.S. Adults, 1999–2018.* J Am Coll Cardiol (12 July, 2022); Saklayen M. G. (2018) *The Global Epidemic of the Metabolic Syndrome.* Curr Hypertens Rep, 20(2):12.

p.257 The 'skinny fat': Carnethon, M. et al. (2012) *Association of Weight Status with Mortality in Adults with Incident Diabetes.* JAMA, 308(6), 581–590.

p.258 American life expectancy: Centers for Disease Control and Prevention (2022) Life Expectancy in the US Dropped for the Second Year in a Row in 2021. *CDC.*

American lower limb amputations: Centers for Disease Control and Prevention (2014) National Diabetes Statistics

Report: Estimates of Diabetes and Its Burden in the United States, 2014. *CDC.*

Per capita health care by country: WHO (n.d.) Global Health Expenditure Database. *WHO.*

p.259   Coral death: Tyler, D. et al. (2021) Global Decline in Capacity of Coral Reefs to Provide Ecosystem Services. *One Earth*, 4(9), 1278–1285.

p.263   Charles C. Mann's (2018) *Wizard and the Prophet: Two Remarkable Scientists and their Battle to Shape Tomorrow's World.* London: Pan Macmillan.

p.265   The Economist (2023) Go to Texas to See the Anti-Green Future of Clean Energy. *The Economist*, 12 January.

Appendix

References and detailed evidence for the recommendations of the National Food Strategy can be found at *National Food Strategy: The Plan*, pp.141–164, 192–263. Available at nationalfoodstrategy.org.

Index

Note: The index covers the Introduction, the numbered Chapters and the Appendix but not the endnotes or acknowledgements.

An *italic* page number denotes an illustration or diagram on that page: the suffix 'n', a footnote.

Where both appear in the text, abbreviations have been preferred to their expansions as main entries, so BMI and BOGOF, not 'body mass index' or 'buy-one-get-one-free'

A

abattoirs/slaughterhouses 160, 163–4, 174–6, 193
active and resting metabolic states 53
addiction (system trap) 26–7
Additive Total Energy Expenditure model 54, *55*, 59
additives
  E-numbers 76
  to reduce methane emissions 155, 216
advertising
  of pharmaceuticals, USA 118
  proposed ban on junk food 51, 112, 214, 262, 273
  revenue, HFSS foods 111
  see also TV watershed
Africa, mapping and malnutrition 233
agriculture *see* farming
Agriculture Act 276–7
agroecological farming 187–90
AI (Artificial Intelligence) 187, 209
airfreight 150
Alaska 123–5
Allen, Myles *155*, 182n
alternative protein technologies

environmental benefits 225
forecast impacts 221–2, 228
lab-grown meat 217–19, *218*
precision fermentation 220–1
regulation 225
research into 278
vegetable protein-based 222–3
Amazon rainforest 147
AMP (Adaptive Multi-Paddock) grazing 161–2
animal fats 97
animal feed 27, 178, 195, 221, 228
Animal Rights and Wrongs, by Roger Scruton 174
animal sentience 163, 168, 170, 172–3, 176
animal welfare concerns
  coexisting with carnivory 173
  GFMC and 136, *137*
  'humane practices' 165–6
  incompatible with demand for meat 174
  and intensive farming 156
  legislation 168
  slaughterhouses 160, 163–4, 174–6, 193
  standards in Australia 238–9

undermined by trade deals
    197, 236–7, 277
US 164
animals
    divinely ordained dominion
        over 168
    experiences of 'higher
        animals' 169
    feelings of 'lower animals' 171
    obesity in 58, 78
    wild or bred for food 11, 12,
        163
Annan, Kofi 233
anorexia 67n
antimicrobials/antibiotics
    antimicrobial resistance
        176–7, 277
    in livestock rearing 163–4,
        177, 236
appetite
    as a biological compulsion
        63–4
    breast milk ratio 44
    effect of ultra-processed
        food 79
    genetic control 41–2
    manipulation 114
    suppression by satiety
        hormones 66–7
    understanding 251
    see also hormones
arable farming 187, 208, 228
Arbib, James 254–5
arthritis 82
artificial sweeteners 94, 273
Asda supermarkets 90
asparagus, imported 150n
Australia
    animal welfare standards
        238–9
    deforestation 158, 236
the author, sampling lab-grown
    meat 218

B
bacteria
    gut microbiome 83
    in the nitrogen cycle 128, 157,
        187
    peat bog emissions 148
balancing feedback loops 22,
    24, 26
Barabási, Albert-László 80–2, 84
bariatric surgery 67–8, 115–16
    see also gastric
basic payments
    under CAP 228
    compared with ELMs 232
    reliance on 231
beef
    abattoir tour 174–5
    carbon-neutral 161–2
    emissions per kg 158, 159
    ex-dairy 160
    imported, deforestation
        effect 236
    production by country 159
bees, sentience 171
'best before' and 'use by' dates
    206, 208
biochemicals recorded in foods
    80–1
biodiversity
    cattle and 160, 162
    government commitment 180
    human activity and 129
    intensive agriculture effect
        on 37, 38
    land-sharing and 189
    paying farmers to support 276
    'priority species' 38
    setting targets 280
'biogeochemical cycles' 127–8
biomass of humans and wild
    animals 10, 11
birth interval 57
Blastocystis 83n

Blickenstaff, Harold 70
'blue carbon' 130
BMI (body mass index)
   calculation 50
   distribution in 1950, 1980 and
     today 42–4
   maintenance through
     exercise 61
   visceral fat problem and 257
BOGOF (buy-one-get-one-free)
   offers 45, 110, 273
'boiled frog syndrome' 25, 40, 49
Borlaug, Norman 31, 33–8, *34*
bottom trawling 25, 129–30
bottom-up reform 248
brain
   calorific expenditure 54
   cooking and brain
     development 57, 166
Brazil 236, 239
breakfast cereals 46
breast milk ratio 44
breeding programmes to reduce
   methane emissions 155, 216
Brexit *see* post-Brexit
Brilliant Planet 219
broadleaf woodland *179*, 185,
   190, 276
bulk-buying, practical limits 94
bull-baiting 167–8, 172
Burger King 219
Burn, by Herman Pontzer 56
butterflies *38*, 188, 199
Buying Standards for Food 280
Byck, Peter 161–2

C

calorie-dense foods 26, 42–7, 79
   inherited preference for 44
calorie intake
   children seeing junk food
     advertising 111–12
   population 108

calorie restriction after-effects
   70–1
calories burned
   by average adult 53–6
   largely constant worldwide
     56
   measuring through exhaled
     CO_2 54
   by orangutans 57
cancer and diet 49, 60–1, 78,
   82, 88
cancer treatments 130
cannibalism 63
canola *see* rapeseed oil
CAP (Common Agricultural
   Policy, EU) 135, 138, 202, 228,
   276
capital
   Dasgupta's three forms 133
   indicators of human and
     natural capital 27–8, 132
   see also natural capital
capitalism 47, 85–6, 192, 205,
   264–5
carbon dioxide
   concentration 145
   measuring exhaled 54
   removal from the atmosphere
     181–2
   see also greenhouse gases
carbon dioxide equivalents
   (CO_2eq) 148, 156, *157*, 182n
carbon emissions
   food production and 37, 150,
     185
   offsetting contrasted with
     sequestration 180
carbon footprints
   ex-dairy beef 158
   food manufacturers reducing
     150, 155
   imported vs local food 18, *159*,
     236, 240

intensively reared food 156–8, *157*
mob grazing and 162
carbon sequestration
'blue carbon' 130n
defined 180
as difficult to measure 137–8
under ELMs 231–2, 234
by growing plants and trees 148, 182–4
limitations of technology 181
by peat 148, 183
potential of land released from livestock farming *184*, 189, 215, 222–3
proposal to reward farmers for 232, 234, 276
carbon storage in plants and soils 138, 148
cardiovascular disease 78, 81, 88
cars
availability 91, 95
supplanting horses 253–4
cassava 27
cats 171
cattle
distress of dairy cows 171–2
emissions per kg beef in different countries 158, *159*
CCC (Climate Change Committee, UK) 182, 209, 278, 281
cereal crops and national self-sufficiency 35
change, pace of 253–4, 262–3
Chefs in Schools charity 14n
chicken farming 156, *157*
chicken goujons (fake) 222–3
chickens, maternal instincts 172
Chief Medical Officer 48
children
average sugar consumption 108

cooking lessons 14n, 52, 249n, 251
food unsuitable for marketing to 13n, 47
inequality and height 86–7
junk food advertising to 110–11, 113, 273
leptin-deficient 66
in refugee camps 257n
unhealthy preferences 92
Chilean plane crash 63
China 164, *165*, 221
chlorinated chicken 237
chocolate 44–5
chocolate cake 68
chocolate ice-cream 44
choice
and food imports 197
illusion of 9, 47, 49, 94, 100–2, 248
chronic inflammation 60
climate change
cost to governments 133
food system contribution 125, 258–9
responsible gases 146
short-term improvements 154
snow crab decline 124
see also global warming
Climate Change Committee, UK 182, 209, 278, 281
climate regulation 144
coal-fired power stations 141
Coase, Ronald 140
cod stocks, overfishing 25, 130
cognitive dissonance 173
Common Agricultural Policy, EU (CAP) 135, 138, 202, 228, 276
'common sense' solutions 49, 51–2, 225
complex systems
approach to nutrition 80

approach to sustainability 264

system dynamics 21, 233

see also feedback loops

confectionery market size 47

conscience

food industry 47, 113

meat eaters 176

conscientious objectors 69–70

Constrained Total Energy Expenditure model 55

consultation *see* deliberative dialogues

consumers' responsibility 51, 89–95, 101

see also choice

consumption

debate on cutting back 263–4

food, over a lifetime 82

influencing through prices 216–17, 265

salad, weather dependent 204

sugar, daily, in UK 106–7

ultra-processed food in Britain 77–8

see also meat consumption

'consumption effect' 45

convenience food 224, 246–7

see also ready-meals

cookers, availability 92

cookery skills gap 52, 92, 95, 206, 246–7, 249n

cooking, and human dominance 10, 166

cooking lessons

for children 14n, 52, 249n, 251, 278

food education and 207, 275–6

see also nutritional education

The Corn Laws, introduction and repeal 196

coronary heart disease 82

cost of living crisis 89, 207, 255

Covid-19 12, 88, 119, 192, 194, 207, 255–6 16

diet-related disease

compared 49, 256

effects on UK food industry 15, 192

crisps *46*, 46–7, 79

crop rotation using ruminants 160, 188, 189

crop yields, improving 126, 208–10, *209*

cruelty 168, 237–8

see also animal welfare

crustaceans, feeling pain 170–1

D

Daily Mail newspaper 106

Darwin, Charles 169–70

Dasgupta, Sir Partha 27, 132–3, 135, 142–3

Deadliest Catch TV series 123

deforestation 12, 36

imported beef and 236

Defra (the Department for the Environment, Food and Rural Affairs), 110, 198, *281*

author's involvement in 14–15, 227, 239

'deliberative dialogues' and focus groups 15, 106, 213, 237, 260

Deming, WE 19

depression 49, 78, 82, 118, 120

dextrose 77

diabetes 58, 61, 82, 257

type 2 13, 49, 50, 116, 258

diet, in North Karelia 97

diet-related disease

as cause of illness and death 13

challenge of 17

correlation with income 88
cost 102, 256
deficiency diseases 87
libertarian arguments
exhausted 101
limits to drug therapy 118
as a negative externality 134
as a systemic problem 105
visible effects 86
dieting
after-effects of crash diets 68
as predictor of obesity 41
typical progress 71–2
digestion, role of gut
microbiome 83
Dimbleby Report *see* National
Food Strategy
The Diversity of Life, by Edward
O Wilson 130
doubly labelled water method
54–7, 62
droughts
European, 2022 125
farming contribution 127
frequency 181
drug prevention policies 24
drugs as alternatives to surgery
116
Dutch 'hunger winter' 71

E
E-numbers 76
the 'Eatwell Plate'/Eatwell
Programme 89, 272, 275
economics
cost of obesity 48–9
'negative externalities' 85,
134, 139–41
The Economics of Biodiversity,
by Sir Partha Dasgupta 27, 132
ecosystem-wide effects 125
ecosystems, allocating values
142

educational attainment and
diet 87
Egypt 96, 194–6
Eisenstadt, Naomi 92
ELMs (Environmental Land
Management schemes) 138,
199, 231–4, 276–7
Elwood, Robert 170–1
energy
industry as a model for
change 265
prospect of limitless energy
254
energy expenditure and
exertion 53–6, 59
English Pastoral, by James
Rebanks 234–5
Environment Bill 280
environmental benefits, pricing
142
environmental damage
cost of intensive agriculture
17
cost to governments 133
governments subsidising 135,
138, 240
urgency of the problem 18
environmental impacts, farming
136–7
escalation (system trap) 26–7,
262
EU *see* Common Agricultural
Policy
Eustice, George 239–40
eutrophication 128–9
'evidence-based policymaking'.
103
'evidence-informed
policymaking'. 104
ex-dairy meat 158, 160
exercise
benefits 61–2
and heart disease 97

and the obesity crisis 52
weight loss and 52–5, 60–2
extreme weather events 181, 200

F
famine 36, 71
farm shops 95
farmers
demands on 185–6
payment for public goods 231,
263, 276
supermarket contracts 204
unfair competition from
imports 237, 240
use of fresh water 127
farming
agricultural innovation 216,
266, 278
agricultural subsidies, UK
199–200, 202, 227
agroecological farming 187–90
arable 228
carbon emissions 37, 150, 185
impacts, according to GFMC
136–7
labour shortages through
urbanisation 245
land-sharing and land-
sparing approaches 186,
188–90
as a 'mining' operation 186
symbiotic 'per plant' farming
187, 209
'Three Compartment Model'
189–90, 231, 277
see also livestock
farmland birds 38, 188, 189
fast-food outlets, siting 90–1,
214, 257n
'fat acceptance' movement
257
fat deposits, regulation 65, 70
fat to sugar ratio 44

feedback loops
affecting food waste 206–7
avoiding system traps 24
balancing 21–4, 26
as balancing and reinforcing
21–3
biological, in humans 58–60,
64–5, 68
financial 101
see also reinforcing feedback
fertilisers
Haber–Bosch process 128, 148
manure 128, 148, 151–2, 156,
161–2, 254
pasture for ruminants 151
recent price rises 195
reliance on pesticides and 27,
37, 148, 160–1, 221, 230
water pollution by 134
fibre, dietary 13, 45, 68, 87, 272
Finland 96–9
First Bite, by Bee Wilson 243
fish
imports 195
memory in 171
overfishing 25, 129–30
fish farming 156, *157*
'five a day' recommendation
52, 272
flexitarianism 225, 250
flour shortages 192–3
focus groups and deliberative
dialogues 15, 106, 213, 237, 260
food
biochemicals recorded in
80–1
calorie-dense food 26, 42–7,
79
carbon costs per kg *184*
families cutting back on 89
hidden environmental costs
139
scoring for healthiness 47

Food and Agriculture
  Organization, UN *126*
food budgets
  proportion of income spent
    on food *198*, 199, 206
  vulnerability 93
food crops, reliance on wheat,
  maize and rice 131
food culture
  Britain 245–7, 278–81
  Japan 242–5
food designers 84
Food for Life, by Tim Spector
  82–3
food industry
  embrace of renewables 150
  lobbying by 110, 249–50
  mandatory reporting 273–4
  matters of conscience 47, 113,
    250
  pressure to sell unhealthy
    foods 13, 26, 45–7
'food miles' 150
food production
  under agroecological farming
    190
  and carbon emissions 37
  climate change threat 259
  greenhouse gases from 146–7
  UK, in World War II 32
  use of sugar and salt 107
Food Resilience Industry Forum
  15–16
food security
  climate change threat 200
  definitions 196–7
  household concerns 89
  Japan 245
  justifying farm subsidies 227,
    232
  land-sharing and 189
  national concerns 12, 17, 189,
    191–2, 194–200

Russian invasion of Ukraine
    12, 194, 200, 255–6
  UK Food Security Assessment
    198
  UK self-sufficiency over time
    201–2
  World War Two 32
Food Standards Agency 280–1
food surpluses, EU 202, 228
'food swamps' 91
food system
  bottom-up reform 248
  capitalism and conscience
    47, 113
  cheapness of sugars and fats
    12–13
  coping with population
    growth 31–7
  Covid-19 and 15–16
  defined 19
  environmental degradation
    effects 125
  importance of diversity 265–7
  importance of trade
    agreements 236–7
  myths and misconceptions
    18
  'negative externalities' 85,
    134, 139–41
  overproduction built in 204
  price inflation 195
  prioritising quantity over
    quality 39
  reform undermined by in-
    fighting 264
  scope 10, 14, 19–20
  'system dynamics' and 21,
    80, 233
food technologists 84
food waste *139*, 198, 203
  domestic food waste 203,
    205, 207
  government target 207

Foresight Obesity System Map
20, 20–1
forest clearance for pasture 158
forest cover, Britain 147
fossil fuels
industries depending on 182
transition, as model 141
use in agriculture 147
'free from' labelling 72
free school meals (FSM)
for children up to Year 2 14n
proposed expansion 109,
274–5, 279
free will and the food system
9–10
freezers, availability and
capacity 92, 94
fresh ingredients
local unavailability 90
as percentage of household
budgets 46
fruit and vegetables
cosmetic criteria and waste
204–5
'five a day' recommendation
52, 272
high-rise greenhouses 266
importance of variety 250
market size 46
as perishable 207–8
reflecting inequality 87
'social prescribing' 266, 275–6

G
garlic 80–1
gastric bands 67–8
gastric bypass surgery 114–15
see also bariatric
gastric sleeves 115–16
GDP (Gross Domestic Product)
28, 102, 133
genetic diversity, utilitarian
arguments 130–1

genetically modified organisms
immune defences 266
yeast for precision
fermentation 220
genetics and appetite 41–3
GFMC (Global Farm Metric
coalition) 136–7
ghrelin 65, 67–8, 72, 79, 115–16
global markets, undermining
subsidies 199–200
global warming *155,* 180–1, 259
see also climate change
GLP-1 (glucagon-like peptide-1)
65–6, 115–16
goals, incorrect or incomplete
27–8
Good Food Bill proposal 280
government actions,
recommended in the National
Food Strategy 271–81
government departments,
involved in food strategy 21–2
Government Food Strategy 17
see also National Food
Strategy
government institutions
reducing meat consumption
215
governments
abundance of caution 109
broken pledges on trade
deals 238
near paralysis 17
subsidising environmental
damage 135, 138, 240
targets 261
grain harvests, Europe, 2022 125
The Great Leveller, by Walter
Scheidel 85–6
Great Ormond Street Institute
of Child Health 111
The 'Green Revolution' *33–4,* 37,
45, 160, 186, 194

greenhouse gases
from agriculture and fertiliser
manufacture 149, 152, 230
emitted by the food system
12, 37, 125–6, 134
from the Haber–Bosch
process 128
potency and persistence 146
representing food uneaten
203
from various protein sources
156, *157*, 223
see also carbon dioxide;
methane; nitrous oxide
Guardian newspaper 142, 224
Gulf Stream, threats *126*, 200
gut microbiome 82–3, 250, 265
GWP (Global Warming Potential)
scale 153, 156

H
Haber–Bosch process 128, 148
habitat creation 136, 184
habitat destruction 37–8, 129–
30, 136, 186, 188
The Hadza people of Tanzania
56
HAF (holiday activities and
food) schemes 93, 109, 261,
274–5
Haldane, Andy 102
'half a Smartie' argument 111–12,
249
Hall, Kevin 78–9
Hanke, David 224
Hardin, Garrett 24–5
harvest failures 36, *126*, 127,
196–7, 200
healthcare, UK see NHS
healthy eating, practical
difficulties 90–2, 93–5
Healthy Start programme 94,
109, 261, 275

heart attack risk 97
heart failure 49, 96, 98
heating, economising on 94–5
Hegarty, John 112–13
herbicides 148, 266
HFSS (high in fat, sugar or salt)
foods 52, 106–7, 111–12, 223,
272
'high nature value farming' see
agroecological
highly processed food
as cheap source of calories 13
see also ultra-processed
Hilton, Boyd 196
Hog Farm Management (trade
journal) 164
Holocene era 10
honey 42, 44, 77
hormones
affecting appetite 64–7, 79
treating cattle with 160, 237
see also hunger hormones;
satiety hormones
household food waste 203, 205
housework as exercise 53
How to Love Animals, by Henry
Mance 172–3
human body, cell numbers 83
human capital 27–8, 133
human exceptionalism 172
humans
as endurance athletes 57–8
fat reserves 58
the three ages of mankind
254n
hunger hormones
genetic control 41, 65–7, 68n
ghrelin 65, 67–8, 72, 79, 115–16
semaglutide inhibition 117
hunter-gatherers 44, 56, 58, 60
hydroxyl radicals 152
'hyperpalatable' processed
foods 77, 79–80

hypothalamus, and appetite
64–7

I
ice-cream 44, 108
ice melting, polar 124, 180
ignorance *see* public awareness
Imagindairy, non-dairy milk 221
immigration 247, 274
immune system and gut
microbiome 83
imported food
compliance with standards
277
compromised environmental
goals 239–40
environmental benefits 236
national dependence on
194–5, 245–6
see also trade agreements
the Impossible Burger/
Impossible Foods 219–20, 223
income
correlation with diet-related
illness *87–8*
proportion spent on food *198*,
199, 206
industrial farming *see* intensive
Industrial Revolution 201, 245,
258
inequality
global 126
history of 85–6
income inequality, UK 256
reducing diet-related
inequality 274–6
ingredients, fresh 46, 90–1, 101,
208, 245
ingredients lists, inadequacies
73–4, 76
Institute for Economic Affairs
100
Institute for Fiscal Studies 53

Institute for Public Policy
Research 256
institutional catering, call for
action 215, 249, 279–80, *281*
insulin 65n, 116, 220, 257
intensive agriculture
addiction problem 27
birth of 35
carbon emissions 156
dairy farming, New Zealand
229–30
effect on biodiversity 37, *38*
effect on the nitrogen cycle
128
environmental cost 17
livestock production miseries
163–77
pigs 164, *165,* 173
'sustainable intensification'
186–7
virus replication risk 177
intra-gastric balloons 68
Ishige, Noamichi 244
ITV executives 110, 249
Ivy Farm Technologies 218

J
Jagger, Mick 107
Japan
author's accident 241–2
changing national diet 243–5
view of other food cultures
247n
jaw-wiring 67–8
Jenkinson, Andrew 67
Johnson, Boris 106–7
Joint Nature Conservation
Committee *38*
Jones, Liz 106
Juniper, Tony 142n
junk food
advertising ban 51, 112, 214,
262, 273

made from plants 222–3
visible effects 86
Junk Food Cycle
  escaping 105, 114, 116–17,
    273–4
  'fat shaming' and 257–8
  introduced 251
  need for state intervention
    102, 105–6, 247
  as a reinforcing feedback
    loop 45–6
  risk to vegetarians 223–4
'just in time' logistics 192

K
'Kate' (author's friend) 117,
  119–20
Kenya 36n
Keyes, Ancel 68–9
Kipling, Rudyard 201
kitchen equipment, availability
  of cookers and freezers 92
kitchen skills *see* cooking

L
lab-grown meat 217–19, *218*
labour-saving devices 53
land area
  to be set aside for nature
    261, 272
  farmland as proportion, UK
    37, 178–9
  freed from livestock farming
    223
  required to feed growing
    populations 31–3, 36–7
land-sharing and land-sparing
  approaches 186, 188–90
land use
  calories per hectare 209
  and climate change 147
  digitised map for the UK
    232–3, 277

and national self-sufficiency
    198
  optimisation 272, 276–7
  repurposing unproductive
    land 183–5
  'Three Compartment Model'
    189–90, 277
  within the UK and for the UK
    market 178–9
Land Use Framework 17
landmass, UK, occupied by
  farmland 37
Lang, Tim 197n
leghaemoglobin 219–20
legislation on junk food 47
legislative framework for
  sustainability 281
lemons, shortage of 193
lentils 89
Leon restaurants 14, 100, 101
leptin 65–6, 78
Levelling Up White Paper 106,
  276, 278
libertarian view of blood sports
  168
libertarian view of nutrition
  47–9, 100–1
life expectancy
  and deprivation 88–9
  in Finland 99
  increase from 1950 35
  reduction in US 258
  in UK, USA and Japan 242
  years lost by cause 48–9
lifetime food consumption 82
Linked, by Albert-László
  Barabási 79–80
livestock farming
  and food security 199
  land area 178–9
  and methane 154, 155, 216
  predicted disruption 221
  see also ruminants

Lloyd, William Foster 24
lobbying by the food industry
110, 249–50
'local' food
effective inaccessibility 95
government procurement 280
misconceptions 18, 196
lockdown, Covid-19 16, 192, 194
lodging problem 34
'low fat' food, misconceptions
18, 72
low-intensity farming 190
'Lucy' (author's friend) 114–16

M
machine learning 220
maize 125–7, *126*, 131, *184*, 187,
194
mammals, threatened with
extinction 129
Mance, Henry 172–3
Mann, Charles C 263
manual labour, decline 52–3
manure 128, 148, 151–2, 156,
161–2, 254
mapping land use 232–3, 277
marathon runners 59
Marr, Andrew 85
mass extinction, trend 133
Meadows, Donella H 23–4, 26–7
Means, Casey 84, 258
meat consumption
beef and lamb 153–4, *216*,
217
chicken *216*, 217
in Japan 243
land use benefits 209–10
reducing through state
procurement 215
reducing to meet government
targets 272
reductions by individuals 250
trends 153, *216*, 217

see also alternative protein
technologies
the 'meat paradox' 173, 176
'meat tax' proposal 214–15
medical training, nutrition in 84
medicines, natural products as
130–1
megafauna extinctions 12
Melton, Douglas 25n
men, calories burned by
average 53–6
metabolic syndrome 256–7
methane
atmospheric breakdown 152–3
as a greenhouse gas 146
from ruminant animals 151,
155, 216
Mexico 33–5
microbiomes 82–3, 250, 265
micronutrients 80–1
milk powder 221
Minnesota hunger project
68–70
mob grazing 161–2
Monbiot, George 142
monocultures 37, 131, 188
Monteiro, Carlos 76–8
MSG (monosodium glutamate)
66–7
'mulesing' 239
Musk, Elon 117
myths and misconceptions 18

N
'nanny state' interventions 17,
52, 96, 100
NASA *126*
National Diet and Nutrition
Survey 87
National Farmers Union 185
National Food Strategy
Boris Johnson's reaction
106–7

deliberative dialogues and focus groups 106, 213, 237, 260
on food security 197
government departments involved 21–2
mapping proposal 232–3, 277
objectives 247
online availability 272
recommended government actions summarised 271–81
supporters 93, 107, 260
Three Compartment Model of farming 189–90, 231, 277
unproductive land proposals 185, 190
National Food System Data programme 279
natural capital 27–8, 132–3, 135, 139, 234, 262
concept criticised 142
Natural Capital Committee 135–6
nature, intrinsic and utilitarian value 131
'negative externalities' 85, 134, 139–41
Nestlé 150, 155
'net zero ' commitment 181–3, 185–6, 236, 261, 277
New York street scenes 253–4
New Zealand 209n, 229–30
Newfoundland Grand Banks 25
NHS (National Health Service, UK)
cost of diet-related disease 13, 48–9, 50, 102, 266
semaglutide availability 117, 119
spending on prevention 275
NICS (National Institute for Clinical Excellence) 117
nitrogen cycle 128

nitrous oxide
from agriculture 147, 149, 151–2, 153
as a greenhouse gas 146, 153–4, 181
non-meat protein 242
see also alternative protein technologies
North Karelia 96–9
NOVA food categorisation system 76–7
'nudge theory' 99, 217
Nutrient Profile Model (WHO) 13n, 47
nutrition
as a complex system 80–1
status of research and training 81, 83–4
nutritional education 207, 275–6
nutritional values, claimed 72

O
obesity
in animals 58, 78
attempted treatment 66
BMI definition 42–3
Chief Medical Officer on 48
in childhood 88, 261
contributing genes and variants 41
economic cost 48–9
Foresight System Obesity Map 20–1
health effects 49
increase since 1950 13, 42–4
Japan 242
and metabolic syndrome 256–7
modern food production and 38, 259
mood and side-effects 48–9, 68
politicisation 100

urgency of the problem 18, 48–9
'obesity epidemic' 44
'obesogenic environments' 101, 105, 116, 119
oceans, carbon dioxide absorption 181
OECD (Organisation for Economic Co-operation and Development) 49, 102, 158
OEP (Office for Environmental Protection) 281
offsetting and carbon sequestration 180, 223
OHID (Office for Health Improvement and Disparities) 281
Oliver, Jamie 26
opportunity costs of carbon *184*
orangutans 57
Origin of Species, by Charles Darwin 169
Our World in Data *157*
overfishing 25, 129–30
overweight people
    BMI definition 42–3
    as unhappy 48–9, 68, 119
Ozempic *see* semaglutide

P
panic buying 192–3
Parsons, Kelly *22*
pasture for ruminants
    area *179*
    repurposing for carbon sequestration 183–4
    usually fertilised 151
patchwork landscape ideal 189, 210
'peak meat' 153
peat bogs/soils 147–8, *179*, 183, 185, 189–90, 276
'per plant' farming 187, 209

periwinkle *(Catharanthus roseus)* 130
personal responsibility *see* consumers'
pesticides
    banned in UK 237
    reducing use 188, 235, 266
    see also fertilisers; herbicides
photosynthesis
    carbon dioxide removal by 181–2
Pigou, Arthur 139–41
pigs
    castration 164
    intensive production 164, *165*
    sow pens/stalls/cages 164, 237–8
Pisani, Nicole 14n
plane crash survivors 63
plant alternatives to food crops 131
'policy evaluation' science 103
Policy Resistance trap 24
political inaction 104, 259
    see also governments
polluter pays principle 136, 139, 182n
Pontzer, Herman 56–60
population
    growth, while avoiding famine 31–7
    weight distribution, 1950 to date 42–3
portion sizes
    misleading 72
    supermarket 91
post-Brexit
    shortcomings of trade deals 237, 277
    support for farmers 228
poverty in the UK 89–90, 95, 109, 260, 274
pre-diabetes 117, 257

precision fermentation 220–2, 254, 266
   nutritional aspects 224
pregnant women 109, 261, 275
preserved meats 97
primates, non-human 57
The Problem of Social Cost, by Ronald Coase 140
processed food
   categories 77
   as cheaper per calorie 92
   levels of salt and sugar 107
   as low in water and fibre 45, 79
   misleading claims 18, 72
   proportion deemed unhealthy 13
   see also highly processed food
produce prescription/'social prescribing' 266, 275–6
productivity
   of land 17, 37 +
   of the workforce 49, 102
promotions, in-store of unhealthy food 110, 262, 273
   see also BOGOF
Prophets and Wizards 263–5
Protein Industries Supercluster (Canada) 226
public attitudes
   enthusiasm for food standards 237, 277
   to food waste 205
   support for junk food advertising ban 112, 214
public awareness
   access to company data 274
   of health guidelines 51–2
   perception of risk 119
public goods defined 136, 138
Puska, Pekka 96–9, 103–4

PYY (peptide tyrosine tyrosine) 65–7, 79, 115

Q
Quorn 220

R
rapeseed oil
   industrial processing 74–5
   pesticide use 237
Rashford, Marcus 109, 260–1
ready-meals 41, 45, 77, 224–5, 246–7
   see also convenience food
Rebanks, James 234–5
reinforcing feedback loops
   cooking skills and 57, 92, 247
   distinguished from balancing 22–3, 26
   Junk Food Cycle as 45–6, 262
rennet replacement 220
restaurants, UK 247
resting metabolic state 53–4, *55*, 59–60, 62, 72
   immune system and 60
Rethinking Humanity, report 254
RethinkX, think tank 221–2, 254
rewilding 37, 160, 185, 190, 210
rice, predicted yields *126*, 127
Ritchie, Hannah *157*
Ronnie (author's cat) 171
the Royal Society 222
RSPCA (Royal Society for the Prevention of Cruelty to Animals) origins 166–8
rule-beating behaviour 27
ruminants
   area of pasture devoted to *179*
   environmental damage from grazing 230
   methane from 151, 155, 216

use of fertilisers on pasture 151

using in crop rotation 160, 188, 189

Rural Land Use Framework for England 233, 279

Russia 12, 37, 195

see also Ukraine

Rycroft, Tim 250

S

SACN (Scientific Advisory Committee on Nutrition) 272

salad

consumption as weather dependent 204

as the most discarded food 207

sandwich ingredients list 73–4, 76

satiety hormones 45, 84, 115

GLP-1 (glucagon-like peptide-1) 65–6, 115–16

leptin 65–6, 78

PYY (peptide tyrosine tyrosine) 65–7, 79

satiety signals, slowed by processed food 45

sausages 99

Scheidel, Walter 85–6

The School Food Plan 14n, 26, 249n, 278

The School Food Standards 274–5

school kitchens

Covid-19 and 15

meals in Finland 99

meals in school holidays 93, 109, 261

school meals

Japan 244–5

reducing meat consumption 215

sampling by parents 248–9

see also free school meals

schools, Eat and Learn initiative 278

Scruton, Roger 174

sea-level rise 127, 180–1

seaweed, potential feed additive 216n

Seba, Tony 254–5

self-sufficiency

national 35, 196, 198–9

UK, over time 201–2

semaglutide (Ozempic, Wegavy) 116–19

sentience, in animals 163, 168, 170, 172–3, 176

severely obese classification 43, 44, 78

sheep farming, New Zealand 229

slaughter of animals in epidemics 164

slaughterhouses/abattoirs 160, 163–4, 174–6, 193

SLCP (short lived climate pollutants) 155

Smith, Rod (farmer) 208

smoking 48, 49, 98, 102

snow crab fishermen 123–5

social media 117, 256, 264

'social prescribing'/produce prescription 266, 275–6

Soft Drinks Industry Levy 52, 103–4, 108

Soil Carbon Cowboys (documentary) 161

soils

AMP grazing 162

carbon release from 147

soil ecosystems 142, 264–5

see also peat

solvents in rapeseed processing 74–5

Somalia 36n

sow pens/stalls/cages 164, 237–8
soy protein isolates 77
Spector, Tim 81–3, 250
starvation
    Dutch 'Hunger Winter' 71
    experiments 68–9
    in postwar Japan 243–4
state, disputed role in UK 99–100
state intervention
    as inadequate by itself 248, 265
    Japanese diet changes 243–5
    public support for 214
    see also subsidies
state procurement
    healthy and sustainable food 279–80, 281
    meat consumption and 215
Stein, Rick 170
stem cells 217, 218
Stemple, Daisy 93–5
strokes 82, 97
subsidies
    agricultural, UK 199–200, 202, 227
    of environmental damage 135, 138, 240
    helping energy transitions 265
    removal 229
sugar
    average consumption, UK 107–8
    'free from added' claim 72
    sweetened foods as cheaper 94
Sugar and Salt Reformulation Tax (proposed) 107, 108–9, 273, 281
Summer Kitchen schemes 93–4
Sun newspaper 51–2

sunflower oil 194–5, 199–200
Sure Start programme 92
sustainability
    GFM indicators 136
    possible legislative framework 281
    rewarding farmers for 138, 232, 234, 237
    'sustainable intensification' 186–7, 189
    undermined by trade deals 237
    Wizards and Prophets 263
Sutton, Marshall 69–70
system dynamics 21
'system traps' 24–8, 262

T
targets, UK government 261, 280
tastebuds 44, 67
tax
    on agricultural emissions 230
    equivalent of diet-related disease costs 102
    legislation as an alternative 143
    proposed on salt and sugar 106–9, 273
    revenues 108
    subsidies as alternatives 140–1
Thinking in Systems, by Donella H Meadows 23–4, 26–7
'Three Compartment Model' 189–90, 231, 277
Timonen, Esa 96
tooth decay 88
trade agreements
    broken pledges 238
    importance of agreements 236–7
    need to support farmers 276

shortcomings of post-Brexit deals 237
undermining animal welfare concerns 236
undermining sustainability 237
Tragedy of the Commons 24–5
transparency, food data 274, 279
trees
  age for effective CO_2 removal 182
  planting negated by imports 238
  removed by grazing 184
Truss, Liz 238–9
TV series *Deadliest Catch* 123
TV show about healthy living 99
TV watershed for junk food advertising 110–12, 273
twin studies 41, 82–3
Tyndall, John 144–5

U
UK
  ambiguity toward animals 173
  reputation for bad food 247n
  slow embrace of alternative protein technologies 225–6
Ukraine,
  EU imports 125
  pesticide use 237
  Russian invasion 12, 194–5, 200, 255
ultra-processed food
  in the British diet 46, 77–8
  as a category 77
  coinage of the term 76
  'handmade' sandwich 73–4
  health impacts 78, 265
  micronutrient profile 80–1
  scope for alternative protein products 223
  weight gain from 79

'umami' flavour 66–7
unhealthy food, defined 13
Universal Credit 89, 94, 274–5
USDA (United States Department of Agriculture) 80–1

V
vegetables
  and gut microbiome 83
  overcoming disdain for 97–8
  see also flexitarianism; fruit and vegetables
vegetarians, junk food risks 223–4
vicious and virtuous circles 23, 45, 71, 125, 200
  see also feedback loops
Vincent, John 14n, 249n
viruses
  intensive agriculture and 158, 177
  see also Covid

W
Waite, Richard 123
walking
  decline since mid-1970s 53
  encouraging in the elderly 98
waste
  see food waste
water and fibre in foods 45
water cycle 127, 146
water pollution 129, 134
water vapour and climate 145
Watson-Jones, Sam 187
weight control
  genetic element 41
  'Metabo law' in Japan 244
weight loss
  and exercise 52–5, 60–2
  and social prescribing 276
  using drugs 116

see also bariatric surgery
What are we Feeding our Kids?
    (TV documentary) 250
What Has Nature Ever Done For
    Us?, by Tony Juniper 142n
wheat, yields 33–5, 126, 208
wheat rust 33–4
Whitty, Chris 48
Why We Eat (Too Much), by
    Andrew Jenkinson 67
Wilberforce, William 166–8
wild bird populations 129
wildlife, farmers role in caring
    for 234
wildwoods, Britain 147
willpower 9, 13, 51–2, 101
Wilson, Bee 243–4
Wilson, Edward O 130–1
Wittgenstein, Ludwig 171
The Wizard and The Prophet, by
    Charles C Mann 263

Wizards and Prophets 263–5
women, calories burned by
    average 53–6
women, working and cooking
    246–7
workforce productivity 49, 102
World Health Organization 13n,
    47
World War I 128
World War II 32, 97, 147, 198, 243
World Wars and food security
    201–2
WRAP, anti-waste charity 205,
    207

Y

yeast, precision fermentation
    technology 220

Z

zoonotic diseases 177, 277